IEE CONTROL ENGINEERING SERIES 7

SERIES EDITORS: G.A. MONTGOMERIE
PROF. H. NICHOLSON

Feedback and Multivariable Systems

Previous volumes in this series:

Feedback
and
Multivariable
Systems

D.H. Owens, B.Sc., A.R.C.S., Ph.D., A.F.I.M.A.
Lecturer in Control Engineering,
University of Sheffield,
England

PETER PEREGRINUS LTD.
on behalf of the
Institution of Electrical Engineers

Published by Peter Peregrinus Ltd.
Southgate House, Stevenage, Herts. SG1 1HQ, England

ISBN: 0 906048 03 6

Composed at the Alden Press Oxford, London and Northampton
Printed in England by A. Wheaton & Co., Ltd., Exeter

Contents

Contents

Man only thinks when you prevent him from acting

JEAN JACQUES ROUSSEAU

Preface

This text is concerned with the provision of a firm basis for the analysis and design of unity-negative multivariable (or multi-input/multi-output) feedback systems using error-actuated dynamic output feedback networks. It was conceived in the conviction that the theoretical basis of linear multivariable feedback design should be set in a physical context

(a) reflecting known dynamic behavioural characteristics
(b) providing useful intuitive guidelines for attaining design objectives
(c) identifying design difficulties in terms of system properties, and
(d) bridging the conceptual gap between classical techniques and the various computer-aided-design techniques suggested in the period 1969–77.

It may be inconsistent to attempt such a task in a theoretical context but the author feels that such an attempt is the only feasible starting point and draws his justification from the all-pervading importance of the (physical) theory of classical mechanics.

It has not been possible to include discussions of many important topics in feedback theory in a text of this length. It is hoped, however, that a fairly complete treatment has been provided of the important features of dynamic output feedback of linear, time-invariant system models. An attempt has been made to minimise the mathematical machinery required for the understanding of the material. Any reader familiar with elementary matrix algebra and transfer-function methods should have no problem in following the material (a summary of essential results in matrix theory is provided in Chapter 1) and, as such, the text could be useful for advanced undergraduate and postgraduate study. The reader should not expect to find explicit recipes for control design. Rather, he should search for the underlying themes of modal dynamics and approximation methods for revealing the essential structure of the multivariable design problem. In this way, it is hoped that he will develop the intuition necessary for the systematic consideration of practical problems.

The material is organised in a logical (rather than a chronological) order. In Chapter 2 the basic mathematical and conceptual framework is set up for the developments of the later chapters. Limitations in space have precluded detailed considerations of many important system-theoretical topics (e.g. controllability, observability and pole allocation) and many other topics are regretfully excluded (e.g. realisation theory, observers, system matrix techniques and geometric methods). In contrast, a fairly detailed discussion of poles, zeros, feedback and stability criteria has been provided. The approach is rigorous in the main although the knowledgable reader will notice a few short-cuts justified by intuitive arguments rather than precise mathematical rigour.

Chapter 3 should be regarded as an introductory account of the basic problems and properties encountered in multivariable feedback design. The objective is to introduce the reader to control possibilities and control difficulties by detailed analyses of specific classes of multivariable structures possessing strong intuitive links to well understood low order classical transfer functions. This provides a (relatively) painless entry to multivariable studies and provides physical examples of the concepts required in later chapters.

The general conclusions of Chapter 3 are extended in Chapter 4 to provide a general theoretical framework for the use of eigenvalue (modal) concepts in stability analysis and feedback design. This is motivated by the techniques used in commutative control and is generalised to permit the use of characteristic loci and characteristic directions as basic design parameters. The idea of eigenvalue approximation is introduced in the form of Gershgorin's theorem in the context of the method of dyadic expansion. This provides a link with the material of Chapter 3 and leads naturally to the discussion of the inverse Nyquist array and contraction mapping results in Chapter 5.

Chapter 6 is probably the most technically difficult. It attempts to provide an introductory conceptual and computational treatment of recent results on the properties of multivariable root-locus plots by analysis of the system Markov parameter matrices. Limitations in space have precluded the inclusion of the methods developed by MacFarlane and Postlethwaite. It is hoped, however, that the material is thought provoking and that the reader will be encouraged to apply the ideas and to add to the stockpile of results available.

Throughout the text, examples are provided of the application of the ideas. Whenever possible, several techniques are applied to the same problem to enable the reader to assess the relationships of the techniques to the physical structure of the system. I have resisted the temptation to compare the usefulness of the various methods, being content simply to distinguish between their mathematical basis and physical emphasis.

I am grateful to Professor H. Nicholson for providing the facilities to undertake this task and to Mrs. J. Stubbs, Mrs. P. Turner and Mrs. E. Halse for preparation of the typescript. Finally, I dedicate this text to my wife Rose and my son Benjamin with thanks for their patience during its preparation.

David H. Owens
September 1977

Chapter 1

Mathematical background

It is a fact that a theoretical text requires the development of certain minimal mathematical skills before the full relevance of the material to practice becomes apparent. It is also true that a familiarity with the more sophisticated branches of mathematics lightens the burden of technical detail leaving time for the development of insight into the need and potential impact of the material. The mathematical techniques required for the understanding of this text are not excessive, namely (i) basic matrix algebra, (ii) elementary differential equations, (iii) Laplace transforms and transfer-function methods and (iv) a little knowledge of continuity and the properties of infinite sequences. There are many excellent texts covering the material required (References 6, 9, 11, 16, 30, 33, 54, 56) but, to help the reader, the following sections outline the basic matrix techniques that have proved particularly relevant to multivariable feedback theory. The material is only reviewed, the proof of many of the results being found in the references.

1.1 Vector space R^n

A *set* X is a collection of objects. If x is an object lying in the set X then x is said to be an element of X and we write

$$x \in X$$

A *real (complex) vector space* X is a set in which operations of 'addition of elements' and 'multiplication of elements by real (complex) numbers' are defined. The elements of X are termed *vectors* and it is required that the following rules hold for arbitrary elements $x, y, z \in X$ and real (complex) numbers α, β.

(*a*) $x + y = y + x$

(b) $(x + y) + z = x + (y + z)$

(c) There exists an element $0 \in X$ (termed the null-vector or the origin of X) so that the product of the number 0 with any element $x \in X$ is equal to the vector 0.

(d) $1 \cdot x = x$

(e) $\alpha(\beta x) = (\alpha\beta)x$

(f) $(\alpha + \beta)x = \alpha x + \beta x$

(g) $\alpha(x + y) = \alpha x + \alpha y$

The *(real) vector space* R^n is the set of columns

$$x = \begin{pmatrix} x_1 \\ x_2 \\ \cdot \\ \cdot \\ \cdot \\ x_n \end{pmatrix}$$

of real numbers $x_1, x_2, \ldots, x_n$. The law of addition is defined by

$$\begin{pmatrix} x_1 \\ x_2 \\ \cdot \\ \cdot \\ \cdot \\ x_n \end{pmatrix} + \begin{pmatrix} y_1 \\ y_2 \\ \cdot \\ \cdot \\ \cdot \\ y_n \end{pmatrix} = \begin{pmatrix} x_1 + y_1 \\ x_2 + y_2 \\ \cdot \\ \cdot \\ \cdot \\ x_n + y_n \end{pmatrix} \in R^n$$

and multiplication by real numbers λ is defined by

$$\lambda \begin{pmatrix} x_1 \\ x_2 \\ \cdot \\ \cdot \\ \cdot \\ x_n \end{pmatrix} = \begin{pmatrix} \lambda x_1 \\ \lambda x_2 \\ \cdot \\ \cdot \\ \cdot \\ \lambda x_n \end{pmatrix} \in R^n$$

The reader should verify (a)–(g) above and note that the origin of R^n is the vector satisfying $x_1 = x_2 = \ldots = x_n = 0$. The scalars $x_1, x_2, \ldots, x_n$ are called *co-ordinates*.

The *(complex) vector space* C^n is defined in an analogous manner by allowing $x_1, \ldots, x_n$ and λ to be complex.

A finite number of vectors $x_1, x_2, \ldots, x_l \in X$ are called *linearly dependent* if there exists numbers $\alpha_1, \alpha_2, \ldots, \alpha_l$, not all zero, such that

$$\alpha_1 x_1 + \alpha_2 x_2 + \ldots + \alpha_l x_l = 0$$

If such a linear dependence does not hold, the vectors $x_1, x_2, \ldots, x_l$ are called *linearly independent*. If the vectors $x_1, x_2, \ldots, x_l$ are linearly dependent then one of the vectors can be represented as a linear combination of the remaining vectors e.g. if $\alpha_1 \neq 0$

$$x_1 = -\frac{\alpha_2}{\alpha_1}x_2 - \ldots - \frac{\alpha_l}{\alpha_1}x_l$$

The vector space X is called *finite-dimensional* and the number dim X is called the *dimension* of X if there exists dim X linearly independent vectors in X and any set of dim $X + 1$ vectors in X are linearly dependent. A system of n linearly-independent ordered vectors $x_1, x_2, \ldots, x_n$ in an n-dimensional space X is called a *basis* for X. It follows from the definition that, if $x \in X$, the collection $x, x_1, x_2, \ldots, x_n$ is linearly dependent and

$$x = \alpha_1 x_1 + \alpha_2 x_2 + \ldots + \alpha_n x_n$$

for some scalars $\alpha_1, \alpha_2, \ldots, \alpha_n$. For example, the vectors

$$x_1 = \begin{pmatrix} 1 \\ 1 \end{pmatrix}, \quad x_2 = \begin{pmatrix} -1 \\ 1 \end{pmatrix}$$

form a basis for R^2 (and, in fact, C^2) and, in general,

$$\dim R^n = \dim C^n = n$$

The *natural (or standard) basis* for R^n (and C^n) is formed by the sequence

$$e_1 = \begin{pmatrix} 1 \\ 0 \\ 0 \\ . \\ 0 \\ 0 \end{pmatrix} \quad e_2 = \begin{pmatrix} 0 \\ 1 \\ 0 \\ . \\ . \\ 0 \\ 0 \end{pmatrix}, \ldots, \quad e_n = \begin{pmatrix} 0 \\ 0 \\ 0 \\ . \\ 0 \\ 0 \\ 1 \end{pmatrix}$$

1.2 Matrices

A rectangular array of real (complex) numbers

$$A = \begin{pmatrix} A_{11} & A_{12} & . & . & .A_{1n} \\ A_{21} & A_{22} & . & . & .A_{2n} \\ . & & & & . \\ . & & & & . \\ . & & & & . \\ A_{m1} & & . & . & .A_{mn} \end{pmatrix}$$

is termed an $m \times n$ real (complex) *matrix*. If $m = n$, A is said to be square and $n = m$ is termed its *order*. The scalars A_{ij} are called the *elements* of A, A_{ij} is the element in the ith row and jth column, and, for notational simplicity, it is sometimes convenient to write

$$A = [A_{ij}]_{m \times n}$$

The basic operations of addition, multiplication by scalars and multiplication of matrices are assumed known.[11]

The reader should note that the set of real (complex) $m \times n$ matrices is a real (complex) vector space and that if A and B are square, it is not generally true that $AB = BA$ i.e. multiplication is not, in general, *commutative*.

The *transpose* of the $m \times n$ real (complex) matrix A is denoted A^T where

$$A^T = [(A^T)_{ij}]_{n \times m}, \quad (A^T)_{ij} = A_{ji}$$

The reader should verify that, for given matrices A, B, we have $(AB)^T = B^T A^T$.

A related concept is the *adjoint* A^+ of A defined by

$$A^+ = [(A^+)_{ij}]_{n \times m}, \quad (A^+)_{ij} = \bar{A}_{ji}$$

where the bar denotes complex conjugate. If A is real then $A^T = A^+$, and $(AB)^+ = B^+ A^+$.

The *trace* of a square matrix A of dimension n is defined by

$$\operatorname{tr} A = A_{11} + A_{22} + \ldots + A_{nn}$$

and the reader should verify that if $A = [A_{ij}]_{n \times m}$, $B = [B_{ij}]_{m \times n}$, then

$$\operatorname{tr}(AB) = \operatorname{tr}(BA)$$

The *rank* of an $m \times n$ matrix A is defined to be the maximum number of linearly independent columns (regarded as vectors) of A. It can be shown that

$$\operatorname{rank} A = \operatorname{rank} A^T$$

$$\operatorname{rank}(A + B) \leqslant \operatorname{rank} A + \operatorname{rank} B$$

and

$$\text{rank } AB \leqslant \min (\text{rank } A, \text{rank } B)$$

equality holding, in particular, if either A or B is square of dimension n and rank equal to n.

The *inverse* of a square matrix A of dimension n is a matrix A^{-1} satisfying

$$AA^{-1} = A^{-1}A = I_n$$

where I_n is the $n \times n$ unit matrix

$$(I_n)_{ij} = \delta_{ij}$$

(δ_{ij} is the Kronecker delta, equal to 1 if $i = j$ and zero if $i \neq j$). Noting that

$$\text{rank } I_n = n = \text{rank } AA^{-1} \leqslant \min(\text{rank } A, \text{rank } A^{-1}) \leqslant n$$

it follows directly that A^{-1} can only exist if rank $A = n$. This condition is also sufficient and the inverse is uniquely defined.

It is very often convenient to consider a *partitioning* of an $m \times n$ matrix A of the form

$$A = \begin{pmatrix} \tilde{A}_{11} & \cdots & \tilde{A}_{1l} \\ \vdots & & \vdots \\ \tilde{A}_{q1} & \cdots & \tilde{A}_{ql} \end{pmatrix}$$

where $\tilde{A}_{ij}$ is a matrix of dimension $q_i \times l_j$, $m = \Sigma_{i=1}^q q_i, n = \Sigma_{j=1}^l l_j$. For example,

$$A = \begin{pmatrix} 1 & 2 & 1 \\ 2 & 1 & 0 \\ 1 & 1 & 1 \end{pmatrix} = \begin{pmatrix} \tilde{A}_{11} & \tilde{A}_{12} \\ \tilde{A}_{21} & \tilde{A}_{22} \end{pmatrix}$$

where

$$\tilde{A}_{11} = \begin{pmatrix} 1 & 2 \\ 2 & 1 \end{pmatrix}, \quad \tilde{A}_{12} = \begin{pmatrix} 1 \\ 0 \end{pmatrix}, \quad \tilde{A}_{21} = (1 \quad 1), \quad \tilde{A}_{22} = (1)$$

and the partitioning is obviously nonunique. The reader should verify that block matrices multiply as follows:

$$C = AB = \begin{pmatrix} \tilde{A}_{11} & \cdots & \tilde{A}_{1r} \\ \vdots & & \vdots \\ \tilde{A}_{q1} & \cdots & \tilde{A}_{qr} \end{pmatrix} \begin{pmatrix} \tilde{B}_{11} & \cdots & \tilde{B}_{1l} \\ \vdots & & \vdots \\ \tilde{B}_{r1} & \cdots & \tilde{B}_{rl} \end{pmatrix} = \begin{pmatrix} \tilde{C}_{11} & \cdots & \tilde{C}_{1l} \\ \vdots & & \vdots \\ \tilde{C}_{q1} & \cdots & \tilde{C}_{ql} \end{pmatrix}$$

$$\tilde{C}_{ij} = \sum_{k=1}^{r} \tilde{A}_{ik}\tilde{B}_{kj}$$

provided the block multiplications are defined. A partitioned matrix A is said to be *block-diagonal* if $\tilde{A}_{ij} = 0, i \neq j, q = l$ when we write

$$A = \text{block diag } \{\tilde{A}_{11}, \tilde{A}_{22}, \ldots, \tilde{A}_{ll}\}$$
$$= \text{block diag } \{\tilde{A}_{jj}\}_{1 \leqslant j \leqslant l}$$

If $\tilde{A}_{jj}$ is square of dimension 1, $1 \leqslant j \leqslant l$, then A is said to be *diagonal* and we write,

$$A = \text{diag } \{\tilde{A}_{jj}\}_{1 \leqslant j \leqslant n} = \text{diag } \{\tilde{A}_{11}, \ldots, \tilde{A}_{nn}\}$$

A is said to be *block triangular* if $q = l$ and $\tilde{A}_{ij} = 0, i < j$ (block lower triangular) or $\tilde{A}_{ij} = 0, i > j$ (block upper triangular) and *triangular* if $q_i = l_i = 1, 1 \leqslant i \leqslant n$, also holds.

1.3 Determinants

It is assumed that the concept of the *determinant* of a square matrix A of order n is known, so we content ourselves with a summary of basic properties and useful results in the context of this text. The determinant of A is denoted det A or $|A|$, or, in some cases,

$$|A| = \begin{vmatrix} A_{11} & \cdots & A_{1n} \\ \vdots & & \vdots \\ A_{n1} & \cdots & A_{nn} \end{vmatrix}$$

Particularly useful formula are

$$|A| = |A^T|$$
$$|AB| = |A| \, |B| = |BA|$$
$$|\text{diag } \{\lambda_j\}_{1 \leqslant j \leqslant n}| = \lambda_1 \lambda_2 \ldots \lambda_n$$

If A is partitioned and is block-diagonal or block-triangular with square diagonal blocks $\tilde{A}_{ii}$, then

$$|A| = |\tilde{A}_{11}| \, |\tilde{A}_{22}| \ldots |\tilde{A}_{ll}|$$

The matrix A is *singular* if $|A| = 0$ and *nonsingular* if $|A| \neq 0$. A is *invertible* if, and only if, it is nonsingular when

$$|AA^{-1}| = |A|\;|A^{-1}| = |I_n| = 1$$

yields

$$|A^{-1}| = (|A|)^{-1}$$

and $|A| = 0$ if, and only if, rank $A < n$ or, equivalently, if, and only if, there exists a nonzero vector $x \in R^n$ such that $Ax = 0$.

A particularly useful formula is *Schur's formula*. Suppose that A is partitioned as follows,

$$A = \begin{pmatrix} A_{11} & A_{12} \\ A_{21} & A_{22} \end{pmatrix}$$

where A_{11} is square and nonsingular. Consideration of the identity

$$\begin{pmatrix} I & 0 \\ -A_{21}A_{11}^{-1} & I \end{pmatrix} \begin{pmatrix} A_{11} & A_{12} \\ A_{21} & A_{22} \end{pmatrix} = \begin{pmatrix} A_{11} & A_{12} \\ 0 & A_{22} - A_{21}A_{11}^{-1}A_{12} \end{pmatrix}$$

and taking determinants yields the desired result i.e.

$$|A| = |A_{11}|\;|A_{22} - A_{21}A_{11}^{-1}A_{12}|$$

Suppose that A and B have dimension $m \times n$ and $n \times m$, respectively, then a frequently encountered result is stated below without proof, (problem 11)

$$|I_m + AB| = |I_n + BA|$$

In particular, if α, β are vectors (essentially $n \times 1$ matrices)

$$|I_n + \alpha\beta^T| = 1 + \beta^T\alpha$$

If also $\beta^T\alpha \neq -1$, the matrix $A = I_n + \alpha\beta^T$ is nonsingular and it is easily verified that

$$A^{-1} = I_n - \frac{1}{1 + \beta^T\alpha}\alpha\beta^T$$

by substitution into the relation $AA^{-1} = I_n$.

1.4   Eigenvector, eigenvalues and dyadic expansions

Let A be a square (real or complex matrix) of dimension n. A real or complex number λ is an *eigenvalue* of A if, and only if, there exists a (complex) nonzero vector $x \in C^n$ such that the following *eigenvalue equation* is satisfied

$$Ax = \lambda x$$

when x is said to be an *eigenvector* of A corresponding to the eigenvalue λ. Rewriting in the form $\{\lambda I_n - A\}x = 0$, it follows directly that λ is a zero of the *characteristic polynomial* of A

$$\rho(s) = |sI - A|$$

Conversely if $\rho(\lambda) = 0$ then rank $\{\lambda I_n - A\} < n$ and there exists a nonzero eigenvector x corresponding to the eigenvalue λ and satisfying the eigenvalue equation.

The characteristic polynomial of A has degree n and can be factored in the form

$$\rho(s) = |sI_n - A| = (s - \lambda_1)(s - \lambda_2) \ldots (s - \lambda_n)$$

$$= \prod_{j=1}^{n} (s - \lambda_j)$$

and, to each λ_j, there exists an eigenvector x_j. If A is a real matrix, then the eigenvalues exist in complex-conjugate pairs i.e. if λ_j is an eigenvalue then $\lambda_{l(j)} = \bar{\lambda}_j$ is an eigenvalue with eigenvector $x_{l(j)} = \bar{x}_j$. If λ_j is real it is also possible to choose x_j to be real. Note that αx_j is an eigenvector of A corresponding to the eigenvalue λ_j provided that $\alpha \neq 0$, and hence that eigenvectors are not unique. Some of the nonuniqueness can be removed by replacing x_j by $x_j / \|x_j\|$ where

$$\|x_j\| = \sqrt{x_j^+ x_j}$$

The resulting set of eigenvectors is said to be *normalised*.

The *dual eigenvectors* of A are defined as nonzero solutions of the relations

$$v_j^+ A = \lambda_j v_j^+$$

or, taking adjoints,

$$A^+ v_j = \bar{\lambda}_j v_j$$

It follows directly that

$$(\lambda_j - \lambda_k) v_j^+ x_k = 0$$

i.e. the vectors v_j, x_k are *orthogonal* if $\lambda_j \neq \lambda_k$, or, equivalently

$$v_j^+ x_k = 0$$

If A has distinct eigenvalues then the eigenvectors x_j, $1 \leqslant j \leqslant n$, are linearly independent, for, scaling x_j, $1 \leqslant j \leqslant n$, such that

$$v_j^+ x_k = \delta_{jk}$$

the relation $\alpha_1 x_1 + \alpha_2 x_2 + \ldots + \alpha_n x_n = 0$ gives $v_j^+(\alpha_1 x_1 + \alpha_2 x_2 + \ldots + \alpha_n x_n) = \alpha_j = 0$, $1 \leqslant j \leqslant n$. In particular, defining the *eigenvector matrix* or *modal matrix*

$$E = (x_1, x_2, \ldots, x_n)$$

then E is nonsingular. Noting that

$$AE = E \operatorname{diag}\{\lambda_j\}_{1 \leqslant j \leqslant n}$$

(from the eigenvalue equations) it follows that

$$E^{-1}AE = \operatorname{diag}\{\lambda_j\}_{1 \leqslant j \leqslant n}$$

The matrix E is an example of a *similarity transformation* and the above expression is termed the *diagonal canonical form* of A.

A useful formula is obtained by noting that

$$\begin{pmatrix} v_1^+ \\ v_2^+ \\ \cdot \\ \cdot \\ \cdot \\ v_n^+ \end{pmatrix} (x_1, x_2, \ldots, x_n) = I_n$$

and hence that the jth row of E^{-1} is simply v_j^+, $1 \leqslant j \leqslant n$.

The matrix A may have a diagonal canonical form even if some of its eigenvalues are repeated e.g. the matrix

$$A = \begin{pmatrix} 2 & 1 & 0 \\ 1 & 2 & 0 \\ 0 & 0 & 3 \end{pmatrix}$$

has an eigenvector matrix

$$E = \begin{pmatrix} 1 & -1 & 0 \\ 1 & 1 & 0 \\ 0 & 0 & 1 \end{pmatrix}$$

and diagonal canonical form $E^{-1}AE = \operatorname{diag}\{3, 1, 3\}$. In the general case of repeated eigenvalues, the diagonal canonical form does not exist. It is possible in such cases to construct the *Jordan canonical form* of A by choice of similarity transformation T such that

$$T^{-1}AT = \operatorname{block\ diag}(J_1, J_2, \ldots, J_l)$$

where the matrices J_j, $1 \leqslant j \leqslant l$, one square of dimension n_j, $J_j = \eta_j$ if $n_j = 1$ and

$$J_j = \begin{pmatrix} \eta_j & 1 & 0 & \dots & 0 \\ 0 & \eta_j & 1 & & \vdots \\ \vdots & & & & \vdots \\ & & & & 0 \\ \vdots & & & & 1 \\ 0 & \dots & \dots & 0 & \eta_j \end{pmatrix} \quad (n_j > 1)$$

where η_j is an eigenvalue of A, and the following identities hold:

$$n = n_1 + n_2 + \dots + n_l$$

$$\rho(s) = (s - \eta_1)^{n_1} (s - \eta_2)^{n_2} \dots (s - \eta_l)^{n_l}$$

Note that the η_j need not be distinct but that the integers n_j are uniquely defined. In this text the Jordan form is required only rarely. This has little effect on the generality of the results as it can be shown[1] that 'almost every' square matrix A has a diagonal canonical form and, if A has a Jordan form, arbitrary small perturbations of its elements enables the construction of a diagonal canonical form.

The use of the Jordan form yields the following useful properties:

$$|A| = |ATT^{-1}| = |T^{-1}AT| = \lambda_1 \lambda_2 \dots \lambda_n$$

$$\operatorname{tr} A = \operatorname{tr} ATT^{-1} = \operatorname{tr} T^{-1}AT = \lambda_1 + \lambda_2 + \dots + \lambda_n$$

If A has a diagonal canonical form the identity

$$A = E \operatorname{diag} \{\lambda_j\}_{1 \leqslant j \leqslant n} E^{-1}$$

can be written in the form of a *spectral expansion*

$$A = \sum_{j=1}^{n} \lambda_j x_j v_j^+$$

which is a special case of the concept of a *dyadic expansion* of A. A *dyad D* is a nonzero matrix of the form

$$D = \alpha\beta^+$$

(or $D = \alpha\beta^T$ by replacing β by $\bar{\beta}$) where α, β are real or complex vectors. The matrix D is a dyad if and only if rank $D = 1$. A dyadic expansion of A is a relation of the form

$$A = \sum_{j=1}^{r} \alpha_j \beta_j^+$$

(where r is not necessarily equal to n). There are an infinite number of possible dyadic expansions of A as is seen by choosing an arbitrary nonsingular $n \times n$ matrix M and writing

$$A = M(M^{-1}A)$$

with

$$M = (\alpha_1, \alpha_2, \ldots, \alpha_n), \quad M^{-1}A = \begin{pmatrix} \beta_1^+ \\ \beta_2^+ \\ . \\ . \\ . \\ \beta_n^+ \end{pmatrix}$$

and noting that $A = \alpha_1\beta_1^+ + \ldots + \alpha_n\beta_n^+$.

The ideas of spectral and dyadic expansion together with the concept of eigenvalue estimation play a central role in this text. Eigenvalue estimation is achieved by the use of *Gershgorin's theorem* which states that, if A is a complex square matrix of order n with eigenvalues $\lambda_1, \lambda_2, \ldots, \lambda_n$, each eigenvalue λ_j satisfies an inequality of the form

$$|\lambda_j - A_{l_1 l_1}| \leqslant \sum_{\substack{k=1 \\ k \neq l_1}}^{n} |A_{l_1 k}|$$

for some l_1 dependent on j. Applying the theorem to A^T yields

$$|\lambda_j - A_{l_2 l_2}| \leqslant \sum_{\substack{k=1 \\ k \neq l_2}}^{n} |A_{k l_2}|$$

for some l_2 dependent on j. In general l_1, l_2 are unknown and, in such cases, the result is best expressed in a graphical way. Let A be an $n \times n$ complex matrix and plot the n diagonal terms A_{jj}, $1 \leqslant j \leqslant n$, as points in the complex plane. At each point A_{jj}, plot a circle of centre A_{jj} and radius

$$r_j = \sum_{\substack{k=1 \\ k \neq j}}^{n} |A_{jk}| \qquad \text{(row estimate)}$$

(Each circle is called a *Gershgorin circle*). Gershgorin's theorem can then be stated in the form: every eigenvalue lies in the union of the Gershgorin circles of A. Application of the result to A^T indicates the dual result that every eigenvalue of A lies in the *union* of the circles of centre A_{jj}, $1 \leqslant j \leqslant n$, and radius

$$r_j = \sum_{\substack{k=1 \\ k \neq j}}^{n} |A_{kj}| \qquad \text{(column estimate)}$$

These ideas are illustrated in Fig. 1.4.1 by consideration of

$$A = \begin{pmatrix} 1+2i & -2i \\ i & 1-i \end{pmatrix}, \quad (i^2 = -1)$$

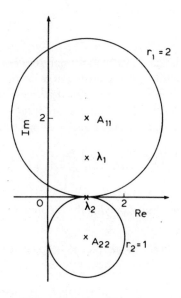

Fig. 1.4.1 Gershgorin circles for eigenvalue estimation

and the use of Gershgorin circles based on row estimates. Note, however, that it is quite possible that all eigenvalues lie in one Gershgorin circle leaving others empty i.e. it is not generally true that every circle contains an eigenvalue. For example, consider

$$A = \begin{pmatrix} 0 & -3 \\ 8 & 10 \end{pmatrix}$$

with eigenvalues $\lambda_1 = 4$, $\lambda_2 = 6$ and Gershgorin circles based on row estimates.

Finally, an $n \times n$ complex matrix A is said to be *row (column) dominant* if

$$|A_{jj}| > \sum_{\substack{k=1 \\ k \neq j}}^{n} |A_{jk}| \left(\sum_{\substack{k=1 \\ k \neq j}}^{n} |A_{kj}| \right), \qquad 1 \leqslant j \leqslant n$$

i.e. the matrix A is row (column) dominant if, and only if, the Gershgorin circles based on row (column) estimates do not contain the origin of the complex plane. Applying Gershgorin's theorem it follows directly that row- or column-dominant matrices are nonsingular. Later in the text, when it is not necessary to distinguish between row and column dominance, A will simply be termed *dominant*.

1.5 Functions of a matrix

Let $g(x) = g_0 + g_1 x + g_2 x^2 + \ldots + g_k x^k$ be a polynomial in the scalar variable x of degree k. Then we define

$$g(A) = g_0 I_n + g_1 A + g_2 A^2 + \ldots + g_k A^k$$

A particular useful result is the *Cayley-Hamilton theorem* which states that every matrix A satisfies its characteristic polynomial,

$$p(A) = a_0 I_n + a_1 A + a_2 A^2 + \ldots + a_n A^n = 0 \qquad (a_n = 1)$$

and hence that any power A^k of A can be written as a linear combination of $I, A, A^2, \ldots, A^{n-1}$.

The idea of a function of a matrix can be extended by considering a function $g(x)$ expressed in the form of a power series

$$g(x) = \sum_{j=0}^{\infty} g_j x^j$$

absolutely convergent for $|x| < R$. If $\max_{1 \leqslant j \leqslant n} |\lambda_j| < R$, it can be shown that the matrix

$$g(A) = g_0 I_n + g_1 A + g_2 A^2 + \ldots$$

is well defined in the sense that the series converges absolutely element by element. An important feature is that the Cayley-Hamilton theorem can be applied to eliminate the terms in A^k, $k \geqslant n$, to express $g(A)$ in terms of $I, A, A^2, \ldots, A^{n-1}$ i.e.

$$g(A) = \tilde{g}_0 I_n + \tilde{g}_1 A + \ldots + \tilde{g}_{n-1} A^{n-1}$$

for some scalars $\tilde{g}_k, 0 \leqslant k \leqslant n-1$.

The most important application of the above ideas is the construction of the *matrix exponential*. Suppose that A is a complex $n \times n$ matrix, then the exponential function

$$e^x = 1 + x + \frac{x^2}{2!} + \frac{x^3}{3!} + \ldots$$

is used to define the exponential of A

$$e^A = I_n + A + \frac{1}{2!}A^2 + \frac{1}{3!}A^3 + \ldots$$

the series converging independent of the choice of A. Note, however, that, in general

$$e^A e^B \neq e^{A+B}$$

unless A and B *commute* i.e. $AB = BA$. It will be useful to note the formula

$$E^{-1}e^A E = e^{E^{-1}AE} = \text{diag}\{e^{\lambda_1}, e^{\lambda_2}, \ldots, e^{\lambda_n}\}$$

whenever A has a diagonal canonical form. If A has a Jordan form, then

$$T^{-1}e^A T = e^{T^{-1}AT} = \text{block diag}\{e^{J_k}\}_{1 \leqslant k \leqslant l}$$

where

$$e^{J_k} = e^{\eta_k}\begin{pmatrix} 1 & 1 & \frac{1}{2} \cdots & \frac{1}{(n-1)!} \\ 0 & 1 & \cdots \cdots & \vdots \\ \vdots & & \cdots \cdots \cdots & \frac{1}{2} \\ \vdots & & & 1 \\ 0 & \cdots \cdots & 0 & 1 \end{pmatrix}$$

1.6 Matrix-valued functions

The elementary idea of a scalar function of a real or complex variable is easily extended to cope with matrix valued functions. Let $A_{ij}(t)$, $1 \leqslant i \leqslant m$, $1 \leqslant j \leqslant n$ be mn scalar-valued functions of the real or complex variable t defined in some domain. Then these functions can be used to construct the matrix-valued function

$$A(t) = [A_{ij}(t)]_{m \times n}$$

If all the elements of $A(t)$ are differentiable then the derivative of $A(t)$

is defined by

$$\frac{d}{dt}\,A(t) = \left[\frac{dA_{ij}(t)}{dt}\right]_{m\times n}$$

In a similar manner, if the elements of $A(t)$ are integrable,

$$\int_a^b A(t)dt = \left[\int_a^b A_{ij}(t)dt\right]_{m\times n}$$

Those readers familiar with the differential calculus on Banach spaces will be familiar with the fact that all the rules of differentiation and integration remain valid with the above definitions.

1.7 Problems

1 Show that the natural basis in R^n is indeed a basis.

2 Prove that $(A_1A_2\ldots A_k)^T = A_k^T A_{k-1}^T \ldots A_1^T$ and prove an analogous result if transposition is replaced by taking the adjoint.

3 Two $m\times n$ matrices A, B are said to be equivalent if, and only if, there exists nonsingular square matrices P, Q of dimension n, m, respectively, such that

$$PAQ = B$$

Show that A and B are equivalent if, and only if, they have the same rank.

4 If A, B have dimensions $m\times n$ and $n\times l$, respectively, and are partitioned by rows and columns, respectively,

$$A = \begin{pmatrix}\alpha_1\\ \vdots\\ \alpha_m\end{pmatrix}, \quad B = (\beta_1, \beta_2, \ldots, \beta_l)$$

Prove that

$$AB = \begin{pmatrix}\alpha_1\beta_1 & \ldots & \alpha_1\beta_l\\ \vdots & & \\ \alpha_m\beta_1 & \ldots & \alpha_m\beta_l\end{pmatrix}$$

5 Prove that the eigenvalues of A^{-1} are simply the inverses of the eigenvalues of A.

6 Prove that the eigenvalues of $\alpha I_n - A$ are equal to α minus the eigenvalues of A.

7 If A has a diagonal canonical form $E^{-1}AE = \text{diag}\,\{\lambda_1, \lambda_2, \ldots, \lambda_n\}$, show that $(sI_n - A)$ is nonsingular if, and only if, $s \neq \lambda_j (1 \leqslant j \leqslant n)$ when

$$(sI_n - A)^{-1} = E \,\text{diag}\left\{\frac{1}{s - \lambda_j}\right\}_{1 \leqslant j \leqslant n} E^{-1}$$

Show also that, for $|s| > \max_{1 \leqslant j \leqslant n} |\lambda_j|$,

$$(sI_n - A)^{-1} = \frac{1}{s} I_n + \frac{1}{s^2} A + \frac{1}{s^3} A^2 + \ldots$$

8 Verify the following dyadic expansions,

$$\begin{pmatrix} 2 & 1 \\ 1 & 2 \end{pmatrix} = \begin{pmatrix} 3 \\ 3 \end{pmatrix} \;(0{\cdot}5 \quad 0{\cdot}5) + \begin{pmatrix} -1 \\ 1 \end{pmatrix} \;(-0{\cdot}5 \quad 0{\cdot}5)$$

$$= \begin{pmatrix} 1 \\ 0 \end{pmatrix} \;(3 \quad 3) + \begin{pmatrix} -1 \\ 1 \end{pmatrix} \;(1 \quad 2)$$

$$= \begin{pmatrix} 3 \\ 1 \end{pmatrix} \;(0 \quad -3) + \begin{pmatrix} 2 \\ 1 \end{pmatrix} \;(1 \quad 5)$$

9 Verify that a square matrix A is diagonal if, and only if, its Gershgorin circles all have zero radius.

10 Apply Gershgorin's theorem to estimate the eigenvalues of

$$A = \begin{pmatrix} 4 & 6 \\ 1 & 12 \end{pmatrix}, \quad A = \begin{pmatrix} 10 & 1 \\ 2 & -8 \end{pmatrix}$$

Check you result by direct evaluation of the eigenvalues.

11 If A and B have dimension $m \times n$ and $n \times m$, respectively, prove the identity

$$|I_m + AB| = |I_n + BA|$$

(Hint: If $m = n$ and A is nonsingular then $|I_m + AB| = |A(A^{-1} + B)|$ $= |(A^{-1} + B)A| = |I_m + BA|$. If $m = n$ and both A and B are singular, note that $A + \epsilon I_m$ is nonsingular in some range $0 < \epsilon < \delta$, apply the above procedure and set $\epsilon = 0$. If $m < n$, write

$$|I_m + AB| = \left| I_n + \begin{pmatrix} A \\ 0 \end{pmatrix} \begin{pmatrix} B & 0 \end{pmatrix} \right|$$

12 If $g(x) = g_0 + g_1 x + g_2 x^2 + \ldots$, use the relation $(T^{-1}AT)^k = T^{-1}A^k T$, $k \geqslant 1$, to show that $T^{-1}g(A)T = g(T^{-1}AT)$. If A has a diagonal canonical form with eigenvector matrix E, prove that

$$E^{-1}g(A)E = \text{diag}\,\{g(\lambda_1), g(\lambda_2), \ldots, g(\lambda_n)\}$$

and hence that

$$\text{tr}\,g(A) = \sum_{j=1}^{n} g(\lambda_j), \quad |g(A)| = \prod_{j=1}^{n} g(\lambda_j)$$

Use these results to verify that e^A is always nonsingular.

Chapter 2

System models and feedback concepts

This Chapter provides the setting and basic concepts within which the later discussion of system structure and controller design will take place. Emphasis is placed on the formulation of the description of system dynamics by mathematical models and the investigation of the mathematical properties of such models. A distinction is made between the description of the input-output behaviour of the system by the internal or state-vector description in the time-domain and the input-output description in the frequency domain in terms of the system transfer-function matrix. The mathematical level is consistent with that provided in Chapter 1 but the results required are used in their simplest form. In this way, it is hoped that the reader can attain a high level of understanding of the basic physical and mathematical concepts of system structure relevant to the discussion of feedback controller design of later chapters, without the more abstract mathematical detail of recent research texts.[57, 63, 64] However, those readers so inclined are referred to the references if they wish to widen the generality of the results.

2.1 System models

The concept of a model of the dynamics of a complex engineering process is, in itself, a complicated concept embodying both *a priori* and *a posteriori* information concerning its structure, its past and anticipated behaviour and the known physical laws governing the dynamics of its individual components. Possible components of such a model are as follows:

(*a*) experimental data obtained by injecting known test signals (e.g. step inputs, sinusoids) at the system inputs and measurement of the system outputs (*b*) a small-scale or pilot plant facility for the investigation of the feasibility of a new process

(*c*) a set of linear or nonlinear algebraic and ordinary or partial-differential equations obtained by a consideration of the known physical laws governing the dynamics of system components. The various parameters appearing in such equations are estimated experimentally

(*d*) the results of statistical analysis of system data to quantify the effects of noise on system components

(*e*) a set of assumptions required to approximate the description of system components for which both theoretical and experimental information available is inadequate.

A consideration of all such approaches is outside the scope of this text so we leave the general discussion of system modelling with the observation that many of the components described above can be used to construct mathematical models of the system dynamics. For example, both experimental data and experience with pilot plant may be used, together with a suitable set of assumptions, to derive a set of algebraic and ordinary or partial-differential equations which approximately describe the dynamics of the system under a set of external conditions of interest.

For the purposes of this text, we assume that the system or engineering plant can be approximately described by a set of first-order ordinary differential equations of the form

$$\frac{dx_i(t)}{dt} = f_i(x_1(t), \ldots, x_n(t), u_1(t), \ldots, u_l(t), t)$$

$$x_i(0) = x_{i0}, \qquad 1 \leqslant i \leqslant n \tag{2.1.1}$$

where t is the time variable, $x_1(t), \ldots, x_n(t)$ are scalar time functions termed *state variables* and $u_1(t), \ldots, u_l(t)$ are scalar time functions representing *input or control variables*. The state variables are those system variables (e.g. flow, temperature, pressure, position, velocity) required at any time t_0, to compute its behaviour for times $t > t_0$.

It should be noted that the state variables are not all necessarily measurable in the sense that either sensor equipment is installed on the plant to directly measure only a few states or that it is physically impossible to measure all the states. To complete the system description, let $y_1(t), \ldots, y_m(t)$ be measured system variables or *output variables* of the form, $1 \leqslant i \leqslant m$,

$$y_i(t) = g_i(x_1(t), \ldots, x_n(t), u_1(t), \ldots, u_l(t), t) \tag{2.1.2}$$

For notational convenience, define the following vectors:

$$x(t) = \begin{pmatrix} x_1(t) \\ x_2(t) \\ \cdot \\ \cdot \\ \cdot \\ x_n(t) \end{pmatrix}, \quad u(t) = \begin{pmatrix} u_1(t) \\ u_2(t) \\ \cdot \\ \cdot \\ \cdot \\ u_l(t) \end{pmatrix}, \quad y(t) = \begin{pmatrix} y_1(t) \\ y_2(t) \\ \cdot \\ \cdot \\ \cdot \\ y_m(t) \end{pmatrix}, \quad x_0 = \begin{pmatrix} x_{10} \\ \cdot \\ \cdot \\ \cdot \\ x_{n0} \end{pmatrix}$$

(2.1.3)

and the vector functions

$$f(x(t), u(t), t) = \begin{pmatrix} f_1(x_1(t), \ldots, u_l(t), t) \\ \vdots \\ f_n(x_1(t), \ldots, u_l(t), t) \end{pmatrix}$$

(2.1.4)

$$g(x(t), u(t), t) = \begin{pmatrix} g_1(x_1(t), \ldots, u_l(t), t) \\ \vdots \\ g_m(x_1(t), \ldots, u_l(t), t) \end{pmatrix}$$

Rewriting eqns. 2.1.1 and 2.1.2 in vector notation yields

$$\frac{dx(t)}{dt} = f(x(t), u(t), t), \quad x(0) = x_0 \qquad (2.1.5)$$

$$y(t) = g(x(t), u(t), t) \qquad (2.1.6)$$

The time-dependent vector $x(t) \in R^n$ is termed the *state vector*, $u(t) \in R^l$ the *input vector* and $y(t) \in R^m$ the *output vector*. Eqns. 2.1.5, 2.1.6 will be called the *state-vector model* of the process dynamics. It is of interest to note that a differential equation of order n can always be reduced to a set of n first-order differential equations. Consider the following scalar differential equation of order n:

$$\frac{d^n y(t)}{dt^n} = h\left(y(t), \frac{dy(t)}{dt}, \ldots, \frac{d^{n-1} y(t)}{dt^{n-1}}, u(t), t\right) \qquad (2.1.7)$$

where $u(t)$ is a scalar input function. Defining,

$$x_1(t) = y(t)$$

$$x_2(t) = \frac{dy(t)}{dt}$$

$$\vdots \qquad \vdots$$

$$x_n(t) = \frac{d^{n-1}y(t)}{dt^{n-1}}$$

then eqn. 2.1.7 reduces to

$$\frac{dx_1(t)}{dt} = x_2(t)$$

$$\vdots \qquad \vdots$$

$$\frac{dx_{n-1}(t)}{dt} = x_n(t)$$

$$\frac{dx_n(t)}{dt} = h(x_1(t), \ldots, x_n(t), u(t), t)$$

$$y(t) = x_1(t) \qquad\qquad (2.1.8)$$

which is of the form of eqns. 2.1.5 and 2.1.6

Exercise 2.1.1

Obtain a state-variable representation of the following system:

$$\frac{d^n y(t)}{dt^n} + a_1 \frac{d^{n-1}y(t)}{dt^{n-1}} + \ldots + a_{n-1} \frac{dy(t)}{dt} + a_n y(t) = u(t)$$

The analysis of the general nonlinear state-vector model of eqns. 2.1.5, 2.1.6 is a highly complex problem and the theoretical analysis of the control of such systems is a complex and largely unsolved problem. In the remainder of this text we restrict our attention to linear state-vector models. To conclude this Section, the interested reader is referred to the references[6, 33, 56] for an analysis of the state eqns. 2.1.5 in terms of uniqueness of solution and continuity with respect to variations in initial conditions and system parameters.

2.2 Linear state-vector models

The control engineer's task would indeed be an unenviable one if the mathematical description of all physical systems required, for the purposes of control system design, a general nonlinear model of the process dynamics. Fortunately, the behaviour of a large class of physical systems can be approximated, with surprising accuracy, by a set of linear state vector equations using the well known technique of linearisation[3,10] about a known operating point, which leads to a set of first-order differential equations of the form,

$$\frac{dx_i(t)}{dt} = A_{i1}x_1(t) + \ldots + A_{in}x_n(t) + B_{i1}u_1(t) + \ldots + B_{il}u_l(t),$$

$$1 \leqslant i \leqslant n$$

$$x_i(0) = x_{i0}$$

$$y_i(t) = C_{i1}x_1(t) + \ldots + C_{in}x_n(t) + D_{i1}u_1(t) + \ldots + D_{il}u_l(t)$$

$$1 \leqslant i \leqslant m \qquad (2.2.1)$$

where A_{ij}, B_{ij}, C_{ij}, D_{ij} are real constants. Defining the following constant matrices:

$$A = \begin{pmatrix} A_{11} & \cdots & A_{1n} \\ \vdots & & \vdots \\ A_{n1} & \cdots & A_{nn} \end{pmatrix}_{(n \times n)}, \quad B = \begin{pmatrix} B_{11} & \cdots & B_{1l} \\ \vdots & & \vdots \\ B_{n1} & \cdots & B_{nl} \end{pmatrix}_{(n \times l)}$$

$$C = \begin{pmatrix} C_{11} & \cdots & C_{1n} \\ & & \\ C_{m1} & \cdots & C_{mn} \end{pmatrix}_{(m \times n)}, \quad D = \begin{pmatrix} D_{11} & \cdots & D_{1l} \\ & & \\ D_{m1} & \cdots & D_{ml} \end{pmatrix}_{(m \times l)}$$

$$(2.2.2)$$

and using the notation $\dot{x}(t) = \dfrac{dx(t)}{dt}$, it is easily checked that eqns. 2.2.1 can be written in the state vector form.

$$\dot{x}(t) = Ax(t) + Bu(t), \quad x(0) = x_0$$

$$y(t) = Cx(t) + Du(t) \qquad (2.2.3)$$

where $x(t) \in R^n$, $u(t) \in R^l$, $y(t) \in R^m$ are as defined by eqn. 2.1.3. Such a mathematical model is conventionally termed a linear, time-invariant state-vector model of the process dynamics and can be represented in the block diagram form shown in Fig. 2.2.1. The diagram illustrates immediately the intuitive interpretation of D as the direct transmission or feedforward element in the system structure, the observation that B and C describe the effect of the inputs on the state dynamics and the effect of the state on the outputs, respectively, and the expectation that the A matrix (which appears in a feedback loop) will dominate the stability of the system. These topics and their relevance to design are discussed in later sections.

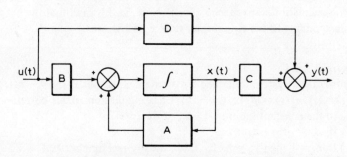

Fig. 2.2.1 Block representation of the state-vector model

2.3 Steady-state solutions to the state equations

Consider a system described by the state-vector model

$$\dot{x}(t) = f(x(t), u(t), t) \qquad (2.3.1)$$

$$y(t) = g(x(t), u(t), t) \qquad (2.3.2)$$

An equilibrium state of this system corresponding to an input $u(t)$ is a *constant* state vector x_e satisfying

$$0 = f(x_e, u(t), t) \quad \text{for all } t \qquad (2.3.3)$$

Such an equilibrium state may fail to exist, may be defined uniquely or there may exist a finite or infinite number of equilibrium states corresponding to the input $u(t)$. It is easily shown that the solution of the state-vector equation

$$\dot{x}(t) = f(x(t), u(t), t), \quad x(0) = x_e \qquad (2.3.4)$$

is simply $x(t) \equiv x_e \ (t \geqslant 0)$ and hence that an equilibrium state x_e corresponding to an input $u(t)$ is simply a constant solution to the state equations. Note, however, that the corresponding output $y(t) = g(x_e, u(t), t)$ may fail to be constant.

In practical applications, the most common situation is that f, g do not depend explicitly on the time variable t and that it is required to find the equilibrium state corresponding to a known constant input $u(t) \equiv u_0$ i.e. the equilibrium state is a solution of the equation

$$f(x_e, u_0) = 0 \qquad (2.3.5)$$

which is of a much simpler form than eqn. 2.3.3 owing to the absence of the time variable t, and can be solved for the solution vectors x_e using standard iterative techniques.[51] Note, in this case, that the output corresponding to the equilibrium state x_e is constant.

Exercise 2.3.1
Show that a system described by the state equations $\dot{x}_1(t) = -x_1(t) + u(t)x_2(t)$, $\dot{x}_2(t) = u(t)x_1(t) - x_2(t)$ has equilibrium states corresponding to the constant input $u(t) \equiv u_0$ of the form
(a) If $u_0^2 \neq 1$ then $x_e = 0$
(b) If $u_0 = 1$ then $x_e = \lambda\{1, \quad 1\}^T$, for any real number λ.
(c) If $u_0 = -1$ then $x_e = \lambda\{-1, \quad 1\}^T$, for any real number λ.

Of particular interest in applications is a consideration of the equilibrium states of a linear time-invariant state-vector model of the form of eqn. 2.2.3. In this case an equilibrium state x_e corresponding to the input $u(t)$ is a solution of the relation,

$$Ax_e = -Bu(t) \quad \text{for all } t \qquad (2.3.6)$$

from which it follows directly that, if rank $B = l$, the system possesses equilibrium states x_e corresponding to the input $u(t)$ only if $u(t)$ is constant, $u(t) \equiv u_0$ i.e.

$$Ax_e = -Bu_0 \qquad (2.3.7)$$

If A is nonsingular then the unique equilibrium state is $x_e = -A^{-1}Bu_0$. If A is singular then there may exist no equilibrium state or an infinite number of equilibrium states. To prove this statement, let $\tilde{x}_e$ be a known equilibrium state and let u be a nonzero eigenvector of A corresponding to the eigenvalue zero, then $Au = 0$ and it is easily checked that $x_e = \tilde{x}_e + \lambda u$ is an equilibrium state for any real number λ. Conversely, if x_e is any equilibrium state then $A(x_e - \tilde{x}_e) = 0$ so that $x_e = \tilde{x}_e + u$ where u is an eigenvector of A with zero eigenvalue.

Exercise 2.3.2

Calculate all possible equilibrium states of the linear time-invariant system described by the matrices

$$A = \begin{pmatrix} -1 & 1 & 0 \\ 1 & -2 & 1 \\ 0 & 1 & -1 \end{pmatrix}, \quad B = \begin{pmatrix} 1 \\ -1 \\ 0 \end{pmatrix}$$

corresponding to the constant input $u(t) \equiv u_0 = 1$. (Hint: calculate a single solution of the algebraic equation $A\tilde{x}_e = -B$ and show that the equation $Au = 0$ has only one linearly independent solution vector u. Finally write $x_e = \tilde{x}_e + \lambda u$, where λ is an arbitrary real number).

2.4 Transformation of scalar differential equations to state-vector form

Consider the problem of deriving a state-vector representation of the scalar differential equation with constant coefficients,

$$\overset{(n)}{y} + a_1 \overset{(n-1)}{y} + \ldots + a_{n-1}\dot{y} + a_n y = b_0 \overset{(n)}{u} + b_1 \overset{(n-1)}{u} + \ldots + b_n u \tag{2.4.1}$$

or, equivalently, the problem of deriving a state vector representation of a single-input, single-output system described by the transfer function

$$g(s) = \frac{s^n b_0 + s^{n-1} b_1 + \ldots + b_n}{s^n + a_1 s^{n-1} + \ldots + a_n} \tag{2.4.2}$$

There are many ways of obtaining a solution to this problem. Three methods of particular simplicity and interest are described below.

Method 1: A characterisation of a state-vector model in terms of the coefficients $b_0, b_1, \ldots, b_n, a_1, \ldots, a_n$ is obtained by defining state variables

$$x_1 = y - b_0 u$$
$$x_2 = \dot{x}_1 + a_1 y - b_1 u$$
$$x_3 = \dot{x}_2 + a_2 y - b_2 u$$
$$\vdots \qquad \vdots$$
$$x_n = \dot{x}_{n-1} + a_{n-1} y - b_{n-1} u \tag{2.4.3}$$

from which, using eqn. 2.4.1, it is easily shown that

$$\dot{x}_n = -a_n y + b_n u \qquad (2.4.4)$$

from which, the derived state-vector model is obtained as

$$
\begin{pmatrix} \dot{x}_1 \\ \dot{x}_2 \\ \vdots \\ \vdots \\ \vdots \\ \dot{x}_n \end{pmatrix} =
\begin{pmatrix}
-a_1 & 1 & 0 & \cdots & 0 \\
-a_2 & 0 & 1 & \cdots & 0 \\
\vdots & & & & \vdots \\
& & & & 0 \\
& \vdots & 0 & 0 & \cdots & 1 \\
-a_n & 0 & 0 & \cdots & 0
\end{pmatrix}
\begin{pmatrix} x_1 \\ x_2 \\ \vdots \\ \vdots \\ \vdots \\ x_n \end{pmatrix} +
\begin{pmatrix}
b_1 & -a_1 b_0 \\
b_2 & -a_2 b_0 \\
\vdots & \vdots \\
\vdots & \vdots \\
b_n & -a_n b_0
\end{pmatrix} u
$$

$$
y = (1 \quad 0 \quad \cdots \quad 0)
\begin{pmatrix} x_1 \\ x_2 \\ \vdots \\ \vdots \\ x_n \end{pmatrix} + b_0 u \qquad (2.4.5)
$$

Exercise 2.4.1

Show that the state variables of eqn. 2.4.3 can be defined by the relation

$$
\begin{pmatrix} x_1 \\ x_2 \\ \vdots \\ \vdots \\ x_n \end{pmatrix} =
\begin{pmatrix}
1 & 0 & \cdots & 0 \\
a_1 & 1 & \cdots & 0 \\
\vdots & & \vdots \\
\vdots & & \vdots \\
a_{n-1} & a_{n-2} & \cdots & 1
\end{pmatrix}
\begin{pmatrix} y \\ \dot{y} \\ \vdots \\ \vdots \\ \overset{(n-1)}{y} \end{pmatrix}
$$

$$
+
\begin{pmatrix}
-b_0 & 0 & \cdots & 0 \\
-b_1 & -b_0 & & \vdots \\
\vdots & & \vdots \\
\vdots & & \vdots \\
-b_{n-1} & -b_{n-2} & \cdots & -b_0
\end{pmatrix}
\begin{pmatrix} u \\ \dot{u} \\ \vdots \\ \vdots \\ \overset{(n-1)}{u} \end{pmatrix}
\qquad (2.4.6)
$$

and consider how this equation can be used to define the initial condition on the states $x_1(0), x_2(0), \ldots, x_n(0)$ in terms of the boundary conditions $y(0), \ldots, \overset{(n-1)}{y}(0)$ and knowledge of the system input.

In many cases of practical interest $b_0 = 0$ when eqn. 2.4.5 takes a particularly simple form which can be obtained by inspection from the system transfer function. If, as is often the case in control applications, $y(0) = \dot{y}(0) = \ldots = \overset{(n-1)}{y}(0) = u(0) = \ldots = \overset{(n-1)}{u}(0) = 0$ then $0 = x_1(0) = x_2(0)) \ldots = x_n(0)$ i.e. the assumption of zero initial conditions on the output and input is equivalent to the use of zero initial conditions for the state variables. For example, if a system is described by the scalar differential equation

$$\ddot{y} + 2\dot{y} + y = \dot{u} + 2u$$

$$y(0) = \dot{y}(0) = u(0) = 0 \qquad (2.4.7)$$

then a suitable set of state variables are defined by eqn. 2.4.6 as

$$\begin{pmatrix} x_1 \\ x_2 \end{pmatrix} = \begin{pmatrix} 1 & 0 \\ 2 & 1 \end{pmatrix} \begin{pmatrix} y \\ \dot{y} \end{pmatrix} + \begin{pmatrix} 0 & 0 \\ -1 & 0 \end{pmatrix} \begin{pmatrix} u \\ \dot{u} \end{pmatrix} \qquad (2.4.8)$$

which gives the state-vector model,

$$\dot{x}(t) = \begin{pmatrix} -2 & 1 \\ -1 & 0 \end{pmatrix} x(t) + \begin{pmatrix} 1 \\ 2 \end{pmatrix} u(t)$$

$$x(0) = (0 \quad 0)^T$$

$$y(t) = (1 \quad 0)x(t) \qquad (2.4.9)$$

Method 2: (a decomposition using poles) Method one requires no knowledge of the system poles and zeros. If, however the system poles are known the following technique can be applied. Suppose that the system poles are $\lambda_1, \lambda_2, \ldots, \lambda_n$ (not necessarily distinct and possibly complex) then the transfer function eqn. 2.4.2 can be decomposed into the form

$$g(s) = \left\{ \gamma_0 + \frac{1}{(s-\lambda_1)} \left\{ \gamma_1 + \frac{1}{(s-\lambda_2)} \left\{ \gamma_2 + \frac{1}{s-\lambda_3} \right\} \ldots \right. \right.$$

$$+ \frac{\gamma_n}{(s - \lambda_n)} \Bigg\} \Bigg\} \Bigg\} \cdots \Bigg\} \tag{2.4.10}$$

which has the form shown in Fig. 2.4.1. Defining the states x_j, $1 \leqslant j \leqslant n$, to be the output from the first-order lag $1/(s - \lambda_j)$ in Fig. 2.4.1, the following equations are obtained:

$$y = x_1 + \gamma_0 u$$

$$\dot{x}_1 = \lambda_1 x_1 + x_2 + \gamma_1 u$$

$$\dot{x}_2 = \lambda_2 x_2 + x_3 + \gamma_2 u$$

$$\vdots \qquad \vdots$$

$$\dot{x}_n = \lambda_n x_n + \gamma_n u \tag{2.4.11}$$

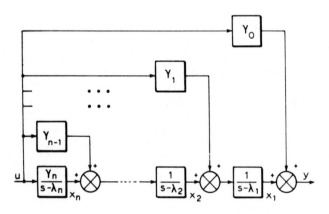

Fig. 2.4.1

or, in state-vector form,

$$
\begin{pmatrix} \dot{x}_1 \\ \dot{x}_2 \\ \vdots \\ \vdots \\ \dot{x}_n \end{pmatrix} =
\begin{pmatrix} \lambda_1 & 1 & 0 & \cdots & 0 \\ 0 & \lambda_2 & 1 & & \cdot \\ \vdots & & & & \vdots \\ \vdots & & & \lambda_{n-1} & 1 \\ 0 & \cdots & \cdots & 0 & \lambda_n \end{pmatrix}
\begin{pmatrix} x_1 \\ x_2 \\ \vdots \\ \vdots \\ x_n \end{pmatrix} +
\begin{pmatrix} \gamma_1 \\ \gamma_2 \\ \vdots \\ \vdots \\ \gamma_n \end{pmatrix} u
$$

$$y = (1 \quad 0 \quad \ldots \quad 0) \begin{pmatrix} x_1 \\ \cdot \\ \cdot \\ \cdot \\ x_n \end{pmatrix} + \gamma_0 u \qquad (2.4.12)$$

Note that the poles of $g(s)$ become the eigenvalues of the matrix A (a special case of a general result obtained in later sections).

The initial conditions for the state variables can be obtained by application of the following general technique applied to eqn. 2.2.3 with $m = l = 1$ by sequential differentiation of the output equation $y = Cx + Du$ i.e.

$$y(0) = Cx(0) + Du(0)$$

$$\dot{y}(0) = CAx(0) + CBu(0) + D\dot{u}(0)$$

$$\cdot \qquad \qquad \cdot$$
$$\cdot \qquad \qquad \cdot$$
$$\cdot \qquad \qquad \cdot$$

$$\overset{(n-1)}{y}(0) = CA^{n-1}x(0) + CA^{n-2}Bu(0) + \ldots + CB\overset{(n-2)}{u}(0) + D\overset{(n-1)}{u}(0)$$
$$(2.4.13)$$

Rearranging these equations, it is easily seen that $x(0)$ is a solution of the equation

$$\begin{pmatrix} C \\ CA \\ \cdot \\ \cdot \\ \cdot \\ CA^{n-1} \end{pmatrix} x(0) = d \qquad (2.4.14)$$

where d is defined by eqn. 2.4.13 and the initial conditions on y and u.

Method 3: (a decomposition using zeros) Consider a system described by the linear scalar differential equation with constant coefficients

$$\overset{(n)}{y} + a_1 \overset{(n-1)}{y} + \ldots + a_{n-1}\dot{y} + a_n y = b_1 \overset{(n-1)}{u} + \ldots + b_n u$$
$$(2.4.15)$$

Let k be the smallest integer greater than or equal to one such that $b_k \neq 0$, then the $n - k$ zeros of the system $z_1, z_2, \ldots, z_{n-k}$ satisfy the relation

$$b_k s^{n-k} + \ldots + b_{n-1}s + b_n = b_k(s - z_1) \ldots (s - z_{n-k})$$
$$(2.4.16)$$

The inverse transfer function takes the form

$$g^{-1}(s) = b_k^{-1}\left\{ s^k + \hat{a}_1 s^{k-1} + \ldots + \hat{a}_k + \frac{c_1 s^{n-k-1} + \ldots + c_{n-k}}{(s-z_1)(s-z_2)\ldots(s-z_{n-k})}\right\}$$

which indicates that eqn. 2.4.15 is equivalent to the two scalar differential equations

$$\overset{(k)}{y} + \hat{a}_1 \overset{(k-1)}{y} + \ldots + \hat{a}_k y = b_k u - v \tag{2.4.17}$$

$$\overset{(n-k)}{v} + \frac{b_{k-1}}{b_k} \overset{(n-k-1)}{v} + \ldots + \frac{b_n v}{b_k} = c_1 \overset{(n-k-1)}{y} + \ldots + c_{n-k} y \tag{2.4.18}$$

Application of method 1 to eqn. 2.4.17 leads to the state-vector model

$$\dot{w}_1 = \begin{pmatrix} -\hat{a}_1 & 1 & 0 & \cdots & 0 \\ -\hat{a}_2 & 0 & 1 & & \vdots \\ \vdots & & & & \vdots \\ & & & & 0 \\ & & & & 1 \\ -\hat{a}_k & 0 & \cdots & \cdots & 0 \end{pmatrix} w_1 + \begin{pmatrix} 0 \\ 0 \\ \vdots \\ \vdots \\ 0 \\ 1 \end{pmatrix} (b_k u - v)$$

$$y = (1 \quad 0 \quad \cdots \quad 0) w_1 \tag{2.4.19}$$

Application of method 2 to eqn. 2.4.18 leads to a state-vector model of the form

$$\dot{w}_2 = \begin{pmatrix} z_1 & 1 & 0 & \cdots & 0 \\ 0 & z_2 & 1 & & \vdots \\ \vdots & & & & \vdots \\ & & & & 1 \\ 0 & \cdots & 0 & & z_{n-k} \end{pmatrix} w_2 + \begin{pmatrix} \gamma_1 \\ \gamma_2 \\ \vdots \\ \vdots \\ \gamma_{n-k} \end{pmatrix} y$$

$$v = (1 \quad 0 \quad \cdots \quad 0) w_2 \tag{2.4.20}$$

Combination of eqns. 2.4.19 and 2.4.20 with the state vector $x(t) = (w_1(t)^T, w_2(t)^T)^T$ yields

$$\dot{x}(t) = \begin{pmatrix} -\hat{a}_1 & 1 & 0 & \cdots & 0 & 0 & \cdots & \cdots & 0 \\ -\hat{a}_2 & 0 & 1 & & & & & & \vdots \\ \vdots & \vdots & & & 1 & 0 & & & \\ -\hat{a}_k & 0 & \cdots & \cdots & 0 & (-1) & 0 & \cdots & 0 \\ \gamma_1 & 0 & \cdots & \cdots & 0 & z_1 & 1 & 0 \cdots & 0 \\ \gamma_2 & 0 & \cdots & \cdots & 0 & 0 & z_2 & 1 & \vdots \\ \vdots & \vdots & & & & & 0 & & \vdots \\ \vdots & \vdots & & & & & & & 1 \\ \gamma_{n-k} & 0 & \cdots & \cdots & 0 & 0 & \cdots & 0 & z_{n-k} \end{pmatrix} x(t)$$

$$+ \begin{pmatrix} 0 \\ \vdots \\ 0 \\ b_k \\ 0 \\ \vdots \\ \vdots \\ 0 \end{pmatrix} u(t)$$

$$y(t) = (1 \quad 0 \quad \cdots \quad 0)x(t) \qquad (2.4.21)$$

The initial condition $x(0)$ can be obtained using the techniques of eqns. 2.4.13 and 2.4.14.

Example 2.4.1 Consider a system described by the transfer function

$$g(s) = \frac{s+1}{s^3 + 5s^2 + 6s} = \frac{(s+1)}{s(s+2)(s+3)} \qquad (2.4.22)$$

Applying method 1, the state-space model is obtained by noting that $n = 3, b_0 = b_1 = 0, b_2 = b_3 = 1, a_1 = 5, a_2 = 6, a_3 = 0$ from which

$$\dot{x} = \begin{pmatrix} -5 & 1 & 0 \\ -6 & 0 & 1 \\ 0 & 0 & 0 \end{pmatrix} x + \begin{pmatrix} 0 \\ 1 \\ 1 \end{pmatrix} u$$

$$y = (1 \quad 0 \quad 0)x \qquad (2.4.23)$$

To apply method 2, decompose the transfer function into the form

$$g(s) = \frac{1}{s} \cdot \frac{1}{s+2} \left\{ 1 - \frac{2}{s+3} \right\} \qquad (2.4.24)$$

from which $\gamma_0 = \gamma_1 = 0$, $\gamma_2 = 1$, $\gamma_3 = -2$ and hence a state-vector model takes the form

$$\dot{x} = \begin{pmatrix} 0 & 1 & 0 \\ 0 & -2 & 1 \\ 0 & 0 & -3 \end{pmatrix} x + \begin{pmatrix} 0 \\ 1 \\ -2 \end{pmatrix} u$$

$$y = (1 \quad 0 \quad 0)x \qquad (2.4.25)$$

Finally, to apply method 3, note that $k = 2, b_2 = 1$, and.

$$g^{-1}(s) = s^2 + 4s + 2 - \frac{2}{s+1} \qquad (2.4.26)$$

from which $\gamma_1 = -2, \hat{a}_1 = 4, \hat{a}_2 = 2$ and

$$\dot{x} = \begin{pmatrix} -4 & 1 & 0 \\ -2 & 0 & -1 \\ -2 & 0 & -1 \end{pmatrix} x + \begin{pmatrix} 0 \\ 1 \\ 0 \end{pmatrix} u$$

$$y = (1 \quad 0 \quad 0)x \qquad (2.4.27)$$

2.5 State-vector model of a two-vessel liquid storage system

Consider the simple two-vessel liquid storage system illustrated in Fig. 2.5.1 consisting of two interconnected tanks each of uniform cross-section and areas a_1, a_2, respectively. Let $q_i(t), i = 1, 2$, denote the input flow rate into vessel i (m^3/s), $h_i(t), i = 1, 2$, denote the height of the liquid in vessel i and let $V_i(t) = a_i h_i(t), i = 1, 2$, be the volume of liquid in vessel *i*. Assume that the system is subject to disturbances $d_i(t), i = 1, 2$, representing outlet flow rates (m³/s) demanded by the next stage of the process.

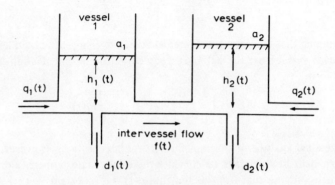

Fig. 2.5.1 Two-vessel liquid storage system

Elementary physical considerations lead to the following differential equations describing the dynamics of the process:

$$\dot{V}_1(t) = q_1(t) - f(t) - d_1(t) = a_1 \dot{h}_1(t)$$
$$\dot{V}_2(t) = q_2(t) + f(t) - d_2(t) = a_2 \dot{h}_2(t) \qquad (2.5.1)$$

where $f(t)$ is the flow rate (m³/s) from vessel one into vessel two. Also if d_{10}, d_{20} are constant disturbances then it is anticipated that the system will have a steady state with constant inlet flow rates q_{10}, q_{20} and constant intervessel flow f_0 satisfying the equations

$$q_{10} = f_0 + d_{10}$$
$$q_{20} = -f_0 + d_{20} \qquad (2.5.2)$$

Let $h_{i0}, i = 1, 2$, to be the corresponding constant levels of liquid in the vessels, and define

$$h_i(t) = h_{i0} + x_i(t), \qquad i = 1, 2$$
$$q_i(t) = q_{i0} + u_i(t), \qquad i = 1, 2$$
$$d_i(t) = d_{i0} + l_i(t), \qquad i = 1, 2$$
$$f(t) \simeq f_0 + \beta\{x_1(t) - x_2(t)\} \qquad (2.5.3)$$

then the following small perturbation model of the system is obtained:

$$u(t) = (u_1(t), u_2(t))^T, x(t) = (x_1(t), x_2(t))^T, l(t) = (l_1(t), l_2(t))$$

$$\dot{x}(t) = \begin{pmatrix} \dfrac{-\beta}{a_1} & \dfrac{\beta}{a_1} \\[2mm] \dfrac{\beta}{a_2} & \dfrac{-\beta}{a_2} \end{pmatrix} x(t) + \begin{pmatrix} \dfrac{1}{a_1} & 0 \\[2mm] 0 & \dfrac{1}{a_2} \end{pmatrix} \{u(t) - l(t)\}$$

$$(2.5.4)$$

Assuming that the output measurements are the changes in liquid height in each vessel from the defined steady state, the output relation takes the form

$$y(t) = \begin{pmatrix} 1 & 0 \\ 0 & 1 \end{pmatrix} x(t) + \begin{pmatrix} 0 & 0 \\ 0 & 0 \end{pmatrix} u(t)$$

$$(2.5.5)$$

A detailed analysis of this model is left for later sections. However, it is convenient at this stage to consider the steady-state properties of the model. Suppose that $l(t) = 0$ and that $u(t) = \alpha$ (constant vector) then, examination of the steady-state relation

$$\begin{pmatrix} \dfrac{-\beta}{a_1} & \dfrac{\beta}{a_1} \\[2mm] \dfrac{\beta}{a_2} & \dfrac{-\beta}{a_2} \end{pmatrix} x_e = - \begin{pmatrix} \dfrac{1}{a_1} & 0 \\[2mm] 0 & \dfrac{1}{a_2} \end{pmatrix} \alpha$$

indicates that the system has no steady state unless $\alpha = \lambda\{-1, 1\}^T$, for some real scalar λ, reflecting the fact that the total volume of fluid in the vessels vary with time unless $\alpha_1 + \alpha_2 = 0$.

Exercise 2.5.1
Show that the liquid-level system has an infinite number of steady states corresponding to constant inputs $\alpha = \lambda\{-1, 1\}^T$. Interpret this result in terms of the physical structure of the plant.

2.6 State-vector model of a coupled spring-mass-damper system

Consider the mechanical system illustrated in Fig. 2.6.1 where m_1, m_2 are constant masses moving on a horizontal friction-free surface. The springs are assumed to have stiffness constants k_1, k_2 and the light damper has a damping constant c. The inputs to the system $u_1(t), u_2(t)$ are taken to be the displacement of the outer ends of each spring from a nominal steady-state position and the system outputs $y_1(t), y_2(t)$ are the displacements of the masses m_1, m_2, respectively, from the steady-state condition. Applying Newton's laws yields the equation of motion

$$m_1 \ddot{y}_1 = k_1(u_1 - y_1) + c(\dot{y}_2 - \dot{y}_1)$$
$$m_2 \ddot{y}_2 = -k_2(y_2 - u_2) - c(\dot{y}_2 - \dot{y}_1) \qquad (2.6.1)$$

Defining the states $x_1 = y_1, x_2 = y_2, x_3 = \dot{y}_1, x_4 = \dot{y}_2$ then it is left as an exercise for the reader to show that the system has a state-vector model of the form

$$\dot{x}(t) = \begin{pmatrix} 0 & 0 & 1 & 0 \\ 0 & 0 & 0 & 1 \\ \dfrac{-k_1}{m_1} & 0 & \dfrac{-c}{m_1} & \dfrac{c}{m_1} \\ 0 & \dfrac{-k_2}{m_2} & \dfrac{c}{m_2} & \dfrac{-c}{m_2} \end{pmatrix} x(t) + \begin{pmatrix} 0 & 0 \\ 0 & 0 \\ \dfrac{k_1}{m_1} & 0 \\ 0 & \dfrac{k_2}{m_2} \end{pmatrix} u(t)$$

$$y(t) = \begin{pmatrix} 1 & 0 & 0 & 0 \\ 0 & 1 & 0 & 0 \end{pmatrix} x(t) + \begin{pmatrix} 0 & 0 \\ 0 & 0 \end{pmatrix} u(t) \qquad (2.6.2)$$

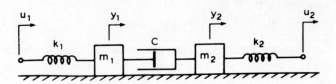

Fig. 2.6.1 Simple mechanical system

2.7 Solution of the state equations

The solution of the state equations for a given initial condition and a known input vector $u(t)$ is obviously an important practical aspect of the assessment of system dynamics, control difficulties and the evaluation of a proposed control scheme. We restrict our attention to linear state-vector models of the form

$$\dot{x}(t) = A(t)x(t) + B(t)u(t), \quad x(0) = x_0$$
$$y(t) = C(t)x(t) \qquad (2.7.1)$$

where $A(t)$, $B(t)$, $C(t)$ are $n \times n$, $n \times l$, $m \times n$ time-varying matrices, respectively.

For simplicity consider the homogeneous (or free response) case of eqn. 2.7.1 i.e. $u(t) \equiv 0$ and

$$\dot{x}(t) = A(t)x(t), \qquad x(0) = x_0 \qquad (2.7.2)$$

The solution of this equation can be characterised in a manner independent of the initial condition by considering the solution of the matrix differential equation,

$$\frac{d}{dt}\Phi(t,s) = A(t)\Phi(t,s)$$

$$\Phi(s,s) = I_n \qquad (2.7.3)$$

where $\Phi(t,s)$ is termed the system transition matrix and is a function of the two variables (t,s). The solution to eqn. 2.7.2 is then easily obtained by setting

$$x(t) = \Phi(t,0)x(0) \qquad (2.7.4)$$

which is the solution of eqn. 2.7.2 as is easily checked by the calculation

$$\dot{x}(t) = \frac{d}{dt}\Phi(t,0)x(0) = A(t)\Phi(t,0)x(0) = A(t)x(t)$$

$$x_0 = \Phi(0,0)x(0) = x(0) \qquad (2.7.5)$$

More generally, we can write for any time points t_1, t_2

$$x(t_2) = \Phi(t_2,t_1)x(t_1) \qquad (2.7.6)$$

i.e. the transition matrix is a linear operation describing the functional relationship between any two points of the system response, in the absence of control input. In particular, from eqn. 2.7.6

$$x(t_1) = \Phi(t_1,t_2)x(t_2) = \Phi(t_1,t_2)\Phi(t_2,t_3)x(t_3) \quad (2.7.7)$$

This relation is valid, in particular, for $t_3 = t_1$ independent of the choice of $x(t_1)$ i.e. for all choices of t_1, t_2.

$$\Phi(t_1,t_2)\Phi(t_2,t_1) = I_n \qquad (2.7.8)$$

so that $\Phi(t,s)$ is nonsingular for all (t,s) and

$$\Phi(s,t) = (\Phi(t,s))^{-1} \qquad (2.7.9)$$

A more detailed discussion of the mathematical properties of the transition matrix can be found in Reference 33.

Turning our attention to the case of linear time-invariant systems when $A(t)$ is simply an $n \times n$ constant matrix A, it is easily verified that

$$\Phi(t, s) = e^{A(t-s)} \tag{2.7.10}$$

as, recalling the definition of the matrix exponential,

$$e^{A(t-s)} = I_n + A(t-s) + \frac{A^2}{2!}(t-s)^2 + \ldots$$

$$= \sum_{j=0}^{\infty} \frac{A^j}{j!}(t-s)^j \tag{2.7.11}$$

it follows directly that $e^{A(t-s)} = I_n$ if $t = s$, and

$$\frac{d}{dt}e^{A(t-s)} = A + A^2(t-s) + \ldots = Ae^{A(t-s)} \tag{2.7.12}$$

as required by eqns. 2.7.3.

Turning our attention to the case of nonzero input vectors $u(t)$, and defining

$$x(t) = \Phi(t, 0)z(t) \tag{2.7.13}$$

then $z(0) = x(0) = x_0$ and differentiating, with subsequent application of eqn. 2.7.3,

$$\dot{x}(t) = A(t)x(t) + B(t)u(t) = \left(\frac{d}{dt}\Phi(t, 0)\right)z(t) + \Phi(t, 0)\dot{z}(t)$$

$$= A(t)x(t) + \Phi(t, 0)\dot{z}(t) \tag{2.7.14}$$

Rearranging and integrating yields the unique solution for $z(t)$

$$z(t) = x(0) + \int_0^t (\Phi(s, 0))^{-1} B(s)u(s)ds \tag{2.7.15}$$

or, using eqns. 2.7.13, 2.7.8 and 2.7.9

$$x(t) = \Phi(t, 0)x(0) + \int_0^t \Phi(t, s)B(s)u(s)ds$$

$$y(t) = C(t)x(t) \tag{2.7.16}$$

This expression is the formal solution of the relations eqn. 2.7.1 expressed in terms of the transition matrix solution of eqn. 2.7.3. In general, the solution of eqn. 2.7.3 can be a formidable computational task as it is necessary to solve the matrix differential equation for each value of s in the time interval of interest. The task is fortunately very much simpler if the system is time-invariant when the transition matrix is defined by the matrix exponential eqns. 2.7.10, 2.7.11 i.e.

$$x(t) = e^{At}x(0) + \int_0^t e^{A(t-s)}Bu(s)ds$$

$$y(t) = Cx(t) \tag{2.7.17}$$

which is the case of interest in the remaining chapters of this text.

2.8 Calculation of e^{At} and system modal behaviour

The systematic calculation of e^{At} has been discussed in detail in many texts[15, 33, 56] so we restrict our attention to three techniques relevant to the spirit of this text:

Method 1: (direct numerical approximation) If t is not too large, then we can truncate the series characterisation after a finite number of terms M,

$$e^{At} \simeq \sum_{j=0}^{M} \frac{A^j}{j!} t^j \tag{2.8.1}$$

This technique is not to be recommended as a means of solving the state equations, however, as it requires excessive computational effort and storage and the reader is better advised to solve the state-vector equating directly using well known numerical integration routines.

Method 2: (Laplace-transformation method) An interesting and conceptionally useful approach to the calculation of e^{At} is obtained by taking the Laplace transform[56] of eqns. 2.7.2 where $A(t)$ is taken to be the constant matrix A, yielding

$$sx(s) - x(0) = Ax(s) \tag{2.8.2}$$

where s is the Laplace transform variable and $x(s)$ is to be interpreted as the Laplace transform of the state vector $x(t)$. Rearranging and denoting the operation of taking the inverse Laplace transform by $\mathcal{L}^{-1}$ yields

$$x(t) = \{\mathcal{L}^{-1}(sI_n - A)^{-1}\}x(0) \tag{2.8.3}$$

Bearing in mind the uniqueness of the solution $x(t) = \Phi(t, 0)x(0) = e^{At}x(0)$, it follows directly that

$$e^{At} = \mathcal{L}^{-1}(sI_n - A)^{-1} \tag{2.8.4}$$

i.e. e^{At} can be computed by evaluating $(sI - A)^{-1}$ as a matrix whose elements are rational polynomials in s and using standard tables to take the inverse Laplace transform of $(sI_n - A)^{-1}$ element by element.

Method 3: (eigenvector transformation and modal behaviour) Suppose, for simplicity that the matrix A has distinct eigenvalues $\lambda_1, \lambda_2, \ldots, \lambda_n$ with corresponding eigenvectors $w_1, w_2, \ldots, w_n$, then, defining the eigenvector matrix or modal matrix

$$E = [w_1, w_2, \ldots, w_n] \tag{2.8.5}$$

it follows that $E^{-1}AE = \text{diag}\{\lambda_1, \lambda_2, \ldots, \lambda_n\}$ and, in particular,

$$e^{At} = Ee^{E^{-1}AEt}E^{-1} = E \,\text{diag}\{e^{\lambda_1 t}, e^{\lambda_2 t}, \ldots, e^{\lambda_n t}\} E^{-1} \tag{2.8.6}$$

That is, the transition matrix can be evaluated by calculation of the eigenvectors and eigenvalues of A (no trivial task if n is large) and construction of e^{At} from eqn. 2.8.6. In practice, the technique is feasible but the decomposition is probably more important to the conceptual understanding of system dynamics as discussed later in this Section and subsequent discussions of system transfer-function matrices.

Eqn. 2.8.6 is seen to hold if A has multiple eigenvalues but n linearly-independent eigenvectors. If, however, A does not have n linearly-independent eigenvectors we can choose a transformation T such that $T^{-1}AT$ is in Jordan canonical form

$$T^{-1}AT = \text{block diag}\{J_1, \ldots, J_p\} \tag{2.8.7}$$

where J_i, $1 \leqslant i \leqslant p$, is a Jordan block corresponding to an eigenvalue λ_i i.e.

$$T^{-1}e^{At}T = \text{block diag}\{e^{J_1 t}, e^{J_2 t}, \ldots, e^{J_p t}\} \tag{2.8.8}$$

Considering this expression block by block it is left as an exercise for the reader to show that, if

$$J_i = \begin{pmatrix} \lambda_i & 1 & 0 & \ldots & 0 \\ 0 & \lambda_i & 1 & & \vdots \\ \vdots & & \ddots & & 0 \\ \vdots & & & \ddots & 1 \\ 0 & \ldots & \ldots & 0 & \lambda_i \end{pmatrix} (n_i \times n_i) \tag{2.8.9}$$

then

$$e^{J_i t} = \begin{pmatrix} e^{\lambda_i t} & te^{\lambda_i t} & \ldots & \dfrac{t^{n_i-1}}{(n_i - 1)!}\, e^{\lambda_i t} \\ 0 & e^{\lambda_i t} & te^{\lambda_i t} & \vdots \\ \vdots & & \ddots & \ddots & te^{\lambda_i t} \\ 0 & \ldots & \ldots & 0 & e^{\lambda_i t} \end{pmatrix} \tag{2.8.10}$$

For example, if $n_i = 2$

$$e^{J_i t} = \begin{pmatrix} e^{\lambda_i t} & t e^{\lambda_i t} \\ 0 & e^{\lambda_i t} \end{pmatrix} \tag{2.8.12}$$

The eigenvector-transformation technique is a powerful tool for revealing the physical nature of a linear time-invariant system. For simplicity, suppose that A has distinct eigenvalues $\lambda_1, \ldots, \lambda_n$ with eigenvector matrix E and define a new state vector $z(t)$ by the relation

$$x(t) = E z(t) \tag{2.8.12}$$

from which the relations $\dot{x} = E \dot{z} = Ax + Bu = AEz + Bu$ immediately yield the state-vector model

$$\dot{z}(t) = E^{-1} AEz(t) + E^{-1} Bu(t)$$

$$y(t) = CEz(t), \quad z(0) = E^{-1} x(0) \tag{2.8.13}$$

which can be regarded as an equivalent description of the system dynamics. It follows from the definition of E that, element by element,

$$\dot{z}_i(t) = \lambda_i z_i(t) + \beta_i^T u(t), \qquad 1 \leqslant i \leqslant n, \tag{2.8.14}$$

where β_i^T is the ith row of $E^{-1} B$. The interesting point here is that the dynamics of the 'modal variables' $z_i(t)$, $1 \leqslant i \leqslant n$, are independent, depending only on the initial condition and input vector $u(t)$, and characterised by the poles λ_i, $1 \leqslant i \leqslant n$. The eigenvectors $w_1, \ldots, w_n$ are termed the modal vectors or simply the modes of the system and describe characteristic behaviour patterns of the state in the absence of inputs. This observation can be strengthened by considering the homogeneous system with the initial condition $x(0) = w_i$, when

$$x(t) = e^{At} w_i = e^{\lambda_i t} w_i \tag{2.8.15}$$

i.e. the state remains unchanged in direction but has an amplitude varying in a characteristic manner dictated by the eigenvalue λ_i. More generally, eqn. 2.8.12 indicates that

$$x(t) = \sum_{j=1}^{n} w_j z_j(t) \tag{2.8.16}$$

or, equivalently, the state response can be represented as a linear combination of the system modes with amplitudes governing by independent first-order scalar differential equations. In the homogeneous case (i.e. $u(t) \equiv 0$) eqn. 2.8.14 indicates that

$$x(t) = \sum_{j=1}^{n} w_j z_j(0) e^{\lambda_j t} \tag{2.8.17}$$

which can yield useful insight into the system behaviour as $t \to \infty$[54].
For example, suppose that $\lambda_n < \lambda_{n-1} < \ldots < \lambda_2 < \lambda_1 < 0$ (all λ_i real)
then, for large values of time t, the state has the asymptotic form

$$x(t) \simeq w_1 z_1(0) e^{\lambda_1 t} \qquad (2.8.18)$$

indicates that the largest eigenvalue of A dominates the asymptotic
state response. If system inputs are considered, the situation becomes
more complex as the magnitude of the row vectors β_i^T, $1 \leqslant i \leqslant n$, plays
an important role in dictating the relative contribution of the modal
variables to the output response and is better discussed in the context
of the system transfer-function matrix.

Finally, if A does not have a diagonal canonical form the transformation T of eqn. 2.8.7 can be used in place of E to generate p noninteracting state-vector models

$$\dot{z}_j(t) = J_j z_j(t) + \beta_j u(t), \qquad 1 \leqslant j \leqslant p \qquad (2.8.19)$$

Here $z^T(t) = \{z_1^T(t), \ldots, z_p^T(t)\}$, $E^{-1}B = [\beta_1^T, \ldots, \beta_p^T]^T$ where $z_i(t)$
is an $n_i \times 1$ vector and β_i is of dimension $n_i \times l$, $1 \leqslant i \leqslant p$.

Exercise 2.8.1
Using the data $a_1 = a_2 = 1$, calculate the transition matrix of the
coupled liquid-level system of eqn. 2.5.4 using methods 2 and 3. Show
that the system has modes $w_1 = (1, 1)^T$, $w_2 = (-1, 1)^T$ corresponding
to eigenvalues $\lambda_1 = 0$, $\lambda_2 = -2\beta$ and hence calculate the differential
equations governing the modal variables. Use your results to evaluate
the response of the system with $u(t) \equiv l(t) \equiv 0$ and $x(0) = (1, 0)^T$.
Check your answers by using eqn. 2.8.3.

2.9 Complete state controllability

An important concept in the mathematical theory of control relates to
the practical problem of assessing the degree of control that can be
imposed on the system. The formulation of this problem yields insight
into system structures and hence is a useful object for study. It must be
stated, however, that the mathematical conditions are of little practical
relevance, other than guaranteeing the existence of certain classes of
control systems (see, for example, the section on pole allocation or
Reference 64).

Definition: The linear time-varying state-vector model eqn. 2.7.1 is completely state-controllable if, given any states x_0, x_f and any initial time t_0, there exists a $t_1 > t_0$ and an input vector $u(t)$ defined on $t_0 < t < t_1$ so that the system state is transferred from the initial state $x(t_0) = x_0$ to the final state $x(t_1) = x_f$.

It is important to recognise that x_0, x_f, t_0 must be arbitrary and that $t_1 > t_0$ should be finite. In essence the definition requires that, by suitable choice of input vector, the system can be controlled from any initial state to any defined final state in a finite time. For simplicity we will replace the cumbersome term 'completely state-controllable' by the term 'controllable'.

There are a variety of techniques[33, 57, 64] for obtaining necessary and sufficient conditions for a system to be controllable. Application of an origin shift in time to eqn. 2.7.16 yields the relation

$$x(t_1) = \Phi(t_1, t_0)x(t_0) + \int_{t_0}^{t_1} \Phi(t_1, t)B(t)u(t)dt \qquad (2.9.1)$$

A necessary and sufficient condition for the system to be controllable is that this equation has a solution $(u(t), t_1)$ independent of the choice of $x(t_0), x(t_1)$. Without loss of generality we may assume that $x(t_1) = 0$ so that, applying eqns. 2.7.7 and 2.7.9, we require that

$$x(t_0) + \int_{t_0}^{t_1} \Phi(t_0, t)B(t)u(t)dt = 0 \qquad (2.9.2)$$

For convenience, define the Gram matrix or controllability Gramian,

$$W(t_0, t_1) = \int_{t_0}^{t_1} \Phi(t_0, t)B(t)B^T(t)\Phi^T(t_0, t)dt \qquad (2.9.3)$$

If $W(t_0, t_1)$ is nonsingular, define

$$u(t) = -B^T(t)\Phi^T(t_0, t)(W(t_0, t_1))^{-1}x(t_0) \qquad (2.9.4)$$

from which, substituting eqn. 2.9.2,

$$x(t_0) + \int_{t_0}^{t_1} \Phi(t_0, t)B(t)u(t)dt = (I_n - W(t_0, t_1)(W(t_0, t_1))^{-1})x(t_0) = 0 \qquad (2.9.5)$$

as required and the system is controllable. If $W(t_0, t_1)$ is singular for some t_0 and for all $t_1 > t_0$, then there exists a nonzero constant vector α_{t_1} satisfying $W(t_0, t_1)\alpha_{t_1} = 0$ i.e.

$$0 = \alpha_{t_1}^T W(t_0, t_1)\alpha_{t_1} = \int_{t_0}^{t_1} \| B^T\Phi^T(t_0, t)\alpha_{t_1} \|^2 dt \qquad (2.9.6)$$

or equivalently

$$\alpha_{t_1}^T \Phi(t_0, t)B \equiv 0, \qquad t_0 \leqslant t \leqslant t_1 \qquad (2.9.7)$$

Letting t_1 tend to $+\infty$ we can always choose a nonzero vector α so that

$\alpha^T \Phi(t_0, t)B = 0$, $t_0 \leqslant t < \infty$. Choosing $x(t_0) = \alpha$ in eqn. 2.9.2 indicates that, independent of the choice of input $u(t)$, and for all $t_1 > t_0$,

$$\alpha^T \alpha + \int_{t_0}^{t_1} \alpha^T \Phi(t_0, t)Bu(t)dt = \alpha^T \alpha \neq 0 \qquad (2.9.8)$$

and the system must be uncontrollable i.e. we have proved the result:

Theorem 2.9.1: A linear time-varying system characterised by the matrices $A(t), B(t)$ is completely state-controllable if, and only if, the Gram matrix $W(t_0, t_1)$ is nonsingular for some $t_1 > t_0$ for each t_0.

The theorem is obviously valid if the system is time invariant when,

$$W(t_0, t_1) = \int_{t_0}^{t_1} e^{A(t_0 - t_1)} BB^T e^{A^T(t_0 - t_1)} dt \qquad (2.9.9)$$

and, in this case, the conditions of theorem 2.9.1 can be simplified. Suppose that $W(t_0, t_1)$ is singular and choose a nonzero vector α satisfying $W(t_0, t_1)\alpha = 0$. In a similar manner to eqn. 2.9.7 it can be shown that

$$\alpha^T e^{A(t_0 - t)} B = 0, \quad t_0 \leqslant t \leqslant t_1 \qquad (2.9.10)$$

or, equivalently,

$$(-1)^j \frac{d^j}{dt^j} \{\alpha^T e^{A(t_0 - t)} B\}|_{t = t_0} = \alpha^T A^j B = 0, \qquad j \geqslant 0 \qquad (2.9.11)$$

Defining the $n \times ln$ controllability matrix

$$M_c = [B, AB, A^2 B, \ldots, A^{n-1} B] \qquad (2.9.12)$$

then $\alpha^T M_c = 0$ so that rank $M_c < n$. Conversely, suppose that α is a nonzero vector satisfying $\alpha^T M_c = 0$ i.e. $\alpha^T A^j B = 0$, $0 \leqslant j \leqslant n-1$. Applying the Cayley-Hamilton theorem it follows directly that $\alpha^T A^j B = 0$, $j \geqslant 0$ and hence that $\alpha^T e^{A(t_0 - t)} B \equiv 0$, $t_0 \leqslant t \leqslant t_1$, independent of the choice of $t_1 > t_0$. Substituting into eqn. 2.9.9, it follows that $W(t_0, t_1) \alpha = 0$ and hence (theorem 2.9.1) the system is not controllable. We can summarise this analysis in the form of the theorem:

Theorem 2.9.2: A linear time-invariant system characterised by the matrices A, B is completely state controllable if, and only if, the controllability matrix M_c has rank equal to n.

The absence of t_0, t_1 from the definition of M_c indicates that the system can be driven from any initial state to any final state on any time interval $t_0 \leqslant t \leqslant t_1$ $(t_0 < t_1)$ and, in particular, we can always take $t_0 = 0$ without any loss of generality.

Exercise 2.9.1
Calculate a state-vector model of the single-input, single-output system described by the transfer function $g(s) = (s + \beta)/s(s + 1)$ using method 1 of Section 2.4. Hence prove that the system is controllable only if $\beta \neq 0$ and $\beta \neq 1$.

The most useful vehicle for illustrating the physical nature of controllability (or its absence!) is the modal decomposition discussed in Section 2.8. For simplicity, suppose that A has distinct eigenvalues, that $l = 1$ and let E be the eigenvector matrix of A satisfying the relation

$$E^{-1}AE = \text{diag}\{\lambda_1, \lambda_2, \dots, \lambda_n\} \qquad (2.9.13)$$

where $\lambda_1, \dots, \lambda_n$ are the eigenvalues of A. Defining $x(t) = Ez(t)$ then, from eqn. 2.8.13,

$$\dot{z}(t) = E^{-1}AEz(t) + E^{-1}Bu(t) \qquad (2.9.14)$$

Noting that $(E^{-1}AE)^j E^{-1}B = E^{-1}A^jB$, for all $j \geq 0$, then

$$\text{rank } M_c = \text{rank } [E^{-1}B, (E^{-1}AE)E^{-1}B, \dots, (E^{-1}AE)^{n-1}E^{-1}B] \qquad (2.9.15)$$

from which we deduce that controllability is invariant under transformation of the state variables. As $l = 1$, it is easily shown that rank $M_c = n$ if, and only if, $|M_c| \neq 0$ i.e. writing $E^{-1}B = (\gamma_1, \gamma_2, \dots, \gamma_n)^T$

$$|M_c| = \gamma_1 \gamma_2, \dots, \gamma_n \begin{vmatrix} 1 & 1 \dots 1 \\ \lambda_1 & \lambda_2 & \lambda_n \\ \cdot & & \cdot \\ \cdot & & \cdot \\ \cdot & & \cdot \\ \lambda_1^{n-1} & \dots & \lambda_n^{n-1} \end{vmatrix} \qquad (2.9.16)$$

which is nonzero if, and only if, all the eigenvalues of A are distinct and $\gamma_i \neq 0$, $1 \leq i \leq n$. In particular, writing the modal equations in the form

$$\dot{z}_i(t) = \lambda_i z_i(t) + \gamma_i u(t), \qquad 1 \leq i \leq n, \qquad (2.9.17)$$

the system is controllable only if none of the modal amplitudes are governed by a differential equation of the form $\dot{z}_i(t) = \lambda_i z_i(t)$. In general terms, a necessary condition for a linear time-invariant system to be controllable is that every mode of the system is affected by the control input vector.

The above discussion is hardly exhaustive as the idea of controllability has been well studied. Those readers interested in more detailed analyses of the idea are referred to Reference 64 for the geometric interpretation and to Reference 57 for the definition in terms of polynomial matrices.

2.10 Complete state observability

The concept of controllability is concerned with the degree of control that can be imposed on the state dynamics. This Section is concerned with the related problem of reconstructing the state dynamics from measurements of the output vector over a finite time interval. This is an important concept in output feedback control where the state is to be controlled by feedback controllers responding to signals generated from output data only.

Definition: The linear time-varying state-vector model eqn. 2.7.1 is completely state-observable (or, for simplicity, observable) if, for any t_0, there exists a $t_1 > t_0$ such that a knowledge of the output vector $y(t)$ and input vector $u(t)$ on the interval $t_0 \leqslant t \leqslant t_1$ is sufficient to determine the initial state $x(t_0)$ uniquely.

It is left as an exercise for the reader to convince himself that, in the analysis of mathematical conditions for observability, no generality is lost by taking $u(t) \equiv 0$, $t_0 \leqslant t \leqslant t_1$ i.e.

$$y(t) = C(t)\Phi(t, t_0)x(t_0) \qquad (2.10.1)$$

and the analysis of the system property of observability is equivalent to the analysis of the simplified problem – 'given $y(t)$ in eqn. 2.10.1 on some interval $t_0 \leqslant t \leqslant t_1$, can we deduce $x(t_0)$ uniquely?' This problem can be answered using a similar analysis to that of Section 2.9 by defining the observability Gramian.

$$W_0(t_0, t_1) = \int_{t_0}^{t_1} \Phi^T(t, t_0)C^T(t)C(t)\Phi(t, t_0)dt \qquad (2.10.2)$$

Theorem 2.10.1: The linear time-varying system eqn. 2.7.1 is observable if, and only if, the Gram matrix $W_0(t_0, t_1)$ is nonsingular for each t_0 and some $t_1 > t_0$.

To prove this result suppose that $W_0(t_0, t_1)$ is singular for some t_0 and for all $t_1 > t_0$ then it is easily shown that there exists a nonzero vector α_{t_1} such that

$$C(t)\Phi(t, t_0)\alpha_{t_1} = 0, \qquad t_0 \leqslant t \leqslant t_1 \qquad (2.10.3)$$

Letting $t_1 \to + \infty$ it follows that we can choose a nonzero vector α so that

$$C(t)\,\Phi(t, t_0)\alpha = 0, \qquad t \geqslant t_0 \qquad (2.10.4)$$

Hence we cannot distinguish between the initial condition $x(t_0) = \alpha$ and the condition $x(t_0) = 0$ i.e. the system is unobservable. Conversely suppose that $W(t_0, t_1)$ is nonsingular, multiply eqn. 2.10.1 by $\Phi^T(t, t_0)\,C^T(t)$ and integrate from t_0 to t_1,

$$W(t_0, t_1)x(t_0) = \int_{t_0}^{t_1} \Phi^T(t, t_0)C^T(t)y(t)dt \qquad (2.10.5)$$

This relation has a unique solution for $x(t_0)$ and hence theorem 2.10.1 is proved.

The case of greatest practical interest is that of a linear time-invariant system when

$$W(t_0, t_1) = \int_{t_0}^{t_1} e^{A^T(t-t_0)}C^T Ce^{A(t-t_0)}dt \qquad (2.10.6)$$

Comparing with eqn. 2.9.9 and noting the similarity in form of theorems 2.9.1 and 2.10.1 then the reader should easily prove the following analogue to theorem 2.9.2:

Theorem 2.10.2: A linear time-invariant system characterised by matrices C, A of dimension $m \times n$, $n \times n$, respectively, is observable if, and only if, the observability matrix

$$M_0 = \begin{pmatrix} C \\ CA \\ \cdot \\ \cdot \\ \cdot \\ \cdot \\ CA^{n-1} \end{pmatrix} \quad (nm \times n) \qquad (2.10.7)$$

has rank equal to n.

As the condition for observability is independent of t_0, t_1 it is easily verified that we can, without loss of generality, take $t_0 = 0$ and that the initial state $x(0)$ can be deduced from output records on any finite time interval $0 \leqslant t \leqslant t_1$ $(0 < t_1)$.

Observability has a useful intuitive interpretation in terms of modal dynamics. Let A have distinct eigenvalue $\lambda_1, \ldots, \lambda_n$ and eigenvector matrix E. Choosing $u(t) \equiv 0$, and $x(t) = Ez(t)$ then (see eqns. 2.8.13)

$$\dot{z}_i(t) = \lambda_i z_i(t)$$

$$y(t) = \gamma_1 z_1(t) + \gamma_2 z_2(t) + \ldots + \gamma_n z_n(t) \qquad (2.10.8)$$

where $CE = [\gamma_1, \gamma_2, \ldots, \gamma_n]$, Noting that

$$M_0 = \begin{pmatrix} CE \\ CE(E^{-1}AE) \\ . \\ . \\ . \\ CE(E^{-1}AE)^{n-1} \end{pmatrix} E^{-1} \qquad (2.10.9)$$

then observability is unchanged by the transformation of state variables. Choosing $l = 1$ then

$$|M_0| = \gamma_1 \gamma_2, \ldots, \gamma_n \begin{vmatrix} 1 & 1 \ldots 1 \\ \lambda_1 & \lambda_2 & \lambda_n \\ . & & . \\ . & & . \\ \lambda_1^{n-1} & \ldots & \lambda_n^{n-1} \end{vmatrix} \qquad (2.10.10)$$

so that the system is observable if, and only if, the eigenvalues of A are distinct and $\gamma_i \neq 0$, $1 \leqslant i \leqslant n$. Comparing with eqn. 2.10.8 it is easily deduced that, in general terms, the system is observable only if every mode of the system can make a nonzero contribution to the output.

Exercise 2.10.1
Use theorems 2.9.2 and 2.10.2 to show that the state vector models of Sections 2.5 and 2.6 are both controllable and observable, independent of the particular values of the parameters (assumed to be nonzero) occurring in the models. Is this obvious from the physical structure of the systems?

2.11 Stability and oscillation

Those readers familiar with the idea of stability in classical control methods will remember that the stability of the system can be defined in terms of the poles of the transfer function i.e. in terms of the input-output description of systems dynamics. This is a natural approach as, in applications of control theory, attention is normally restricted to the response of the system output to input signals of interest. This approach can be formalised in the time domain using a variety of definitions[15, 33]

valid for general nonlinear state-vector models possessing a finite
number of equilibrium states. For simplicity, our attention is restricted
to the case of a linear time-invariant system of the form,

$$\dot{x}(t) = Ax(t) + Bu(t), \quad u(t) \in R^l$$

$$y(t) = Cx(t), \quad y(t) \in R^m, \quad x(t) \in R^n \qquad (2.11.1)$$

Definition (asymptotic output stability): The linear time-invariant
system eqn. 2.11.1 is said to be asymptotically output stable if, and
only if,

$$\lim_{t \to \infty} Ce^{At}x(0) = 0 \qquad (2.11.2)$$

for all initial conditions $x(0)$.

An equivalent statement is that, in the absence of input signals, the
system *output* decays to zero as $t \to +\infty$, independent of the initial
condition on the state vector. Although this definition of stability is
adequate for most practical applications, problems can arise if the system is not observable. For example, suppose that A has an eigenvalue λ
with strictly positive real part corresponding to an eigenvector ω
satisfying $C\omega = 0$, then, choosing $x(0) = \omega$, $y(t) = Ce^{\lambda t}\omega \equiv 0, t > 0$ so
that $\lim_{t \to +\infty} y(t) = 0$, yet the state $x(t) = e^{\lambda t}\omega$ grows without bound as
t becomes large. In applications, the elements of the state vector rep-
resent, for example, flows, temperatures, pressures within the system
structure so that, in this context, asymptotic output stability is not
sufficient to guarantee the 'good behaviour' of the state. For this
reason we will formulate our definition of stability in terms of the
state.

Definition (asymptotic stability): The linear time-invariant system
eqn. 2.11.1 is said to be asymptotically stable if, and only if,

$$\lim_{t \to +\infty} e^{At}x(0) = 0 \qquad (2.11.3)$$

for all initial state conditions $x(0)$.

Equivalently, in the absence of input signals, we require that the
system *state* decays to zero as $t \to +\infty$, independent of the initial state
conditions. This definition is easily transformed into a more convenient
form by examination of a canonical decomposition of A. Assume for
simplicity that A has distinct eigenvalues $\lambda_1, \ldots, \lambda_n$ and eigenvector
matrix E, then

$$e^{At} = E \text{ diag } \{e^{\lambda_1 t}, \ldots, e^{\lambda_n t}\}E^{-1} \qquad (2.11.4)$$

The following theorem is hence easily proved:

Theorem 2.11.1: The linear time-invariant system eqn. 2.11.1 is asymptotically stable if, and only if, the system open-loop characteristic polynomial

$$\rho_0(s) = |sI_n - A| = \prod_{j=1}^{n} (s - \lambda_j) \qquad (2.11.5)$$

has zeros $\lambda_1, \lambda_2, \ldots, \lambda_n$ with strictly negative real parts, Re $\lambda_j < 0$, $1 \leqslant j \leqslant n$. That is the eigenvalues of A must have strictly negative real parts. It is left as an exercise to the reader to prove that asymptotic stability implies asymptotic output stability, and that a sufficient condition for asymptotic output stability to imply asymptotic stability is that the system is observable (Hint: assume that the system is output stable but that A has an eigenvalue λ, Re $\lambda > 0$, and let $x(0)$ be a non-zero eigenvector of A corresponding to the eigenvalue λ). For simplicity, the following terminology is used:

(a) if Re $\lambda_j < 0$, $1 \leqslant j \leqslant n$, the system is stable
(b) if Re $\lambda_j > 0$, for some j, the system is unstable
(c) if Re $\lambda_j \leqslant 0$, $1 \leqslant j \leqslant n$, and Re $\lambda_l = 0$ for some l, the system is critically stable.

It is well known from classical control theory that linear systems can be stable but exhibit wild oscillations sufficiently large as to require strong control action. In state-vector terms, this corresponds to the situation where A has complex eigenvalues. To illustrate this point consider the two-dimensional system,

$$\dot{x}(t) = \begin{pmatrix} \rho & -\omega \\ \omega & \rho \end{pmatrix} x(t) \qquad (2.11.6)$$

where $\omega \neq 0$. It is easily verified that the system has complex-conjugate pair eigenvalues $\lambda_1 = \rho + i\omega$, $\bar{\lambda}_1 = \lambda_2 = \rho - i\omega$ $(i^2 = -1)$ corresponding to eigenvectors $(i, 1)^T$, $(-i, 1)^T$ and hence is stable if, and only if, $\rho < 0$. Also,

$$x(t) = e^{At}x(0) = \frac{1}{2}\begin{pmatrix} i & -i \\ 1 & 1 \end{pmatrix} \begin{pmatrix} e^{(\rho+i\omega)t} & 0 \\ 0 & e^{(\rho-i\omega)t} \end{pmatrix} \begin{pmatrix} -i & 1 \\ i & 1 \end{pmatrix} x(0)$$

$$= e^{\rho t}\begin{pmatrix} \cos \omega t & -\sin \omega t \\ \sin \omega t & \cos \omega t \end{pmatrix} x(0) \qquad (2.11.7)$$

and the trigonometric functions indicate that the system will oscillate with a frequency equal to the magnitude of the imaginary part of the eigenvalue in an envelope proportional to $e^{\rho t}$. In particular, it is seen that, the significance of the oscillation in system performance increases as the ratio $|\omega/\rho|$ increases.

Exercise 2.11.1

Extend the analysis of eqn. 2.11.6 to the case where A has distinct eigenvalues, and possibly more than one pair of complex-conjugate eigenvalues.

2.12 State feedback

Given a linear, time-invariant system of the form

$$\dot{x}(t) = Ax(t) + Bu(t), \quad u(t) \in R^l$$
$$y(t) = Cx(t), \quad x(t) \in R^n, \quad y(t) \in R^m \qquad (2.12.1)$$

a linear constant state-variable feedback law takes the form

$$u(t) = Fx(t) + Gr(t) \qquad (2.12.2)$$

where F, G are constant $l \times n, l \times m$ matrices and $r(t)$ is a new external input variable taken to represent the demanded response from the system output $y(t)$. As can be seen, the control input $u(t)$ depends explicitly on the state vector $x(t)$ and hence represents a closed-loop or feedback law imposed on the system. The feedback character of the control law is illustrated in Fig. 2.12.1.

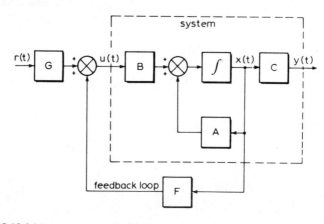

Fig. 2.12.1 Linear state-variable feedback

Substituting eqn. 2.12.2 into expr. 2.12.1 yields the closed-loop system

$$\dot{x}(t) = \{A + BF\}x(t) + BGr(t)$$

$$y(t) = Cx(t) \qquad (2.12.3)$$

from which it is seen that the state feedback law has a significant effect on the state dynamics (both the A and B matrices are transformed) but the output equation remains unchanged. In particular, the stability properties of the system will change by replacing A by $A + BF$. Closed-loop stability can be characterised, by analogy with eqn. 2.11.5, by the closed-loop characteristic polynomial

$$\rho_c(s) = |sI - A - BF| \qquad (2.12.4)$$

and, using theorem 2.11.1, the closed-loop system is stable if, and only if, all the eigenvalues of $A + BF$ have strictly negative real parts. In general, all the eigenvalues of $A + BF$ will differ from the eigenvalues of A and, the reader can easily verify by example that, the eigenvectors of $A + BF$ will differ from those of A. In physical terms the state feedback law eqn. 2.12.2 affects both the stability of the system and the structure of its modes. As the system dynamics are dominated by its eigenvalue — eigenvector structure, it will be anticipated that state feedback is a powerful and flexible tool in the modification and compensation of system response[63, 64]. Some applications of state feedback are discussed in the following sections.

It is natural to anticipate that the application of a linear state-variable feedback law will affect the controllability and observability properties of the system. It is easily shown by example that observability is not invariant under state feedback e.g. consider the linear time-invariant system described by the matrices

$$A = \begin{pmatrix} 1 & 1 \\ 1 & 1 \end{pmatrix}, \quad B = \begin{pmatrix} 1 \\ 0 \end{pmatrix}, \quad C = (1 \quad 0) \qquad (2.12.5)$$

The system is both controllable and observable but, under the effect of the linear state-variable feedback law

$$u(t) = (0, \quad -1)x(t) + r(t) \qquad (2.12.6)$$

the closed-loop system takes the form

$$\dot{x}(t) = \begin{pmatrix} 1 & 0 \\ 1 & 1 \end{pmatrix}x(t) + \begin{pmatrix} 1 \\ 0 \end{pmatrix}r(t), \quad y(t) = (1 \quad 0)x(t) \qquad (2.12.7)$$

which is not observable.

In contrast it is easily shown that controllability is invariant under the modified state feedback

$$u(t) = Fx(t) + v(t) \qquad (2.12.8)$$

by noting that $(A + BF)^k B = A^k B + A^{k-1} BF_{k,k+1} + \ldots + BF_{1,k+1}$, $k > 0$, for some choice of $l \times l$ matrices $F_{i,k}$ and hence the closed-loop controllability matrix

$$(B, (A + BF)B, \ldots, (A + BF)^{n-1}B)$$

$$= (B, AB, \ldots, A^{n-1}B) \begin{pmatrix} I_l & F_{1,2} & F_{1,3} & \cdots & F_{1,n} \\ 0 & I_l & F_{2,3} & & \vdots \\ \vdots & 0 & I_l & & \vdots \\ \vdots & & 0 & & \vdots \\ \vdots & & & & F_{n-1,n} \\ 0 & \cdots & \cdots & 0 & I_l \end{pmatrix}$$

$$(2.12.9)$$

has the same rank as the open-loop controllability matrix $[B, AB, \ldots, A^{n-1}B]$, independent of the choice of feedback matrix F. In the more general case of the feedback law eqn. 2.12.2, the matrix G can have an effect on controllability e.g. consider the linear time-invariant system described by the matrices

$$A + BF = \begin{pmatrix} 1 & 0 \\ 0 & 1 \end{pmatrix}, \quad B = \begin{pmatrix} 2 & 1 \\ 1 & 1 \end{pmatrix}, \quad C = \begin{pmatrix} 1 & 0 \\ 0 & 1 \end{pmatrix}$$

$$(2.12.10)$$

It is left as an exercise to the reader to show, by direct calculation, that the closed-loop system is controllable if, and only if, G is nonsingular. Assuming that $m = l$, the identity,

$$[BG, (A + BF)BG, \ldots, (A + BF)^{n-1}BG]$$

$$= [B, (A + BF)B, \ldots, (A + BF)^{n-1}B] \begin{pmatrix} G & 0 & \cdots & 0 \\ 0 & G & & \vdots \\ \vdots & & & 0 \\ 0 & 0 & \cdots & G \end{pmatrix}$$

$$(2.12.11)$$

indicates immediately that the closed-loop system is controllable if the open-loop system is controllable and if G is nonsingular. In general, however, the closed-loop system may be controllable even if rank $G <$ min (m, l) as is illustrated by the example

$$A = \begin{pmatrix} 0 & 0 \\ 0 & 1 \end{pmatrix}, \quad B = \begin{pmatrix} 1 & 0 \\ 0 & 1 \end{pmatrix}, \quad C = \begin{pmatrix} 1 & 0 \\ 0 & 1 \end{pmatrix}$$

$$F = \begin{pmatrix} 0 & 1 \\ 0 & 0 \end{pmatrix}, \quad G = \begin{pmatrix} 0 & 0 \\ 0 & 1 \end{pmatrix} \tag{2.12.12}$$

2.13 Pole allocation using state feedback

In applications state-variable feedback can be introduced to change the dynamic behaviour of the uncontrolled system expr. 2.12.1 in some desirable way e.g. to achieve stability or speed up the response. The pole-allocation design method (References 5, 15, 53, 57, 60 and 64), assumes that such criteria can be expressed in terms of the eigenvalues of the closed-loop matrix $A + BF$ (the input matrix G plays no part in the problem). For example, the requirement that the eigenvalues μ_j, $1 \leqslant j \leqslant n$, of $A + BF$ satisfy the constraints Re $\mu_j < -\alpha(\alpha \geqslant 0)$ and $| \operatorname{Im} \mu_j | < \beta$ can be interpreted as the choice of F such that the closed-loop system is stable, responds rapidly to demand signals and has a limited frequency of oscillation.

Pole-allocation problem: Given specified desired closed-loop eigenvalues $\mu_1, \mu_2, \ldots, \mu_n$, find a state feedback matrix F such that the closed-loop matrix $A + BF$ has eigenvalues $\mu_1, \mu_2, \ldots, \mu_n$.

The problem of existence of a suitable F, in general, depends upon the choice of closed-loop eigenvalues. If however we demand that a suitable F should exist, independent of how we choose $\mu_1, \mu_2, \ldots, \mu_n$, the conditions for existence are well known[64]:

Theorem 2.13.1: The pole allocation problem is solvable for all choices of $\mu_1, \mu_2, \ldots, \mu_n$ if, and only if, the system expr. 2.12.1 is controllable.

Rather than attempt a proof of this result in the general case we content ourselves with the following simplified treatment, which is, in effect, a direct computational method. The first step is the reduction of the multi-input problem to a single-input problem using the following lemma:

Lemma 2.13.1:[64] Let p be a nonzero constant $l \times 1$ vector, then there exists a feedback matrix F_1 such that

$$\text{rank } [B, AB, \ldots, A^{n-1}B]$$
$$= \text{rank } [Bp, (A + BF_1)Bp, \ldots, (A + BF_1)^{n-1}Bp]$$

In particular, if system eqn. 2.12.1 is controllable, it follows by defining $b = Bp$ and $u(t) = p\hat{u}(t) + F_1 x(t)$ that the following single-input system is controllable:

$$\dot{x}(t) = (A + BF_1)x(t) + b\hat{u}(t)$$
$$y(t) = Cx(t) \tag{2.13.1}$$

and hence, using theorem 2.13.1, there exists a linear state-variable feedback law

$$\hat{u}(t) = F_2 x(t) + G_1 r(t) \tag{2.13.2}$$

solving the pole-allocation problem, independent of the choice of closed-loop eigenvalues. In particular, noting that

$$u(t) = F_1 x(t) + p\hat{u}(t)$$
$$= \{F_1 + pF_2\}x(t) + pG_1 r(t) \tag{2.13.4}$$

then the desired pole-allocation is achieved using the feedback matrix $F = F_1 + pF_2$. It is important to note that, in almost all cases, a suitable choice of p ensures that we can choose $F_1 = 0$. This case is of sufficient importance to merit a name:

Definition: System eqn. 2.12.1 is said to be *cyclic* if, and only if, there exists a constant $l \times 1$ vector p such that

$$\text{rank } [B, AB, \ldots, A^{n-1}B] = \text{rank } [Bp, ABp, \ldots, A^{n-1}Bp] = n \tag{2.13.4}$$

In particular every cyclic system is controllable, and the pole-allocation problem is solvable using a state-variable feedback law

$$u(t) = pF_2 x(t) + pG_1 r(t) \tag{2.13.5}$$

Also, if a system is cyclic, almost every choice of vector p will satisfy eqn. 2.13.4. The feedback matrix $F = pF_2$ has rank one and hence expr. 2.13.4 is termed a unity-rank state feedback law.

At this stage, the pole-allocation problem has been reduced to the problem of pole allocation for the single-input system of eqn. 2.13.1 using the feedback system shown in Fig. 2.13.1. It remains to provide a solution technique for controllable single-input systems. This is achieved using the idea of controllable companion forms.[63] Suppose, for simplicity that $F_1 = 0$ (if $F_1 \neq 0$, replace A by $A + BF_1$ in the following analysis) and consider the solutions of the matrix equations

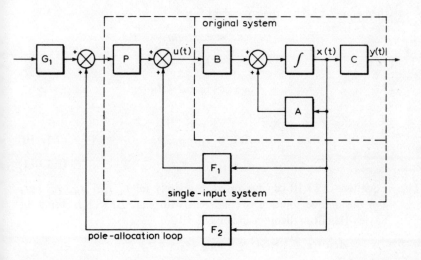

Fig. 2.13.1 Control scheme for pole allocation

$$AT = TA_c, \quad b = Te_n \qquad (2.13.6)$$

when T is the $n \times n$ solution matrix, e_n is the $n \times 1$ vector with a unit element in the nth position and zeros elsewhere and A_c in the $n \times n$ *companion matrix*

$$A_c = \begin{pmatrix} 0 & 1 & 0 & \ldots \ldots & 0 \\ 0 & 0 & 1 & 0 & \vdots \\ \vdots & & & & 0 \\ 0 & & & 0 & 1 \\ -a_n & -a_{n-1} & \cdots \cdots & & -a_1 \end{pmatrix} \qquad (2.13.7)$$

where the coefficients $a_1, \ldots, a_n$ are defined in terms of the open-loop characteristic polynomial

$$\rho_0(s) = |sI_n - A| = s^n + a_1 s^{n-1} + \ldots + a_{n-1}s + a_n \qquad (2.13.8)$$

The pair (A_c, e_n) is termed the *controllable canonical form* of the pair (A, b).

Writing,

$$T = [t_1, t_2, \ldots, t_n] \qquad (2.13.9)$$

then eqn. 2.13.6 has the equivalent form,

$$t_n = b = Bp$$

$$At_n = t_{n-1} - a_1 t_n$$

$$At_{n-1} = t_{n-2} - a_2 t_n$$

$$\vdots \qquad \vdots \qquad \vdots$$

$$At_2 = t_1 - a_{n-1} t_n \qquad (2.13.10)$$

$$At_1 = -a_n t_n \qquad (2.13.11)$$

Equations 2.13.10 can be solved recursively for $t_n, t_{n-1}, t_{n-2}, \ldots, t_1$ and the unique solution is consistent with eqn. 2.13.11 as, using the Cayley-Hamilton theorem and eqn. 2.3.10,

$$\begin{aligned}
At_1 + a_n t_n &= A^2 t_2 + a_{n-1} At_n + a_n t_n \\
&= A^3 t_3 + a_{n-2} A^2 t_n + a_{n-1} At_n + a_n t_n \\
&= \{A^n + a_1 A^{n-1} + \ldots + a_{n-1} A + a_n I_n\} b \\
&= 0 \qquad (2.13.12)
\end{aligned}$$

In particular, the reader can easily verify that T takes the form

$$T = [A^{n-1}b, A^{n-2}b, \ldots, Ab, b] \begin{pmatrix} 1 & 0 & . & . & . & . & . & 0 \\ X & 1 & & & & & & \vdots \\ X & & & & & & & \vdots \\ \vdots & & & & X & 1 & 0 \\ \vdots & & & & & & & \\ X & . & . & . & X & X & 1 \end{pmatrix}$$

$$(2.13.13)$$

where the X's denote unspecified scalars, and hence that T is nonsingular if, and only if, the system given by eqn. 2.13.2 is controllable.

Defining $z(t) = T^{-1}x(t)$, system eqn. 2.13.2 has the equivalent form

$$\dot{z}(t) = A_c z(t) + e_n \hat{u}(t)$$

$$y(t) = CTz(t) \qquad (2.13.14)$$

Suppose that, by direct calculation,

$$(s - \mu_1)(s - \mu_2) \ldots (s - \mu_n) = s^n + b_1 s^{n-1} + \ldots + b_{n-1} s + b_n$$

$$(2.13.15)$$

and consider the state-feedback law

$$\begin{aligned}
\hat{u}(t) &= (a_n - b_n, a_{n-1} - b_{n-1}, \ldots, a_1 - b_1) z(t) + G_1 r(t) \\
&= (a_n - b_n, \ldots, a_1 - b_1) T^{-1} x(t) + G_1 r(t) \\
&= F_2 x(t) + G_1 r(t)
\end{aligned}$$

$$(2.13.16)$$

It is easily verified that

$$\dot{z}(t) = \begin{pmatrix} 0 & 1 & 0 & \ldots & 0 \\ 0 & 0 & 1 & & \vdots \\ \vdots & & & & 0 \\ 0 & \ldots & \ldots & 0 & 1 \\ -b_n & -b_{n-1} & \ldots & \ldots & -b_1 \end{pmatrix} z(t) + \begin{pmatrix} 0 \\ 0 \\ \vdots \\ 0 \\ 1 \end{pmatrix} G_1 r(t)$$

$$(2.13.17)$$

or, equivalently,

$$\dot{x}(t) = T \begin{pmatrix} 0 & 1 & 0 & \ldots & 0 \\ 0 & 0 & 1 & \ldots & 0 \\ \vdots & & & & 0 \\ 0 & \ldots & \ldots & 0 & 1 \\ -b_n & -b_{n-1} & \ldots & & -b_1 \end{pmatrix} T^{-1} x(t) + b G_1 r(t)$$

$$(2.13.18)$$

The closed-loop characteristic polynomial is simply

$$\rho_c(s) = |sI_n - A - bF_2| = |sI_n - T^{-1}(A + bF_2)T|$$

$$= \begin{vmatrix} s & -1 & 0 & \ldots & \ldots & 0 \\ 0 & s & & & & \vdots \\ \vdots & & & & & 0 \\ 0 & \ldots & 0 & & s & -1 \\ b_n & \ldots & \ldots & & b_2 & s + b_1 \end{vmatrix}$$

$$= s^n + b_1 s^{n-1} + \ldots + b_{n-1} s + b_n$$
$$= (s - \mu_1)(s - \mu_2) \ldots (s - \mu_n) \qquad (2.13.19)$$

as required.

In summary, the following procedure is a simple approach to the solution of the pole-allocation problem:

Step 1: Check that the system eqn. 2.12.1 is controllable.

Step 2: Choose F_1, p such that eqn. 2.13.1 is controllable. If the system is cyclic then we can always choose $F_1 = 0$ and a suitable p by trial and error.

Step 3: Evaluate the coefficients $a_1, a_2, \ldots, a_n$ in the open-loop characteristic polynomial expr. 2.13.8 and hence compute T from eqns. 2.13.9 and 2.13.10.

Step 4: Evaluate the coefficients $b_1, b_2, \ldots, b_n$ in the desired closed-loop characteristic polynomial eqn. 2.13.5 to obtain the state feedback matrix F_2 from eqn. 2.13.16.

Step 5: The final closed-loop control law is obtained $u(t) = (F_1 + pF_2)x(t) + pG_1 r(t)$.

The method is easily programmed on a digital computer and can play a valuable role as a computer-aided-design tool. There are, however, a number of unsolved problems which throw more doubt on the long term usefulness of pole-allocation as a complete design method.

(*a*) Implicit in the use of a state-feedback control system is the assumption that the system states $x_1(t), \ldots, x_n(t)$ can be measured. This is not feasible in many practical applications particularly if the state dimension n is large.

(*b*) For the case of single-input, single-output systems the classical root-locus method provides some insight into the relationship between eigenvalue positions and transient performance. No such relationship is known in general for multi-input/multi-output systems.

(*c*) The assumption of a unity-rank state feedback restricts the number of degrees of freedom available for system compensation. It is not clear how these other degrees of freedom can be used in design.

To illustrate the application of the pole allocation method using state feedback, consider the simplified coupled liquid-level model (c.f. Section 2.5)

$$\dot{x}(t) = \begin{pmatrix} -1 & 1 \\ 1 & -1 \end{pmatrix} x(t) + \begin{pmatrix} 1 & 0 \\ 0 & 1 \end{pmatrix} u(t) \qquad (2.13.20)$$

The first step is to check that the system is controllable (theorem 2.13.1) which is easily verified as $n = 2$ and

$$[B, AB] = \begin{pmatrix} 1 & 0 & -1 & 1 \\ 0 & 1 & 1 & -1 \end{pmatrix} \tag{2.13.21}$$

has rank equal to two. The system is also cyclic as can be seen by setting $u(t) = (p_1, p_2)^T \hat{u}(t)$ and noting that

$$\det [Bp, ABp] = \begin{vmatrix} p_1 & p_2 - p_1 \\ p_2 & p_1 - p_2 \end{vmatrix} = (p_1 + p_2)(p_1 - p_2) \tag{2.13.22}$$

which is nonzero for any choice of vector p satisfying $(p_1 + p_2) \neq 0$ and $(p_1 - p_2) \neq 0$. For simplicity choose $p_1 = 1, p_2 = 0$ i.e. the reduced system is to be controlled by the use of the input $u_1(t)$ only. The state-space model now becomes

$$\dot{x}(t) = \begin{pmatrix} -1 & 1 \\ 1 & -1 \end{pmatrix} x(t) + \begin{pmatrix} 1 \\ 0 \end{pmatrix} \hat{u}(t) \tag{2.13.23}$$

which is to be transformed into controllable companion form using the recursion relations (eqn. 2.3.10) and the identity $\rho_0(s) = s^2 + 2s$ i.e. $a_1 = 2, a_2 = 0$. A simple calculation yields the transformation matrix

$$T = \begin{pmatrix} 1 & 1 \\ 1 & 0 \end{pmatrix} \tag{2.13.24}$$

Suppose that it is required to achieve the closed-loop eigenvalues $\mu_1 = -1$, $\mu_2 = -1$, then the desired closed-loop characteristic polynomial is $\rho_c(s) = s^2 + 2s + 1$ i.e. $b_1 = 2, b_2 = 1$. Substituting into eqn. 2.13.6 yields the control law

$$u(t) = p\hat{u}(t) = \begin{pmatrix} 1 \\ 0 \end{pmatrix} \{(0, \quad -1)x(t) + G_1 r(t)\} \tag{2.13.25}$$

The reader can easily verify that the resulting closed-loop system has the desired eigenvalues.

Exercise 2.13.1
Using the data $k_1 = k_2 = m_1 = m_2 = c = 1$ in the model of Section 2.6, calculate a linear state-variable feedback control law to ensure that the closed-loop system has eigenvalues $\mu_1 = \mu_2 = \mu_3 = \mu_4 = 2$. Choose the control law to achieve the design objective by manipulating the input $u_1(t)$ only.

2.14 Constant output feedback

Bearing in mind the difficulties inherent in the implementation of state feedback control laws, it is natural to consider the possibility of control system design by using output data alone, as, by assumption, the system output is measured directly. Consider the linear time-invariant system

$$\dot{x}_1(t) = A_1 x_1(t) + B_1 u(t), \quad x_1(t) \in R^{n_1}$$

$$y(t) = C_1 x_1(t), \quad y(t) \in R^m, \quad u(t) \in R^l \qquad (2.14.1)$$

then, given an $m \times 1$ vector $r(t)$ of demanded output signals, we can construct an $m \times 1$ *error vector*

$$e(t) = r(t) - y(t) \qquad (2.14.2)$$

which is to be regarded as the input signal to our control unit. A *linear constant output-feedback controller* (or, by analogy with classical control terminology, a *proportional output-feedback controller*) sets the input element $u_i(t)$ equal to a linear combination of the error signal $e_1(t), e_2(t), \ldots, e_m(t)$ i.e. in vector notation,

$$u(t) = D_2 e(t) \qquad (2.14.3)$$

where D_2 is a constant $l \times m$ matrix. The resulting control scheme is indicated in Fig. 2.14.1 where it is seen that eqns. 2.14.2, 2.14.3 simply describe a proportional unity-negative feedback control system for the plant (eqn. 2.14.1).

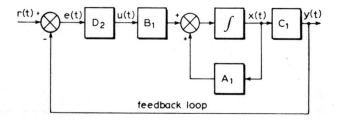

Fig. 2.14.1 Constant output feedback-control system

It is worthwhile noting that

$$u(t) = D_2(r(t) - y(t)) = -D_2 C_1 x_1(t) + D_2 r(t) \qquad (2.14.4)$$

i.e. the output feedback control law is, in fact, a state feedback control law where the rows of F_2 are required to be linear combinations of the rows of C_1 or, more precisely $D_2C_1 = -F_2$ (see eqn. 2.12.2). It is this restriction which would appear to restrict the usefulness of constant output feedback and the attainable system performance e.g. it is not now possible to choose the feedback matrix D_2 to place the eigenvalues of the closed-loop system in arbitrary positions. Later chapters, however, will convince the reader that, despite this apparent limitation, output feedback controllers are capable of producing high performance feedback designs.

The closed-loop state equations are obtained by combining eqns. 2.14.1 to 2.14.3,

$$\dot{x}_1(t) = (A_1 - B_1 D_2 C_1)x_1(t) + B_1 D_2 r(t)$$

$$y(t) = C_1 x_1(t) \qquad (2.14.5)$$

so that the closed-loop characteristic polynomial is

$$\rho_c(s) = |sI_{n_1} - A_1 + B_1 D_2 C_1| \qquad (2.14.6)$$

which provides a complete description of the closed-loop stability. It also gives some indication of the limitations inherent in the use of constant output feedback e.g. denoting the closed-loop eigenvalues by $\mu_1, \ldots, \mu_n$,

$$\sum_{j=1}^{n} \mu_j = \mathrm{tr}\,\{A_1 - B_1 D_2 C_1\}$$

$$= \mathrm{tr}\,A_1 - \mathrm{tr}\,B_1 D_2 C_1$$

$$= \mathrm{tr}\,A_1 - \mathrm{tr}\,C_1 B_1 D_2 \qquad (2.14.7)$$

In particular, if $C_1 B_1 = 0$ (a not uncommon occurrence!), $\sum_{j=1}^{n} \mu_j = \mathrm{tr}\,A_1$ and hence, if $\mathrm{tr}\,A_1 > 0$, at least one closed-loop eigenvalue has a positive real part and the system cannot be stabilised by constant output feedback.

Exercise 2.14.1

By direct calculation of the closed-loop characteristic polynomial, show that an unstable system described by the state-vector model

$$\dot{x}_1(t) = \begin{pmatrix} 0 & 1 \\ 0 & 1 \end{pmatrix} x_1(t) + \begin{pmatrix} 0 \\ 1 \end{pmatrix} u(t)$$

$$y(t) = [1 \quad 0]\, x_1(t)$$

is both controllable and observable but cannot be stabilised by the use of constant output feedback.

Concerning the problem of controllability and observability of the closed-loop control system, similar reasoning to that used in obtaining eqn. 2.12.9 can be used to show that

$$\text{rank } [B_1 D_2, (A_1 - B_1 D_2 C_1) B_1 D_2, \ldots, (A_1 - B_1 D_2 C_1)^{n_1 - 1} B_1 D_2]$$

$$= \text{rank } [B_1 D_2, A_1 B_1 D_2, \ldots, A_1^{n_1 - 1} B_1 D_2] \qquad (2.14.8)$$

i.e. the closed-loop control system is controllable if, and only if, the system

$$\dot{x}_1(t) = A_1 x_1(t) + B_1 D_2 e(t)$$

$$y(t) = C_1 x_1(t) \qquad (2.14.9)$$

is controllable. System eqn. 2.14.9, by analogy with classical terminology will be called the *forward-path system* as it is obtained from Fig. 2.14.1 by removing the feedback loop.

Finally, noting that

$$\text{rank} \begin{bmatrix} C_1 \\ C_1(A_1 - B_1 D_2 C_1) \\ \cdot \\ \cdot \\ \cdot \\ C_1(A_1 - B_1 D_2 C_1)^{n_1 - 1} \end{bmatrix} = \text{rank}[C_1^T, (A_1^T - C_1^T D_2^T B_1^T) C_1^T, \ldots]$$

$$= \text{rank}[C_1^T, A_1^T C_1^T, \ldots, (A_1^T)^{n_1 - 1} C_1^T]$$

$$= \text{rank} \begin{bmatrix} C_1 \\ C_1 A_1 \\ \cdot \\ \cdot \\ \cdot \\ C_1 A_1^{n_1 - 1} \end{bmatrix} \qquad (2.14.10)$$

it follows directly that the closed-loop system is observable if, and only if, the plant (eqn. 2.14.1) is observable.

Exercise 2.14.2
Verify the results on closed-loop controllability and observability by direct application of the basic definitions (Hint: no mathematics is required e.g. in the case of observability, note that a knowledge of $r(t)$ and $y(t)$ enables the evaluation of $u(t)$ and apply the definition).

2.15 Dynamic output feedback

As in classical control theory the use of constant (i.e. proportional) output feedback control limits the performance that can be achieved in the closed-loop system. This problem carries over directly to the multi-input/multi-output case and, as in classical control, dynamic phase compensation is required to improve the system characteristics.

Considering initially the case of a *unity-negative feedback* control system, the error vector $e(t)$ is defined as in eqn. 2.14.2

$$e(t) = r(t) - y(t) \qquad (2.15.1)$$

which is to be the input to the control unit. A *linear dynamic output-feedback controller* constructs the system input vector $u(t)$ as the output from a linear time-invariant system with input $e(t)$ of the form,

$$\dot{x}_2(t) = A_2 x_2(t) + B_2 e(t), \quad x_2(t) \in R^{n_2}$$

$$u(t) = C_2 x_2(t) + D_2 e(t) \qquad (2.15.2)$$

where $x_2(t)$ is the internal state of the controller.

Exercise 2.15.1
For the case of a single-input/single-output system, show that a proportional plus integral controller described by the transfer function $k(s) = k_1 + \dfrac{1}{s} k_2$ can be represented by a state-vector model of the form of eqn. 2.15.2 with $A_2 = 0, B_2 = 1, C_2 = k_2, D_2 = k_1$. Calculate the state-vector model of the phase-compensation network $k(s) = (1 + T_1 s)/(1 + T_2 s)$.

The *forward-path system* is obtained by combining eqns. 2.14.1 and 2.15.2 to yield the composite state-space model

$$\dot{x}(t) = Ax(t) + Be(t), \quad y(t) = Cx(t), x(t) \in R^n \qquad (2.15.3)$$

where $n = n_1 + n_2$, $x(t) = (x_1^T(t), x_2^T(t))^T$ and

$$A = \begin{pmatrix} A_1 & B_1 C_2 \\ 0 & A_2 \end{pmatrix}, \quad B = \begin{pmatrix} B_1 D_2 \\ B_2 \end{pmatrix}$$

$$C = [C_1, \quad 0] \qquad (2.15.4)$$

The closed-loop system is obtained by combining eqns. 2.15.1, 2.15.3 and 2.15.4 to yield

$$\dot{x}(t) = (A - BC)x(t) + Br(t), \quad y(t) = Cx(t) \quad (2.15.5)$$

where

$$A - BC = \begin{pmatrix} A_1 - B_1 D_2 C_1, & B_1 C_2 \\ B_2 C_1, & A_2 \end{pmatrix} \quad (2.15.6)$$

and is illustrated in Fig. 2.15.1.

The open-loop characteristic polynomial of the forward-path system is

$$\rho_0(s) = |sI_n - A| = |sI_{n_1} - A_1| \; |sI_{n_2} - A_2| \quad (2.15.7)$$

which is simply the product of the open-loop characteristic polynomials of the plant eqn. 2.14.1 and that of the controller (eqn. 2.15.2). The closed-loop characteristic polynomial is simply

$$\rho_c(s) = |sI_n - A + BC| \quad (2.15.8)$$

This relationship is fairly complicated and will be discussed in later sections in the context of system transfer-function matrices.

Exercise 2.15.2
Use the techniques of Section 2.14 to prove that the closed-loop system (eqn. 2.15.5) is controllable (respt. observable) if, and only if, the forward-path system (eqn. 2.15.3) is controllable (respt. observable).

The idea of a unity-negative feedback system can be extended to include the possibility of a dynamic (nonunity) feedback loop. In this case, the forward-path system is still described by eqns. 2.15.2 and 2.14.1 (or, equivalently (eqn. 2.15.3)) but the error vector (eqn. 2.15.1) is replaced by an *error measure*

$$e(t) = r(t) - \hat{y}(t) \quad (2.15.9)$$

where the signal $\hat{y}(t)$ is the output from a linear time-invariant dynamical system with input $y(t)$ i.e. (Fig. 2.15.2)

$$\dot{x}_3(t) = A_3 x_3(t) + B_3 y(t), \quad x_3(t) \in R^{n_3}$$
$$\hat{y}(t) = C_3 x_3(t) + D_3 y(t) \quad (2.15.10)$$

In practice the feedback element can, in principle, be used to improve the response of the closed-loop system but, more commonly, it is included to describe dynamic effects within output transducers which provide a dynamic estimate $\hat{y}(t)$ of $y(t)$. As $y(t)$ is not directly available in this case it is natural to use the estimated error vector (eqn. 2.15.9) as input to the control unit.

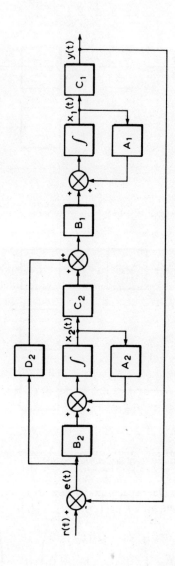

Fig. 2.15.1 Unity-negative feedback configuration

The composite state-space model describing the dynamic effect of $e(t)$ on $y(t)$ is as given in eqns. 2.15.3 and 2.15.4. Of more interest is

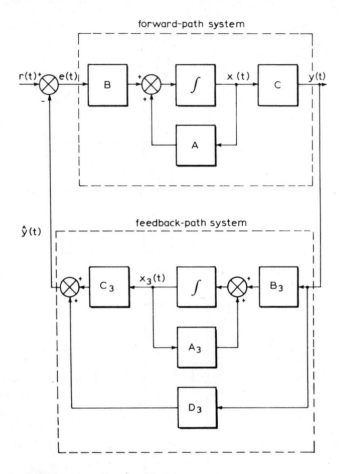

Fig. 2.15.2 Nonunity feedback configuration

the composite state-space model describing the dynamic effect of $e(t)$ on $\hat{y}(t)$. Defining $x(t) = (x_1^T(t), x_2^T(t), x_3^T(t))^T$,

$$\dot{x}(t) = \begin{pmatrix} A_1 & B_1C_2 & 0 \\ 0 & A_2 & 0 \\ B_3C_1 & 0 & A_3 \end{pmatrix} x(t) + \begin{pmatrix} B_1D_2 \\ B_2 \\ 0 \end{pmatrix} e(t)$$

$$\hat{y}(t) = (D_3C_1, \quad 0, \quad C_3)x(t)$$

$$y(t) = (C_1, \quad 0, \quad 0)x(t) \tag{2.15.11}$$

The open-loop characteristic polynomial of this system is easily verified to be

$$\rho_0(s) = |sI_{n_1} - A_1| \ |sI_{n_2} - A_2| \ |sI_{n_3} - A_3| \tag{2.15.12}$$

The state vector model of the closed-loop system is obtained directly by substitution of eqn. 2.15.9 into eqn. 2.15.11 and the closed-loop characteristic polynomial is obtained by inspection. The reader should verify that the resulting expression is a highly complex function of the control parameters $A_2, B_2, C_2, D_2, A_3, B_3, C_3, D_3$ indicating that the problem of system design in the state vector context can be a difficult task. In the next Section consideration is given to the reformulation of the system and controller models in terms of Laplace transform terminology. The approach introduces a notational simplicity and reveals the essential concepts of dynamic output feedback control, and the reader should anticipate its use in control system design using generalisations of the well-known classical design techniques (Nyquist diagram, root-locus etc.) for single-input-output systems. This is discussed in depth in the following chapters.

2.16 Transfer-function matrices

Those readers familiar with the use of transfer functions in classical control systems design will be aware of the wealth of information available by analysis of the system pole-configuration and zero-configuration, the simplifying effect of approximate pole-zero calculation, resonances and the implications of phase and gain characteristics on feedback stability and performance. With those features in mind it is natural to investigate the feasibility of using Laplace transformation methods for the anlysis of multi-input/multi-output systems.

Consider the general linear time-invariant state-vector model,

$$\dot{x}(t) = Ax(t) + Bu(t), \quad x(t) \in R^n$$

$$x(0) = x(0) \qquad \qquad , \quad u(t) \in R^l$$

$$y(t) = Cx(t) + Du(t), \quad y(t) \in R^m \tag{2.16.1}$$

Taking Laplace transforms of these equations, with s as the Laplace transformation variable, yields

$$sx(s) - x(0) = Ax(s) + Bu(s)$$

$$y(s) = Cx(s) + Du(s) \tag{2.16.2}$$

Noting that $sI_n - A$ is nonsingular if s is not equal to an eigenvalue of A, then

$$x(s) = (sI_n - A)^{-1} \{Bu(s) + x(0)\} \qquad (2.16.3)$$

except at a finite number of points in the complex plane. Combining eqn. 2.16.3 with the output equation,

$$y(s) = \{C(sI_n - A)^{-1}B + D\}u(s) + C(sI_n - A)^{-1}x(0) \qquad (2.16.4)$$

where the first term represents the effect of control input (i.e. the 'particular integral') and the second term represents the effect of the initial state vector (i.e. the 'complementary function'). In design work we are primarily interested in the effect of control inputs and hence it is convenient to define

$$G(s) = C(sI_n - A)^{-1}B + D \qquad (2.16.5)$$

to be the *transfer-function matrix* of the system. The matrix $G(s)$ is an $m \times l$ matrix with transfer function elements and will play the role of the transfer function in multi-input/multi-output problems.

The original dynamic system (eqn. 2.16.1) can now be represented in the compact form

$$y(s) = G(s)u(s) + C(sI_n - A)^{-1}x(0) \qquad (2.16.6)$$

and will be represented in the block diagram form of Fig. 2.16.1. In most cases we will be interested in the case of zero initial conditions $x(0) = 0$ when the indication of initial conditions will be deleted from the block diagram.

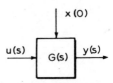

Fig. 2.16.1 Transfer-function-matrix representation of system dynamics

It is important to note that $(sI_n - A)^{-1} = s^{-1}(I_n - s^{-1}A)^{-1}$ has a series expansion of the form

$$(sI_n - A)^{-1} = \frac{1}{s}I_n + \frac{1}{s^2}A + \frac{1}{s^3}A^2 + \dots$$

$$= \frac{1}{s} \sum_{j=0}^{\infty} \frac{1}{s^j} A^j \qquad (2.16.7)$$

valid for large enough $|s|$. It follows directly that

$$\lim_{|s| \to \infty} G(s) = D \qquad (2.16.8)$$

so that the high-frequency behaviour of the system will be dominated by the $m \times l$ transmission matrix D. The following terminology will be used throughout the remainder of this text:

(*a*) the system (eqn. 2.16.1) is said to be *proper* to indicate that the transfer-function matrix is finite at high frequencies

(*b*) if $D = 0$ the system (eqn. 2.16.1) is said to be strictly proper and
$$\lim_{|s| \to \infty} G(s) = 0$$

(*c*) in any other case the system is said to be *improper* or *nonproper*. In general terms a strictly proper system does not respond to high frequency input and hence represents a system possessing inertia (either mechanical, electrical or thermal). If $m = l = 1$, case (*a*) represents a transfer function with n_z zeros and n poles where $n_z \leqslant n$, (*b*) represents the case $n_z < n$ and case (*c*) represents the situation $n_z > n$.

An insight into the structure of $G(s)$ can be obtained by writing eqn. 2.16.5 in the form

$$G(s) = \frac{\{C \operatorname{adj}(sI_n - A)B + \rho_0(s)D\}}{\rho_0(s)} \qquad (2.16.9)$$

where $\rho_0(s) = |sI_n - A|$ is the open-loop characteristic polynomial. Noting that the elements of $N(s) = C \operatorname{adj}(sI_n - A)B + \rho_0(s)D$ are polynomials in s, analytic over the entire complex plane, it can be seen that the poles of $G(s)$ are simply the eigenvalues of the system matrix A. The reader may be tempted to regard the zeros of the elements of $N(s)$ as the 'zeros' of the transfer-function matrix. This temptation must be resisted, however, as, although some insight into transient behaviour can be obtained by pole-zero analysis of the elements of $G(s)$, these zeros do not play the role of zeros in the multivariable case (see Section 2.20 and 6.2).

Given a known initial state $x(0)$ and input signal $u(t)$, $t \geqslant 0$, the output response $y(t)$, $t \geqslant 0$, can be calculated by inverse-Laplace transformation of eqn. 2.16.4 element by element. A convenient technique for hand calculation is to expand the expression using the well known technique of partial-fraction expansion. In state vector terms suppose, for simplicity, that the $n \times n$ matrix A has distinct eigenvalues $\lambda_1, \lambda_2, \ldots, \lambda_n$ with corresponding eigenvectors $w_1, w_2, \ldots, w_n$ and eigenvector matrix $E = [w_1, \ldots, w_n]$ i.e.

$$E^{-1}(sI_n - A)E = \text{diag} \{s - \lambda_1, \ldots, s - \lambda_n\} \quad (2.16.10)$$

so that

$$G(s) = C(sI_n - A)^{-1}B + D = CE \, \text{diag} \left\{ \frac{1}{s - \lambda_j} \right\}_{1 \leqslant j \leqslant n} E^{-1}B + D$$

$$C(sI - A)^{-1}x(0) = CE \, \text{diag} \left\{ \frac{1}{s - \lambda_j} \right\}_{1 \leqslant j \leqslant n} E^{-1}x(0) \quad (2.16;11)$$

Assuming that $x(0) = 0$, $D = 0$ and $u(t)$ is a step-input

$$u(t) = \begin{bmatrix} 0, & t \leqslant 0 \\ \alpha, & t > 0 \end{bmatrix} \quad (2.16.12)$$

then $u(s) = \dfrac{1}{s} \alpha$ and the relation $y(s) = G(s)u(s)$ takes the form

$$y(s) = CE \, \text{diag} \left\{ \frac{1}{s - \lambda_j} \right\}_{1 \leqslant j \leqslant n} E^{-1}B \frac{1}{s} \alpha \quad (2.16.13)$$

Defining $Cw_j = \alpha_j$, $1 \leqslant j \leqslant n$, and $v_j^+ B = \beta_j^+$, $1 \leqslant j \leqslant n$, where v_j^+, $1 \leqslant j \leqslant n$, are the rows of E^{-1}, then the reader can easily verify that

$$G(s) = \sum_{j=1}^{n} \frac{1}{s - \lambda_j} \alpha_j \beta_j^+ \quad (2.16.14)$$

and hence

$$y(s) = \sum_{j=1}^{n} \frac{1}{s(s - \lambda_j)} \alpha_j (\beta_j^+ \alpha) \quad (2.16.15)$$

or, taking the inverse Laplace transform, and assuming that $\lambda_j \neq 0$, $1 \leqslant j \leqslant n$,

$$y(t) = \sum_{j=1}^{n} \frac{(-1)}{\lambda_j} (1 - e^{\lambda_j t}) \alpha_j (\beta_j^+ \alpha) \quad (2.16.16)$$

The corresponding output for the impulse-type input $u(t) = \alpha \delta(t)$ is

$$y(t) = \sum_{j=1}^{n} e^{\lambda_j t} \alpha_j (\beta_j^+ \alpha) \quad (2.16.17)$$

Exercise 2.16.1
The reader should verify the solutions given in eqns. 2.16.16, 2.16.17
directly from the modal description of system dynamics discussed in
Section 2.8.

The following observations should throw more light on the physical
nature of the decomposition eqn. 2.16.4:
(*a*) the $m \times l$ matrix $\alpha_j \beta_j^+$ is the residue of the pole λ_j in the transfer-
function matrix $G(s)$. For the case considered, each residue has rank
one and hence is a dyad. Examination of eqns. 2.16.16 and 2.16.17
indicates that the $m \times 1$ vectors α_j, $1 \leqslant j \leqslant n$, describe the contribution
of the pole λ_j to the output response whereas the $1 \times l$ row vectors β_j^+,
$1 \leqslant j \leqslant n$, described the effect of the input on the pole λ_j e.g. if $\beta_j^+ \alpha =$
0, for some j, then the pole at $s = \lambda_j$ plays no part in the system output
response.
(*b*) if the matrix A has distinct eigenvalues, the system dynamics can be
represented by n classical first-order lags with unity-rank matrix coefficients in a parallel configuration as illustrated in Fig. 2.16.2.

Exercise 2.16.2
Show that a system described by the state-vector model

$$\dot{x}(t) = \begin{pmatrix} -1 & 1 \\ 1 & -1 \end{pmatrix} x(t) + \begin{pmatrix} 2 & 0 \\ 0 & 1 \end{pmatrix} u(t)$$

$$y(t) = \begin{pmatrix} 1 & 0 \\ 0 & 1 \end{pmatrix} x(t)$$

has a transfer-function matrix

$$G(s) = \frac{1}{s(s+2)} \begin{pmatrix} 2(s+1) & 1 \\ 2 & s+1 \end{pmatrix}$$

$$= \frac{1}{s} \begin{pmatrix} 1 \\ 1 \end{pmatrix} \begin{pmatrix} 1 & 0{\cdot}5 \end{pmatrix} + \frac{1}{(s+2)} \begin{pmatrix} -1 \\ 1 \end{pmatrix} \begin{pmatrix} -1 & 0{\cdot}5 \end{pmatrix}$$

By considering step inputs $u(s) = \dfrac{1}{s} \alpha$, calculate those vectors α such
that the output response contains no contribution from the pole at

$s = -2$. Calculate the output response if $\alpha = (1, 1)^T$.

Exercise 2.16.3
Show that a system described by the block diagonal model

$$A = \text{block diag}\{A_1, \ldots, A_p\}, \quad B = \begin{pmatrix} B_1 \\ \vdots \\ B_p \end{pmatrix}$$

$$C = (C_1, C_2, \ldots, C_p)$$

has a transfer-function matrix

$$G(s) = \sum_{j=1}^{p} C_j(sI - A_j)^{-1} B_j + D$$

Use this result and the analysis of Section 2.8 to extend relation eqn. 2.16.4 to the case where A has multiple eigenvalues.

Exercise 2.16.4
Show that two linear, time-invariant systems described by the matrices A, B, C, D and $\tilde{A}, \tilde{B}, \tilde{C}, \tilde{D}$ have identical transfer-function matrices if there exists a nonsingular transformation T such that

$$\tilde{A} = T^{-1}AT, \quad \tilde{B} = T^{-1}B, \quad \tilde{C} = CT, \quad \tilde{D} = D$$

Finally, the relationship of the transfer-function matrix $G(s)$ to the transient performance of the system can be obtained by consideration of the exponential input

$$u(t) = \begin{bmatrix} 0 & ; & t \leqslant 0 \\ \alpha e^{\lambda t} & ; & t > 0 \end{bmatrix} \tag{2.16.18}$$

when, using the formal solution of the state equations, and assuming that λ is not equal to any eigenvalue of A

$$y(t) = Ce^{At}x(0) + \int_0^t Ce^{A(t-s)}Bu(s)ds$$

$$= Ce^{At}x(0) + Ce^{At}\int_0^t e^{(\lambda I - A)s}Bds\alpha$$

$$= Ce^{At}x(0) + C(\lambda I - A)^{-1}(e^{\lambda t}B\alpha - e^{At}B\alpha)$$

$$= Ce^{At}(x(0) - (\lambda I - A)^{-1}B\alpha) + G(\lambda)u(t) \qquad (2.16.19)$$

If the system is asymptotically stable and $\mathrm{Re}\,\lambda > \mathrm{Re}\,\lambda_j$, $1 \leqslant j \leqslant n$, then for large enough values of t,

$$y(t) \simeq G(\lambda)u(t) \qquad (2.16.20)$$

i.e. the transfer-function matrix $G(\lambda)$ describes the asymptotic behaviour of the system in response to exponential inputs of 'frequency' λ.

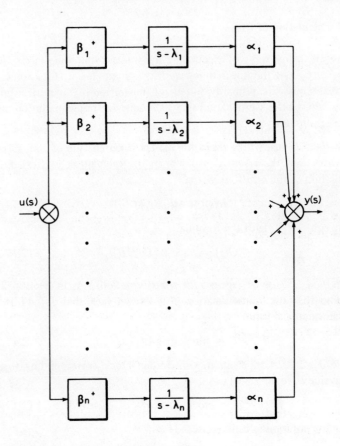

Fig. 2.16.2 Pole-residue decomposition of $G(s)$

In practice we are particularly interested in the case of oscillating inputs represented by the complex exponential,

$$u(t) = \alpha e^{i\omega t}, \qquad t > 0 \qquad (2.16.21)$$

where ω is the (real) frequency of oscillation (rad/unit time). The asymptotic approximation

$$y(t) \simeq G(i\omega)u(t) \qquad (2.16.22)$$

can yield information on the behaviour of the open-loop system by an analysis of the gain and phase characteristics of the elements of the *frequency-response matrix* $G(i\omega)$.

2.17 Calculation of $G(s)$

There are many ways of calculating the transfer-function matrix $G(s)$ (eqn. 2.16.5) of the linear time-invariant system eqn. 2.16.1. Some of the techniques are primarily suited for illustration of theoretical principles whilst others provide a rapid technique for implementation on a digital computer.

Method 1: (use of the transition matrix) Examination of eqn. 2.16.5 indicates that the essential problem in the calculation of $G(s)$ is the calculation of the *resolvent matrix*

$$R(s) = (sI_n - A)^{-1} \qquad (2.17.1)$$

Using eqn. 2.8.4 yields the formula

$$G(s) = D + \mathcal{L}\{Ce^{At}B\} \qquad (2.17.2)$$

Method 2: (use of eigenvector transformations) As in Section 2.8 suppose that the transformation T is known such that $T^{-1}AT$ is in Jordan-canonical form

$$T^{-1}AT = \text{block diag}\{J_1, \ldots, J_p\} \qquad (2.17.3)$$

where J_i, $1 \leqslant i \leqslant p$, is an $n_i \times n_i$ Jordan block corresponding to an eigenvalue λ_i (eqn. 2.8.9) i.e.

$$T^{-1}e^{At}T = \text{block diag}\{e^{J_1 t}, \ldots, e^{J_p t}\} \qquad (2.17.4)$$

Using the notation as in Exercise 2.16.3,

$$CT = (C_1 C_2, \ldots, C_p), \quad T^{-1}B = \begin{pmatrix} B_1 \\ B_2 \\ . \\ . \\ . \\ B_p \end{pmatrix} \qquad (2.17.5)$$

where C_i, B_i are $m \times n_i$, $n_i \times l$ matrices, respectively, then the reader can easily verify that

$$G(s) = D + \sum_{j=1}^{p} \mathcal{L}\{C_i e^{J_i t} B_i\} \qquad (2.17.6)$$

(Hint: use Exercise 2.16.4 and eqn. 2.17.2.) The remaining problem is the calculation of $e^{J_j t}$, $1 \leqslant j \leqslant p$. If $n_i = 1$, $e^{J_i t} = 1/(s - \lambda_i)$ and if $n_i > 1$, the answer is obtained by taking the Laplace transform of eqn. 2.8.10 i.e.

$$\mathcal{L}\{e^{J_i t}\} = \begin{pmatrix} \dfrac{1}{s-\lambda_i} & \dfrac{1}{(s-\lambda_i)^2} & \cdots & \dfrac{1}{(s-\lambda_i)^{n_i}} \\ 0 & \dfrac{1}{s-\lambda_i} & & \vdots \\ \vdots & & \ddots & \vdots \\ \vdots & & & \dfrac{1}{(s-\lambda_i)^2} \\ 0 & \cdots \cdots & 0 & \dfrac{1}{(s-\lambda_i)} \end{pmatrix} \qquad (2.17.7)$$

Exercise 2.17.1
Compare the above derivation with the calculation of $G(s)$ as given by eqn. 2.16.4.

Method 3: (direct evaluation using determinants) Let c_i, $1 \leqslant i \leqslant m$, be the rows of C and b_i, $1 \leqslant i \leqslant l$, be the columns of B then the (i,j)th element of $G(s)$ takes the form

$$G_{ij}(s) = D_{ij} + c_i(sI_n - A)^{-1}b_j \qquad (2.17.8)$$

Applying Schur's formula it follows directly that

$$G_{ij}(s) = \begin{vmatrix} sI_n - A & -b_j \\ c_i & D_{ij} \end{vmatrix} / |sI - A| \qquad (2.17.9)$$

If $D_{ij} \neq 0$, this formula reduces after some manipulation, to

$$G_{ij}(s) = D_{ij} |sI_n - A + b_j(D_{ij})^{-1}c_i| / |sI_n - A| \qquad (2.17.10)$$

and the calculation of the transfer function $G_{ij}(s)$ reduces to the solution of two eigenvalue problems. If, however, $D_{ij} = 0$, the numerator polynomial of eqn. 2.17.9 can be computed by the use of row and column operations on the determinant (Reference 57).

Method 4: (the Faddeev algorithm) A useful technique for the calculation of $G(s)$ which yields some insight into its structure is based on an algorithm due to Faddeev (Reference 9). The algorithm does, however, suffer from some numerical problems[36] in cases where the system matrix A has a large spread in its eigenvalues due to computer rounding errors. This problem can often be removed by the use of double precision arithmetic.

The technique is based upon the systematic calculation of the resolvent $R(s) = (sI_n - A)^{-1}$ by observing that

$$|sI_n - A| = a_0 s^n + a_1 s^{n-1} + \ldots + a_{n-1} s + a_n, \quad a_0 = 1$$

$$\text{adj}(sI_n - A) = H_1 s^{n-1} + \ldots + H_{n-1} s + H_n \qquad (2.17.11)$$

Substituting into the identity,

$$(sI_n - A) \, \text{adj}\,(sI_n - A) = |sI_n - A| I_n \qquad (2.17.12)$$

and equating powers of s^j, $0 \leqslant j \leqslant n$, yields the relations,

$$H_1 = a_0 I_n = I_n$$

$$H_j - AH_{j-1} = a_{j-1} I_n, \qquad 2 \leqslant j \leqslant n \qquad (2.17.13)$$

$$-AH_n = a_n I_n \qquad (2.17.14)$$

In particular, if the coefficients $a_1, a_2, \ldots, a_n$ in the characteristic polynomial are known, eqn. 2.17.13 can be used to sequentially calculate the matrix coefficients $H_1, H_2, \ldots, H_n$. Relation eqn. 2.17.14 can then be used to check the accuracy of the calculation by examination of the magnitude of the elements in the calculated $a_n I_n + AH_n$. Note also that, if A is nonsingular, then $a_n \neq 0$ and

$$A^{-1} = -\frac{1}{a_n} H_n \qquad (2.17.15)$$

If the coefficients a_j, $1 \leqslant j \leqslant n$, are unknown, the algorithm can be easily modified to provide explicit formulas. From eqns. 2.17.13 and 2.17.14, taking the trace

$$na_{j-1} = \text{tr}\, H_j - \text{tr}\, AH_{j-1}, \qquad 2 \leqslant j \leqslant n$$

$$na_n = -\text{tr}\, AH_n \qquad (2.17.16)$$

and noting that, from the definition of $\text{adj}(sI_n - A)$, and the rules for differentiation of a determinant,

$$
\begin{aligned}
\text{tr}\, H_j &= \left. \frac{1}{(n-j)!} \frac{d^{n-j}}{ds^{n-j}} \,\text{tr}\,\{\text{adj}\,(sI_n - A)\} \right|_{s=0} \\
&= \left. \frac{1}{(n-j)!} \frac{d^{n-j}}{ds^{n-j}} \frac{d}{ds}\, |sI_n - A| \right|_{s=0} \\
&= (n+1-j)a_{j-1}
\end{aligned}
\tag{2.17.17}
$$

substitution into eqn. 2.17.16 gives the formula,

$$
a_j = -\frac{1}{j}\,\text{tr}\, AH_j, \qquad 1 \leqslant j \leqslant n \tag{2.17.18}
$$

Using this relation together with eqn. 2.17.13 enables the calculation of the coefficients in the sequence $a_0, H_1, a_1, H_2, a_2, \ldots, H_n, a_n$ with the starting condition $a_0 = 1$.

The transfer-function matrix $G(s)$ takes the form

$$
G(s) = D + \frac{\displaystyle\sum_{j=1}^{n} s^{n-j} C H_j B}{\displaystyle\sum_{j=0}^{n} s^{n-j} a_j} \tag{2.17.19}
$$

Exercise 2.17.2
Apply the four techniques discussed above to the calculation of the transfer-function matrix of the system discussed in Exercise 2.16.2.

Exercise 2.17.3
Use method 1 of Section 2.4 to calculate a state-vector model of a single-input/single-output process described by the transfer function

$$
g(s) = \frac{6(s+1)}{s^2(s+2)}
$$

Use your results to recalculate the transfer function using the methods discussed above.

2.18 Multivariable feedback systems
The purpose of this Section is to reformulate the output feedback

control concepts discussed in Sections 2.14 and 2.15 in transfer-function matrix terms. The system to be controlled is supposed to have a state-vector model (eqn. 2.14.1)

$$\dot{x}_1(t) = A_1 x_1(t) + B_1 u(t), \quad x_1(t) \in R^{n_1}$$

$$y(t) = C_1 x_1(t), \quad y(t) \in R^m, \quad u(t) \in R^l \qquad (2.18.1)$$

possessing a strictly proper $m \times l$ transfer-function matrix

$$G(s) = C_1 (sI_{n_1} - A_1)^{-1} B_1 \qquad (2.18.2)$$

and, in transform terms,

$$y(s) = G(s)u(s) + C_1 (sI_{n_1} - A)^{-1} x_1(0) \qquad (2.18.3)$$

The forward-path control system is described by the model (eqn. 2.15.2)

$$\dot{x}_2(t) = A_2 x_2(t) + B_2 e(t), \quad x_2(t) \in R^{n_2}$$

$$u(t) = C_2 x_2(t) + D_2 e(t) \qquad (2.18.4)$$

(where $e(t)$ is the error signal) with $l \times m$ proper tranfer-function matrix

$$K(s) = D_2 + C_2 (sI_{n_2} - A_2)^{-1} B_2 \qquad (2.18.5)$$

and

$$u(s) = K(s)e(s) + C_2 (sI_{n_2} - A_2)^{-1} x_2(0) \qquad (2.18.6)$$

Considering for simplicity the case of unity-negative feedback, the error signal $e(t)$ is given by

$$e(t) = r(t) - y(t) \qquad (2.18.7)$$

where $r(t)$ is the vector of m demand signals. In transform terms,

$$e(s) = r(s) - y(s) \qquad (2.18.8)$$

Using the block diagram representation, the resulting feedback system is illustrated in Fig. 2.18.1 where, for simplicity, the indications of the initial conditions $x_1(0)$ and $x_2(0)$ are neglected. The reader will recognise the apparent similarity of the configuration to the well known classical unity-negative feedback system for the control of single-input/single-output systems. Note, however, that the blocks and differencing junctions must be interpreted in the vector sense indicated by eqns. 2.18.3, 2.18.6 and 2.18.8.

Noting that the composite system (eqn. 2.15.4) has state $(x_1^T(t), x_2^T(t))^T$ and combining eqns. 2.18.3 and 2.18.6 yields

$$y(s) = G(s) \{ K(s)e(s) + C_2 (sI_{n_2} - A_2)^{-1} x_2(0) \} + C_1 (sI_{n_1} - A_1)^{-1} x_1(0) \qquad (2.18.9)$$

The $m \times m$ forward-path transfer-function matrix relating the output response $y(s)$ to the dynamics of the error $e(s)$ is obtained by setting $x_1(0) = 0$ and $x_2(0) = 0$,

$$Q(s) = G(s)K(s) \qquad (2.18.10)$$

and, assuming zero initial conditions,

$$y(s) = Q(s)e(s) = G(s)K(s)e(s) \qquad (2.18.11)$$

The closed-loop transfer-function matrix $H_c(s)$ relating $y(s)$ and $r(s)$ is obtained by substitution into eqn. 2.18.8 to be

$$H_c(s) = \{I_m + Q(s)\}^{-1}Q(s) \qquad (2.18.12)$$

Note that both $Q(s)$ and $H_c(s)$ are strictly proper as, by assumption, $G(s)$ is strictly proper.

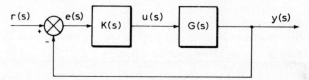

Fig. 2.18.1 Unity-negative feedback system

In the more general case of a nonunity feedback system,

$$e(t) = r(t) - \hat{y}(t) \quad \text{or} \quad e(s) = r(s) - \hat{y}(s) \qquad (2.18.13)$$

where (eqn. 2.15.10) $\hat{y}(t)$ is the output from the system

$$\dot{x}_3(t) = A_3 x_3(t) + B_3 y(t), \quad x_3(t) \in R^{n_3}$$

$$\hat{y}(t) = C_3 x_3(t) + D_3 y(t) \qquad (2.18.14)$$

with $m \times m$ proper feedback transfer-function matrix

$$F(s) = D_3 + C_3(sI_{n_3} - A_3)^{-1}B_3 \qquad (2.18.15)$$

and, in transform terms,

$$\hat{y}(s) = F(s)y(s) + C_3(sI_{n_3} - A_3)^{-1}x_3(0) \qquad (2.18.16)$$

The resulting feedback system is illustrated in Fig. 2.18.2. The closed-loop transfer-function matrix is obtained from eqns. 2.18.3, 2.18.6, 2.18.13 and 2.18.16, by neglecting initial conditions i.e.

$$y(s) = G(s)u(s) = G(s)K(s)e(s) = G(s)K(s)\{r(s) - F(s)y(s)\}$$
$$(2.18.17)$$

so that

$$y(s) = H_c(s)r(s) \qquad (2.18.18)$$

where

$$H_c(s) = \{I_m + G(s)K(s)F(s)\}^{-1} G(s)K(s)$$

$$= \{I_m + Q(s)F(s)\}^{-1} Q(s) \qquad (2.18.19)$$

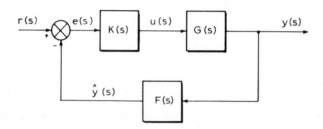

Fig. 2.18.2 Nonunity multivariable feedback system

The reader should note the following points:

(a) for the case of $m > 1$ the ordering of the matrices in eqn. 2.18.10 and 2.18.19 is crucial as, in general, $G(s)K(s) \neq K(s)G(s)$ and $Q(s)F(s) \neq F(s)Q(s)$

(b) the unity-negative feedback system can be regarded as a feedback system with $F(s) = I_m$.

Exercise 2.18.1

Verify eqns. 2.18.10 and 2.18.11 directly from eqns. 2.14.1 and 2.14.2 and 2.14.5 for the case of constant output feedback.

Finally, it is sometimes convenient to consider alternative (but equivalent) expressions for $H_c(s)$. For example, if $m = l$, $|G(s)| \not\equiv 0$, the reader can verify that

$$H_c(s) = \{G^{-1}(s) + K(s)F(s)\}^{-1} K(s) \qquad (2.18.20)$$

Also, the identity

$$Q(s) \{I_m + F(s)Q(s)\} \equiv \{I_m + Q(s)F(s)\} Q(s) \qquad (2.18.21)$$

immediately gives

$$H_c(s) = \{I_m + Q(s)F(s)\}^{-1} Q(s) \equiv Q(s) \{I_m + F(s)Q(s)\}^{-1} \qquad (2.18.22)$$

Alternatively, if we define the $m \times l$ transfer-function matrix $H(s)$ by the identity,

$$G(s) = P_1 H(s) P_2 \qquad (2.18.23)$$

where P_1, P_2 are constant $m \times m, l \times l$ nonsingular matrices then

$$H_c(s) = \{I_m + G(s)K(s)F(s)\}^{-1} G(s)K(s)$$
$$= P_1 \{I_m + H(s)P_2 K(s)F(s)P_1\}^{-1} H(s)P_2 K(s)$$
(2.18.24)

Transformation of this type can be useful if it is possible to choose P_1, P_2 so that $H(s)$ takes a simple form

---

Exercise 2.18.2
The reader should convince himself that the transformation $G(s) \to H(s)$ defined by eqn. 2.18.23 is equivalent to replacing the inputs (outputs) by linear combinations of the inputs (outputs) and hence represents, for example, the operation of scaling the input and output variables.

The interested reader can find several examples of equivalent expressions for $H_c(s)$ in Reference 57.

2.19 Feedback stability and integrity

A glance at the formulation of state-space models of output feedback systems discussed in Sections 2.14 and 2.15 indicates that closed-loop stability can be assessed by examination of the closed-loop characteristic polynomials defined in terms of the matrices in the state-vector representations of $G(s)$, $K(s)$ and $F(s)$. An examination of eqn. 2.18.19 and the identity

$$\{I_m + G(s)K(s)F(s)\}^{-1} = \frac{\text{adj}\{I_m + G(s)K(s)F(s)\}}{|I_m + G(s)K(s)F(s)|}$$
(2.19.1)

suggests that the stability is related to the properties of the *matrix return-difference*

$$T(s) = I_m + G(s)K(s)F(s) = I_m + Q(s)F(s)$$
(2.19.2)

and, in particular, the zeros of the numerator of the *return-difference determinant*

$$|T(s)| = |I + G(s)K(s)F(s)|$$
(2.19.3)

The conjecture is, in fact, correct although the details of the relationship are rather subtle. A detailed treatment of the structure and properties of the relation can be found in Reference 57. For simplicity we restrict our attention to the case of a unity negative feedback system as depicted in Fig. 2.18.1. Regarding $Q(s) = G(s)K(s)$ as the strictly proper transfer-function matrix of a composite system with state-vector model (eqn. 2.15.3)

$$\dot{x}(t) = Ax(t) + Be(t)$$

$$y(t) = Cx(t) \qquad (2.19.4)$$

with transfer-function matrix

$$Q(s) = C(sI_n - A)^{-1}B \qquad (2.19.5)$$

and open-loop characteristic polynomial (eqn. 2.15.7)

$$\rho_0(s) = |sI_n - A| \qquad (2.19.6)$$

The closed-loop characteristic polynomial is defined (eqn. 2.15.8) by the identity

$$\rho_c(s) = |sI_n - A + BC| \qquad (2.19.7)$$

Dividing $\rho_c(s)$ by $\rho_0(s)$ gives

$$\frac{\rho_c(s)}{\rho_0(s)} = \frac{|sI_n - A + BC|}{|sI_n - A|} = \cdot |I_n + (sI - A)^{-1}BC|$$

$$= |I_m + C(sI - A)^{-1}B| = |I_m + Q(s)| = |T(s)| \qquad (2.19.8)$$

i.e. the return-difference determinant relates the forward-path transfer-function matrix $Q(s)$ to both the closed and open-loop characteristic polynomials.

The equivalent expression for the case of a nonunity feedback system is

$$\frac{\rho_c(s)}{\rho_0(s)} = |T(s)| = |I_m + G(s)K(s)F(s)| \qquad (2.19.9)$$

The reader should note that the return difference $T(s)$ not only yields information on closed-loop stability but also can be used to provide information on dynamic behaviour as is suggested by the identity,

$$H_c(s) = T^{-1}(s)Q(s) \qquad (2.19.10)$$

This point is an important but essentially intuitive help in feedback design and is discussed in later chapters.

A feature unique to the single-input/single-output output feedback control configuration is that a failure in either the control actuator and/or the output transducers or sensors such that either the control signal is reduced to zero and/or the output signal fed back is zero totally removes the operation of the feedback control. The system then operates in an open-loop mode. In the case of a multi-input/multi-output system the failure of, for example, a single output sensor affects only part of the control system as, by assumption, the controller can still use the information available from the other output measurements. An important question of relevance to feedback design is: given a stable feedback system, will the failure of specified actuators or sensors introduce instability unless the control policy is modified?

It is not possible, in the theoretical sense, to obtain useful results for all possible system failures so we restrict our attention to two cases of practical interest. Our philosophy will be that stability in the presence of such failures will indicate an overall *integrity* of the closed-loop system in the sense that the control system may be capable of suppressing instabilities induced by a much larger class of failure situations.

(a) Sensor failure in loop k *:* The unity-negative multivariable feedback system of Fig. 2.18.1 is said to have a *sensor failure in loop k,* if the feedback loop returns the erroneous signal $y_k(t) \equiv 0$ due to failure of the kth output transducer.

(b) Actuator failure in loop k *:* The unity-negative feedback system of Fig. 2.18.1 is said to have an *actuator failure in loop k* if the forward-path control system injects the erroneous control input $u_k(t) \equiv 0$ due to failure of the kth control actuator.

Considering the case of sensor failure in loop k, the returned (but erroneous) output vector can be written in the form[35]

$$
\begin{pmatrix} y_1(s) \\ \vdots \\ y_{k-1}(s) \\ 0 \\ y_{k+1}(s) \\ \vdots \\ y_m(s) \end{pmatrix} = \{I_m - e_k e_k^T\} \begin{pmatrix} y_1(s) \\ \vdots \\ y_{k-1}(s) \\ y_k(s) \\ \vdots \\ y_m(s) \end{pmatrix} \tag{2.19.11}
$$

so that the error signal takes the form (where e_k is the $m \times 1$ column vector of zeros everywhere except a unit entry in the kth position)

$$
\begin{aligned}
e(s) &= r(s) - \{I_m - e_k e_k^T\} y(s) \\
&= \{r(s) - (-e_k e_k^T) y(s)\} - y(s)
\end{aligned} \tag{2.19.12}
$$

The block diagram interpretation of this relation is given in Fig. 2.19.1. Analysis of the structure of the failed system will indicate that it can be regarded as a nonunity negative feedback system with formed path system equal to the unity feedback system of Fig. 2.18.1 and a feedback path transfer-function matrix $F(s) = -e_k e_k^T$. By analogy with eqn. 2.19.9 it follows directly that

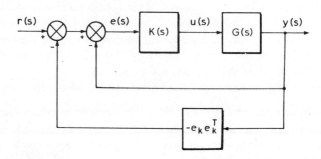

Fig. 2.19.1 Sensor failure in loop k

$$\frac{\text{closed-loop characteristic polynomial of the system with sensor failure in loop } k}{\text{closed-loop characteristic polynomial of the system without sensor failure in loop } k}$$

$$= |I_m + \{I_m + G(s)K(s)\}^{-1}G(s)K(s)(-e_k e_k^T)|$$

$$= 1 - e_k^T \{I_m + G(s)K(s)\}^{-1}G(s)K(s)e_k$$

$$= e_k^T \{I_m - \{I_m + G(s)K(s)\}^{-1}G(s)K(s)\} e_k, \quad (e_k^T e_k = 1)$$

$$= e_k^T \{I + G(s)K(s)\}^{-1}e_k = e_k^T T^{-1}(s)e_k \qquad (2.19.13)$$

It is noted that the matrix return-difference $T(s)$ again dominates the analysis of the failure situations, in the sense that the poles of the failed system are equal to the zeros of the transfer function appearing in the kth diagonal position of $T^{-1}(s)$.

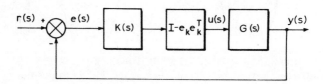

Fig. 2.19.2 Actuator failure in loop k

Turning our attention to the case of actuator failure in loop k, the reader can easily verify that the dynamics of the failed system can be represented by the block diagram of Fig. 2.19.2, where e_k now represents the $l \times 1$ column vector consisting of zero everywhere except the kth position which consists of a unit element. Applying eqn. 2.19.8 with $Q(s) = G(s)K(s)$ replaced by the forward-path transfer-function matrix $G(s)\{I_l - e_k e_k^T\}K(s)$ yields the identity,

$$\frac{\text{closed-loop characteristic polynomial with actuator failure in loop } k}{\text{open-loop characteristic polynomial}}$$

$$= |I_m + G(s)\{I - e_k e_k^T\}K(s)|$$

$$= |I_l + K(s)G(s)\{I - e_k e_k^T\}|$$

$$= |I_l + K(s)G(s)| \; |I_l - \{I + K(s)G(s)\}^{-1}K(s)G(s)e_k e_k^T|$$

$$= |I_m + G(s)K(s)| \, (1 - e_k^T \{I_l + K(s)G(s)\}^{-1}K(s)G(s)e_k)$$

$$(2.19.14)$$

Noting that $|I_m + GK|$ is the ratio of the closed-loop characteristic polynomial (in the absence of a failure) to the open-loop characteristic polynomial it is left as an exercise for the reader to show that

$$\frac{\text{closed-loop characteristic polynomial with actuator failure in loop } k}{\text{closed-loop characteristic polynomial without actuator failure in loop } k}$$

$$= e_k^T \{I_l + K(s)G(s)\}^{-1} e_k \qquad (2.19.15)$$

i.e. the poles of the closed-loop system in the presence of an actuator failure in loop k are the zeros of the transfer function in the kth diagonal position of $\{I_l + K(s)G(s)\}^{-1}$.

In practice the evaluation of the expressions 2.19.13 and 2.19.15 may implicitly introduce cancellation of common terms in the numerator and denominator. This is no problem as failure analysis is normally undertaken when it is known that the original system of Fig. 2.18.1 is stable. It follows directly that any cancelled terms in the numerator must be stable.

Exercise 2.19.1

Show that the stable system described by the data,

$$A = \begin{pmatrix} -1 & 1 \\ 0 & -1 \end{pmatrix}, \quad B = \begin{pmatrix} 1 & 0 \\ 1 & 1 \end{pmatrix}, \quad C = \begin{pmatrix} 1 & 0 \\ 0 & 1 \end{pmatrix}$$

has open-loop characteristic polynomial,

$$\rho_0(s) = s^2 + 2s + 1$$

Using the control elements $K(s) = kI_2$, $F(s) = I_2$, show that the closed-loop system has characteristic polynomial $\rho_c(s) = s^2 + 2(1 + k)s + (1 + k)^2 + k$ and hence is stable for $k > 0$. In the event of a sensor failure in loop 1, show that the closed-loop system has characteristic polynomial $(s + 1)(s + k + 1)$ so that stability is retained. (Hint: apply eqns. 2.19.8 and 2.19.13 and check your result by direct calculation using the state matrices A, B, C).

Replacing C by the matrix

$$C = \begin{pmatrix} 0 & 1 \\ -1 & 0 \end{pmatrix}$$

show that the closed-loop system has characteristic polynomial

$$\rho_c(s) = s^2 + 2(1 + \tfrac{1}{2}k)s + 1 + k^2$$

and hence that the system is stable for all $k > 0$. In the event of a sensor failure in loop 1, show that the closed-loop system has characteristic polynomial

$$\rho_c(s) = s^2 + 2s + 1 - k$$

and hence that stability is retained only if $k < 1$, i.e. the 'gain margin' of the system is drastically reduced in the presence of a failure. This is, by no means, always the case, as will be seen in later chapters, but, in general, the requirement of system integrity may place (severe?) restrictions on the design of the control system, and the achievable performance.

Exercise 2.19.2

If $|Q(s)| \equiv |G(s)K(s)| \not\equiv 0$, prove that the closed-loop system cannot be stable in the presence of a sensor failure if $\lim_{s \to 0} Q^{-1}(s) = 0$. Relate this result to the system steady-state error and the use of integral control action.

2.20 System zeros

The dynamics of a classical single-input/single-output system described by a transfer function $g(s) = D + C(sI_n - A)^{-1}B$, when subject to unity-negative feedback control is critically dependent on the zeros of the transfer function i.e. the zeros of the numerator polynomial of $g(s)$). Writing

$$g(s) = \frac{z(s)}{\rho_0(s)} \tag{2.20.1}$$

where $z(s)$ is the zero polynomial of $g(s)$, application of Schur's formula yields the identity,

$$z(s) = \rho_0(s)g(s) = |sI_n - A| |D + C(sI - A)^{-1}B|$$

$$\equiv \begin{vmatrix} sI_n - A & -B \\ C & D \end{vmatrix} \tag{2.20.2}$$

so that the system zeros can be defined in terms of the state matrices (A, B, C, D). It should be anticipated that the concept of zeros will be of importance in multivariable systems, and that multivariable zeros will have a similar characterisation to eqn. 2.20.2. The most intuitively appealing characterisation of zeros in both the multi-input/multi-output and classical cases can be obtained by the use of the concept of blocking frequency.[17]

Definition 2.20.1: The complex number λ is a zero of the m-input/ m-output system

$$\dot{x}(t) = Ax(t) + Bu(t)$$

$$y(t) = Cx(t) + Du(t) \tag{2.20.3}$$

if, and only if, there exists a vector $\alpha \in R^m$ and an initial state condition $x(0)$ such that either $\alpha \neq 0$ and/or $x(0) \neq 0$ and the output response to the input $u(t) = \alpha e^{\lambda t}$ is identically zero.

In physical terms (assuming, for simplicity that $\alpha \neq 0$), the exponential input $\alpha e^{\lambda t}$ drives the state from the initial condition $x(0)$ in such a way as to leave the output unaffected. To obtain a more useful characterisation of multivariable zeros, suppose that $\lambda, \alpha, x(0)$ satisfy the conditions of Definition 2.20.1, and hence that

$$y(t) = Cx(t) + Du(t) \equiv 0, \qquad t \geq 0 \tag{2.20.4}$$

It follows directly that all the derivatives $y(t)$ vanish identically for $t \geq 0$, and, in particular,

$$\overset{(k)}{y}(0) = 0, \qquad k \geq 0 \tag{2.20.5}$$

The reader should verify that

$$\overset{(1)}{y}(t) = C\{Ax(t) + Bu(t)\} + D\overset{(1)}{u}(t) \tag{2.20.6}$$

or, in general terms, $k \geqslant 1$

$$\overset{(k)}{y}(t) = C\left\{A^k x(t) + \sum_{i=1}^{k} A^{k-i} B \overset{(i-1)}{u}(t)\right\} + D \overset{(k)}{u}(t)$$

$$= C\left\{A^k x(t) + \sum_{i=1}^{k} A^{k-i} \lambda^{i-1} B \alpha e^{\lambda t}\right\} + \lambda^k D \alpha e^{\lambda t} \qquad (2.20.7)$$

Expression 2.20.5 now becomes,

$$C\left\{A^k x(0) + \sum_{i=1}^{k} A^{k-i} \lambda^{i-1} B \alpha\right\} + \lambda^k D \alpha = 0, \qquad k \geqslant 1$$

$$Cx(0) + D\alpha = 0 \qquad (2.20.8)$$

or, for $k \geqslant 1$,

$$0 = C\left\{A^k x(0) + \sum_{i=1}^{k} A^{k-i} \lambda^{i-1} B \alpha\right\} + \lambda^k D \alpha$$

$$= C\left\{A^k x(0) + \sum_{i=1}^{k} A^{k-i} \lambda^{i-1} B \alpha - \lambda\left\{A^{k-1} x(0) + \sum_{i=1}^{k-1} A^{k-1-i} \lambda^{i-1} B \alpha\right\}\right\}$$

$$= CA^{k-1}\{Ax(0) + B\alpha - \lambda x(0)\} \qquad (2.20.9)$$

Combining these equations yields,

$$Cx(0) + D\alpha = 0$$

$$\begin{pmatrix} C \\ CA \\ CA^2 \\ \vdots \\ CA^{n-1} \end{pmatrix} \{\{\lambda I_n - A\}x(0) - B\alpha\} = 0 \qquad (2.20.10)$$

Assuming, for simplicity that the system is observable (theorem 2.10.2) it follows that $\{\lambda I_n - A\}x(0) - B\alpha = 0$, or,

$$\begin{pmatrix} \lambda I_n - A & -B \\ C & D \end{pmatrix} \begin{pmatrix} x(0) \\ \alpha \end{pmatrix} = 0 \qquad (2.20.11)$$

and hence the coefficient matrix is singular i.e. λ is a root of the (suggestively named) *zero polynomial*

$$z(s) = \rho_0(s)|G(s)| \equiv \begin{vmatrix} sI_n & -A & -B \\ C & & D \end{vmatrix} \qquad (2.20.12)$$

Conversely, if λ is a root of $z(s)$, there exists a nonzero solution vector to eqn. 2.20.11. The reader can easily verify that the input $u(t) = \alpha e^{\lambda t}$ and state $x(t) = x(0)e^{\lambda t}$ are a solution of the state eqns. 2.20.3 generating the output $y(t) \equiv 0$. In summary, we have proved the following equivalent to Definition 2.20.1:

Definition 2.20.2: The complex number λ is a zero of the m-input/m-output system eqn. 2.20.3 if, and only if, it is a root of the system zero polynomial $z(s)$.

It is emphasised that the zeros of the system are not the zeros of the elements of the transfer-function matrix $G(s) = D + C(sI_n - A)^{-1}B$.

Exercise 2.20.1
Show that the system

$$A = \begin{pmatrix} 0 & -1 & 0 \\ 0 & 0 & -1 \\ 0 & 0 & 0 \end{pmatrix}, \quad C = \begin{pmatrix} 1 & 0 & 0 \\ 0 & 1 & 0 \end{pmatrix}, \quad B = \begin{pmatrix} 1 & 0 \\ 0 & 0 \\ 0 & 1 \end{pmatrix}, \quad D = 0$$

has no zeros.

Exercise 2.20.2
Show that the zero polynomial of the above system with

$$B = \begin{pmatrix} 0 & 0 \\ 1 & 0 \\ 0 & 1 \end{pmatrix}$$

is identically zero so that every complex number λ is a zero of the system. In general, if $m = 1$, the identity $z(s) \equiv 0$ implies that $g(s)$ is identically zero (eqn. 2.20.2). This is not true however in the case of $m > 1$ as the example will testify.

There are three possible cases,
(*a*) $z(s) \equiv$ constant $\neq 0$ when the system has no zeros.
(*b*) $z(s) \equiv 0$. This is an undesirable system characteristic which, fortu-

nately rarely occurs in practice. In physical terms, it implies that the control inputs used are insufficient to completely control the output. This concept has been discussed in detail by Rosenbrock (Reference 56). For our purposes, it is sufficient to note from eqn. 2.20.12 that $z(s) \equiv 0$ if, and only if, $|G(s)| \equiv 0$.

(c) In general $z(s)$ will take the form

$$z(s) = \beta_0 \{ s^{n_z} + \beta_1 s^{n_z-1} + \ldots + \beta_{n_z} \}$$
$$= \beta_0 (s - z_1)(s - z_2) \ldots (s - z_{n_z}) \qquad (2.20.13)$$

with $\beta_0 \neq 0$, where n_z is the total number of system zeros and the zeros themselves are $z_1, z_2, \ldots, z_{n_z}$. As A, B, C, D are real matrices, the zeros are symmetric about the real axis in the complex plane. If the zeros all have negative real parts, the system is said to be minimum phase. Conversely, if one (or more) zero has a positive real part the system is said to be nonminimum phase. A nonminimum phase multivariable system will introduce control difficulties, as should be expected by analogy with the scalar case.

The following results are important for feedback design studies:

Theorem 2.20.1: Given two systems described by the matrices (A_i, B_i, C_i, D_i), $i = 1, 2$, with transfer-function matrices $G_i(s)$, $i = 1, 2$ and zero polynomials $z_i(s)$, $i = 1, 2$, then the zero polynomial of the composite system

$$\dot{x}_2 = A_2 x_2 + B_2 e$$
$$u = C_2 x_2 + D_2 e$$
$$\dot{x}_1 = A_1 x_1 + B_1 u$$
$$y = C_1 x_1 + D_1 u$$

is simply $z(s) = z_1(s) z_2(s)$.

Proof: The transfer-function matrix of the composite system is simply $G(s) = G_1(s) G_2(s)$ and the characteristic polynomial $\rho_0(s) = |sI - A_1| \, |sI - A_2|$ i.e. $z(s) = \rho_0(s) |G(s)| = |sI - A_1| \, |G_1(s)| \, |sI - A_2| \, |G_2(s)| \equiv z_1(s) z_2(s)$.

Theorem 2.20.2: The zero polynomial of the strictly proper system (A, B, C) subject to state feedback $u(t) = -F_1 x(t) + F_2 r(t)$ with F_1, F_2 constant matrices of dimension $m \times n$, $m \times m$, respectively, is given by the identity,

$$\begin{vmatrix} sI_n - A + BF_1, & -BF_2 \\ C & 0 \end{vmatrix} \equiv |F_2| \begin{vmatrix} sI_n - A & -B \\ C & 0 \end{vmatrix} \qquad (2.20.14)$$

Proof: Noting that $D = 0$, it is easily verified that

$$\begin{vmatrix} sI_n - A + BF_1, & -BF_2 \\ C, & 0 \end{vmatrix} = |F_2| \begin{vmatrix} sI_n - A + BF_1, & -B \\ C & 0 \end{vmatrix}$$

and the result is then proved by suitable column operations on the determinant.

Interpreting these results in terms of the unity-negative feedback system of Fig. 2.18.1, the zero polynomial of the closed-loop system is identical to the zero polynomial of the forward path system $G(s)K(s)$ which, in turn, is identical to the product of the zero polynomials of $G(s)$ and $K(s)$. In essence, the system zeros are independent of unit feedback loops. This fact is obvious in the scalar $(m = 1)$ case and carries over directly to the m-input/m-output case.

Exercise 2.20.3

In Fig. 2.18.1 suppose that the composite system $G(s)K(s)$ has zero polynomial $z(s)$. Use the above results to prove that the closed-loop system has zero polynomial $z_1(s) \equiv z(s)$ in the presence of a sensor failure in any loop and that the zero polynomial $z_2(s) \equiv 0$ if the system has an actuator failure in any loop.

The theoretical analysis of system zeros can be approached in many equivalent ways. The variety of theoretical approaches used can yield great insight into the structure and interpretation of zeros. The interested reader is referred to References 2, 31 and 46 for a geometric treatment, References 57, 58 for an algebraic approach and Reference 13 for numerical techniques.

We now state a result due to Owens[46] giving useful upper bounds on the number of system zeros.

Theorem 2.20.3: A proper m-input/m-output system (A, B, C, D) with transfer-function matrix $G(s) = D + C(sI_n - A)^{-1}B$ has n_z zeros where

$$n_z \leqslant n - \overset{*}{k}m - (m - r_k^*) \tag{2.20.15}$$

and r_k^* is the rank of the matrix $G^{(\overset{*}{k})}$, where k^* is the uniquely defined integer $\geqslant 0$ such that the limit

$$G^{(i)} = \lim_{s \to \infty} s^i G(s) \tag{2.20.16}$$

is finite and nonzero. Moreover, equality holds in expr. 2.20.15 if $r_k^* = m$ (i.e. $|G^{(\overset{*}{k})}| \neq 0$).

For computational purposes k^* is easily evaluated to be

$$k^* = \min_{1 \leqslant i, j \leqslant m} k_{ij} \qquad (2.20.17)$$

where k_{ij} is the transfer function rank (i.e. number of poles − number of zeros) of the (i, j)th element of $G(s)$.

Exercise 2.20.4
Use theorem 2.20.3 to prove that the system

$$A = \begin{pmatrix} 0 & 0 & 1 & 0 \\ 0 & 0 & 0 & 1 \\ 1 & 0 & 0 & 1 \\ 0 & 2 & 1 & 0 \end{pmatrix}, \quad B = \begin{pmatrix} 0 & 0 \\ 0 & 0 \\ 1 & 0 \\ 0 & 2 \end{pmatrix}$$

$$C = \begin{pmatrix} 1 & 0 & 0 & 0 \\ 0 & 1 & 0 & 0 \end{pmatrix}, \quad D = \begin{pmatrix} 0 & 0 \\ 0 & 0 \end{pmatrix}$$

has no zeros. Verify your result by direct evaluation of $z(s)$.

To conclude this Section, eqn. 2.20.12 indicates that

$$|G(s)| = z(s)/\rho_0(s) \qquad (2.20.18)$$

If we regard $|G(s)|$ as a transfer function in its own right and interpret its phase and gain characteristics in terms of the composite effect of all loops in $G(s)$, it might be expected that analysis of $|G(s)|$ could give insight into control difficulties and overall system properties. This will become more apparent during later discussions of system characteristic loci and hence we restrict ourselves to the following observations:
(i) the poles and zeros of $|G(s)|$ are the poles and zeros of $G(s)$
(ii) a resonance in the frequency response $|G(i\omega)|$ indicates the presence of an underdamped mode in the system
(iii) writing $|G(i\omega)| = A(\omega)\exp\{i\phi(\omega)\}$ (gain/phase decomposition), then it is suggested that $\psi(i\omega) \triangleq \phi(i\omega)/m$ is a useful representation of the average phase characteristics of each loop. Analysis of $\psi(i\omega)$ could indicate the degree of phase lag present in $G(s)$ and hence provide an initial estimate of control difficulties and/or the need for phase compensation.

2.21 System inverses

Throughout the remainder of the text it will be seen that it is required to invert transfer function matrices. This possibility is an important system property and plays a useful role in analysis and design (see later chapters and, for example, Reference 2).

Definition 2.21.1: A m-input/m-output system (A, B, C, D) is said to be invertible if, and only if, $z(s) \not\equiv 0$.

Eqn. 2.20.18 implies that invertibility is equivalent to the requirement that $|G(s)| \not\equiv 0$. It should be noted that the requirement that $|G(s)|$ is not identically zero does not preclude the possibility that it is zero at a finite number of points of the complex plane (i.e. at the zeros of $G(s)$), but it does imply that there exists at least one point s_1 so that $|G(s_1)| \neq 0$.

The inverse system is defined by the transfer-function matrix $G^{-1}(s)$

$$G^{-1}(s) = \frac{\text{adj } G(s)}{|G(s)|} \qquad (2.21.1)$$

and hence is defined only if $|G(s)| \not\equiv 0$. The physical interpretation of $G^{-1}(s)$ is obtained from eqn. 2.16.6,

$$u(s) = G^{-1}(s) \{y(s) - C(sI_n - A)^{-1}x(0)\} \qquad (2.21.2)$$

i.e. the inverse system reconstructs the input vector u from knowledge of the output and initial condition on the state vector. Of particular importance is the characterisation of $G^{-1}(s)$ as a function of the complex variable s and the zero polynomial $z(s) = \rho_0(s)|G(s)|$. The essential structure is intuitively suggested by considering the scalar case ($m = 1$). From eqn. 2.20.1

$$g^{-1}(s) = \sum_{j=0}^{k} a_{k-j}s^j + \frac{n(s)}{z(s)} \qquad (2.21.3)$$

where $a_0, a_1, \ldots, a_k$ are real constants, $a_0 \neq 0$, $n(s)/z(s)$ is strictly proper, and k = number of poles – number of zeros $\geqslant 0$ if g is proper. For example, if

$$g(s) = \frac{(s+1)}{s(s+2)}$$

then the inverse system is described by the transfer function,

$$g^{-1}(s) = s + 1 - \frac{1}{s+1}$$

with $k = 1$, $a_0 = 1$, $a_1 = 1$, $n(s) = -1$, $z(s) = s + 1$. The essential features of eqn. 2.21.3 are the presence of the polynomial component $a_0 s^k + a_1 s^{k-1} + \ldots + a_k$ and a strictly proper component $n(s)/z(s)$ with poles equal to the zeros of $g(s)$. A detailed discussion of the inverse system of a system described by an $m \times m$ transfer-function matrix $G(s)$ is given in Reference 2. The essential features of the results can be obtained using the following arguments: write $G(s)$ in the form (c.f. eqn. 2.16.9)

$$G(s) = \frac{M(s)}{\rho_0(s)} \qquad (2.21.4)$$

where $M(s)$ is an $m \times m$ matrix whose elements are polynomials in s. It follows that

$$G^{-1}(s) = \rho_0(s) \frac{\operatorname{adj} M(s)}{|M(s)|} \qquad (2.21.5)$$

but $|M(s)| = \{\rho_0(s)\}^m |G(s)| = \{\rho_0(s)\}^{m-1} z(s)$ so that

$$G^{-1}(s) = \frac{\operatorname{adj} M(s)}{\{\rho_0(s)\}^{m-2} z(s)} \qquad (2.21.6)$$

Taking, for simplicity, the case of $m = 2$, $G^{-1}(s) = \{\operatorname{adj} M(s)\}/z(s)$ so that

$$G^{-1}(s) = \sum_{j=0}^{k} A_{k-j} s^j + \frac{N(s)}{z(s)} \qquad (2.21.7)$$

where $A_0, \ldots, A_k$ are nonzero $m \times m$ matrices, $A_0 \neq 0$, $N(s)$ is an $m \times m$ matrix whose elements are polynomials in s and $N(s)/z(s)$ is strictly proper. It can be shown that $k \geqslant 0$ if $G(s)$ is proper and that

$$H_z(s) \triangleq \frac{N(s)}{z(s)} \equiv C_0(sI_{n_z} - A_0)^{-1} B_0 \qquad (2.21.8)$$

for suitable choice of matrices, C_0, A_0, B_0 where

$$\beta_0 |sI_{n_z} - A_0| \equiv z(s) \qquad (2.21.9)$$

In summary, the general result states that the inverse system of a proper system (A, B, C, D) described by the transfer-function matrix $G(s) = D + C(sI_n - A)^{-1} B$ takes the form

$$G^{-1}(s) = \sum_{j=0}^{k} A_{k-j} s^j + H_z(s) \qquad (2.21.10)$$

where $k \geqslant 0$, $A_0 \neq 0$ and $H_z(s)$ is the transfer-function matrix of a strictly proper system with characteristic polynomial $\beta_0^{-1} z(s)$. A particularly important case in the following chapter is $n_z = 0$, when it can be shown that $H_z(s) \equiv 0$.

Exercise 2.21.1

Show that the system of Exercise 2.20.4 has an inverse of the form $G^{-1}(s) = A_0 s^2 + A_1 s + A_2 + H_z(s)$ with $H_z(s) \equiv 0$. Check your result using the identity $G^{-1}(s)G(s) = I_m$.

2.22 Concluding remarks

This (rather long!) Chapter has discussed the basic ideas of state-vector models, linearity, solution of state equations and modal behaviour, controllability and observability, pole allocation, stability and oscillation, feedback and system transfer-function matrices, multivariable-feedback system stability and integrity, poles, zeros and inverse systems. Those readers familiar with some of the concepts may object to the occasional absence of rigour and generality. These readers are referred to the references for the technical detail they desire and, in this context, they will find that the works given in References 3, 15, 33, 57 and 63–65 will give some alternative approaches. For the majority of readers, however, the Chapter has attempted to provide some useful intuitive and quantitative background to the basic concepts and mathematical techniques required for the discussion, in the following chapters of multivariable control systems design. If forced to attribute a greater importance to any of the material, I suggest that the reader ensures that he is familiar with the material in Sections 2.14–2.15 and 2.18–2.21 before continuing to the remaining chapters.

2.23 Problems and exercises

1 Calculate a state-vector model for the system described by the transfer function $g(s) = 3(s + 1)/s(s + 3)$ and check your result by recalculation of $g(s)$ using the Faddeev algorithm. The system has a zero at $s = -1$. Verify this fact by using eqn. 2.20.12. Is this observation consistent with Theorem 2.20.3?

2 Use all three methods of Section 2.8 to calculate the matrix e^{At} in the cases

$$(a) \quad A = \begin{pmatrix} 0 & 1 \\ 0 & 0 \end{pmatrix} \quad (b) \quad A = \begin{pmatrix} -1 & 0 & 1 \\ 0 & -1 & 1 \\ 0 & 1 & -1 \end{pmatrix}$$

and verify exprs. 2.7.3 and 2.7.9.

3 Consider the proposition that (c.f. eqn. 2.9.15)

rank $[B, AB, \ldots, A^{n-1}B]$

$$= \text{rank } [T^{-1}B, (T^{-1}AT)T^{-1}B, \ldots, (T^{-1}AT)^{n-1} T^{-1}B]$$

for any $n \times n$ nonsingular matrix T. Interpret this result in terms of the invariance of the controllability of the system $\dot{x} = Ax + Bu$ under the state transformation $v(t) = T^{-1}x(t)$. Formulate and prove an analogous result for the observability of the system $\dot{x} = Ax, y = Cx$.

4 Prove that the system $\dot{x} = Ax + Bu, y = Cx$ is observable if, and only if,

$$\text{rank} \begin{pmatrix} \lambda I_n - A \\ C \end{pmatrix} = n \qquad \text{for all complex numbers } \lambda$$

(Reference 57). By noting the similarity between Theorems 2.10.2 and 2.9.2, prove that the system is controllable if, and only if,

rank $[\lambda I_n - A, -B] = n$ for all complex numbers λ.

5 Using the notation of problem 4 and $m = l$, show that

$$\text{rank} \begin{pmatrix} \lambda I_n - A \\ C \end{pmatrix} < n$$

implies that λ is a zero of the system (A, B, C) and that, if x_0 is any unobservable mode of the system with eigenvalue λ, then λ is a zero of (A, B, C). Prove a similar result for uncontrollable modes.

6 Verify that the system with state matrices

$$A = \begin{pmatrix} 1 & 0 & 2 \\ 0 & 1 & 1 \\ 0 & 1 & 1 \end{pmatrix}, \quad B = \begin{pmatrix} 0 \\ 0 \\ 1 \end{pmatrix}$$

is completely state controllable, and compute the controllable canonical form for (A, B). Hence, deduce a state feedback control law allocating the closed-loop poles to the positions $-1, -2, -3$. Check your result by direct evaluation of the closed-loop characteristic polynomial. Hence, or otherwise, show that the system, as above, with B replaced by

$$B = \begin{pmatrix} 1 & -1 \\ 0 & 0 \\ 1 & 1 \end{pmatrix}$$

is cyclic and calculate the corresponding unity rank state feedback for this case.

7 Prove that if $l = n$ and $|B| \neq 0$, the pair (A, B) is always controllable. Formulate and prove the equivalent result for observability. Provide a physical interpretation of the result in each case.

8 If a single-input/single-output system described by a strictly proper transfer function $g(s)$ has a state-space model described by the matrices (A, B, C), show that it is always possible to choose a state-space model described by the matrices (A^T, C^T, B^T). By transforming (A^T, C^T) to controllable canonical form (A_0^T, e_n), the corresponding pair (C, A) can be transformed into the *observable canonical form* (e_n^T, A_0). Consider the form of A_0.

9 A strictly proper system described by the matrices

$$C = \begin{pmatrix} 1 & 0 \\ 0 & 1 \end{pmatrix}, \quad A = \begin{pmatrix} -1 & 2 \\ 2 & -1 \end{pmatrix}, \quad B = \begin{pmatrix} 1 & 0 \\ 0 & 1 \end{pmatrix}$$

is subject to constant output feedback of the form $u(t) = K(r(t) - y(t))$ with $r(t) \equiv 0$

$$K = \begin{pmatrix} k_1 & 0 \\ 0 & k_2 \end{pmatrix}$$

Show that the closed-loop system is asymptotically stable if, and only if,

$$2 + k_1 + k_2 > 0 \quad \text{and} \quad (1 + k_1)(1 + k_2) > 4$$

Plot the region of stability in the plane (with axes k_1, k_2). The situation of sensor failure in loop i can be represented by setting $k_i = 0$. Show that the closed-loop system is stable in the presence of a sensor failure in loop 1 if, and only if $k_2 > 3$. (Hint: prove the result using the state matrices and check using the transfer-function matrix analysis of Section 2.19). Compare the two results graphically.

10 A strictly proper system is described by the matrices

$$A = \begin{pmatrix} -1 & 0 & 1 \\ 0 & -2 & 1 \\ 0 & 1 & -2 \end{pmatrix}, \quad B = \begin{pmatrix} 0 \\ 0 \\ 1 \end{pmatrix}, \quad C = (1 \quad 0 \quad 0)$$

Investigate the controllability and observability of the system and show that the open-loop characteristic polynomial is $|sI_3 - A| = (s + 1)(s + 1)(s + 3)$. Calculate the response of the state $x(t)$ and output $y(t)$ to a unit-step input with initial condition $x(0) = \{1, 1, 1\}^T$ using the eigen-vector method of Section 2.8. Calculate the system transfer function and check your results using eqns. 2.16.3 and 2.16.4 and the inverse Laplace transform.

11 The liquid-level system of Section 2.5, eqns. 2.5.4 and 2.5.5 with $l(t) \equiv 0$ is to be controlled by a unity-negative feedback system with proportional controller $K(s) = K$

$$K = \begin{pmatrix} k_1 & 0 \\ 0 & k_2 \end{pmatrix}$$

i.e. the liquid level in vessel i is to be used to manipulate the input flow to vessel $i, i = 1, 2$. Use the state-vector representation to calculate both the open-loop and closed-loop characteristic polynomials

$$\rho_0(s) = s^2 + \beta \{a_1^{-1} + a_2^{-1}\}s$$

$$\rho_c(s) = s^2 + s \{(\beta + k_1)a_1^{-1} + (\beta + k_2)a_2^{-1}\}$$

$$+ \frac{1}{a_1 a_2} (\beta + k_1)(\beta + k_2) - \frac{\beta^2}{a_1 a_2}$$

Check your result by direct evaluation of the return-difference determinant. With the data $a_1 = a_2 = a$, the symmetry of the system suggests that a design $k_1 = k_2 = k$ will be suitable. Show that the closed-loop system is stable for all $k > 0$ and that stability is retained despite the presence of sensor or actuator failures in any loop.

12 The invariant zeros of a nonsquare ($m \neq l$) system (A, B, C, D) are defined to be the set of complex numbers λ such that,[46]

$$\text{rank} \begin{pmatrix} \lambda I_n - A, & -B \\ C & , & D \end{pmatrix} < n + \min(m, l)$$

Relate this definition in the case of $m = l$ to Definition 2.20.2, and hence show that, in this case, the invariant zeros of the system are just the system zeros. This is not true in the case of $m \neq l$, and the interested reader is referred to Reference 46 for more details, and Reference 2 for the relation to the concept of inverse systems for nonsquare plants.

13 Use eqn. 2.16.7 to show that the strictly proper system (A, B, C) has initial output derivative

$$\frac{dy(0)}{dt} = CB\alpha$$

in response to the step input $\dfrac{1}{s}\alpha$ and zero initial conditions (Hint: use the well known initial-value theorem). If $CA^{j-1}B = 0$, $1 \leqslant j \leqslant k-1$, with similar assumptions, show that

$$\frac{d^k y(0)}{dt^k} = CA^{k-1}B\alpha$$

Chapter 3

Introduction to multivariable frequency-response analysis

The success of classical approaches to the design of compensation networks for the feedback control of single-input/single-output linear time-invariant dynamical systems can be attributed to the insight obtained into both open-loop and closed-loop system dynamics by the introduction of the Laplace-transformation technique and the concept of system transfer function. The design techniques are essentially intuitive extrapolations of analytic results for first-, second- and third-order systems in the framework of general stability theorems (e.g. Nyquist stability theorem). It cannot be claimed that the same level of experience has been obtained in the application of transfer-function matrix methods to the multi-input/multi-output problem, but several design techniques have been suggested and will be discussed in detail in the remaining chapters. The purpose of this Chapter is to define the basic performance specifications commonly required of a multivariable feedback system and to suggest intuitive guidelines for the construction of a unity-negative output feedback controller capable of achieving the desired performance. The approach will essentially be by example, although the reader may be surprised by the scope and insight provided by the examples. One of the important aspects of the material discussed is its strong intuitive correspondence to many classical situations. This is by design and the reader is encouraged to make the comparison whenever possible, in the hope that the transition to the more general material of later chapters will become an obvious generalisation.

3.1 Performance specifications

Our attention is restricted, primarily, to the case of a unity-negative feedback system (Fig. 2.18.1) for the control of an m-input/m-output strictly proper system (A_1, B_1, C_1) with $m \times m$ transfer-function matrix $G(s) = C_1(sI_{n_1} - A_1)^{-1}B_1$. The forward-path controller is assumed to be an m-input/m-output proper system (A_2, B_2, C_2, D_2) with $m \times m$ transfer function matrix $K(s) = C_2(sI_{n_2} - A_2)^{-1}B_2 + D_2$. Using the notation of Section 2.15 the forward-path system has a state-vector model

$$\dot{x}(t) = Ax(t) + Be(t)$$

$$y(t) = Cx(t), \quad x(t) \in R^n, n = n_1 + n_2 \qquad (3.1.1)$$

where

$$A = \begin{pmatrix} A_1 & B_1 C_2' \\ 0 & A_2 \end{pmatrix}, \quad B = \begin{pmatrix} B_1 D_2 \\ B_2 \end{pmatrix}, \quad C = (C_1, 0) \qquad (3.1.2)$$

and eqn. 3.1.1 has transfer-function matrix $Q(s) = G(s)K(s)$. The open-loop characteristic polynomial is

$$\rho_0(s) = |sI_n - A| = |sI_{n_1} - A_1| \, |sI_{n_2} - A_2| \qquad (3.1.3)$$

Unity-negative feedback is represented by the error vector

$$e(t) = r(t) - y(t) \qquad (3.1.4)$$

yielding the closed-loop model

$$\dot{x}(t) = \{A - BC\} x(t) + Br(t)$$

$$y(t) = Cx(t) \qquad (3.1.5)$$

and closed-loop transfer-function matrix

$$H_c(s) = \{I_m + G(s)K(s)\}^{-1} G(s)K(s) \qquad (3.1.6)$$

In general terms, the problem of the design of a suitable feedback system for the plant $G(s)$ can be stated as the systematic search for proper linear systems (or, equivalently, transfer-function matrix $K(s)$) such that the closed-loop system (eqns. 3.1.5–3.1.6) has satisfactory stability properties and transient performance in response to specified demand vectors $r(t)$. The precise design objectives will vary from application to application and may be subjective, but several important general properties can be defined in a reasonably respectable mathematical manner i.e.

(*a*) closed-loop system stability
(*b*) closed-loop transient performance and interaction
(*c*) steady state response and steady state errors
(*d*) closed-loop system integrity

It should be noted however that the similarity to the familiar classical performance specifications is superficial. In fact the multi-input/multi-output case presents several distinct new problems and concepts requiring a change in the nature and emphasis of the analysis.

Closed-loop stability: The stability of the closed-loop system is the obvious necessary condition for the acceptability of a given control system i.e. the zeros of the closed-loop characteristic polynomial

$$\rho_c(s) = |sI_n - A + BC| \tag{3.1.7}$$

must all have strictly negative real parts. Although this relation is used in the following chapters, a more useful characterisation of closed-loop stability for the purposes of applications is the system return-difference determinant,

$$|T(s)| = |I_m + G(s)K(s)| \tag{3.1.8}$$

A justification for the use of $T(s)$ can be obtained by noting that the control matrices A_2, B_2, C_2, D_2 contain $n_2^2 + 2n_2m + m^2 = (n_2 + m)^2$ parameters whereas, $K(s)$ contains m^2 transfer functions. The transfer-function matrix $G(s)$ is, in a similar manner, a more compact representation of the plant dynamics.

If $m = 1$, eqn. 3.1.8 is well known and can be analysed using the Nyquist diagram, root-locus methods, Routh-Hurwitz stability criteria etc. For the case of $m > 1$, although the Routh criterion can still be applied in an obvious manner, the relationships are defined in terms of m^2 gain parameters in $K(s)$. A parametric study of the stability of the system can be a difficult task. Nyquist-diagram techniques are, in a similar manner, difficult to apply as $|T(i\omega)|$ is a complex nonlinear function of the elements of $K(s)$, making it difficult to obtain insight into compensation techniques. With these observations in mind, it will be understood why the multivariable frequency-response design techniques suggested to date attempt to choose $K(s)$ in such a way as to simplify the structure of $|T(s)|$ and enable the application of well known classical design methods.

Exercise 3.1.1
Using the data

$$A_1 = \begin{pmatrix} 0 & 1 \\ 0 & 0 \end{pmatrix}, \quad B_1 = \begin{pmatrix} 1 & 0 \\ 0 & 1 \end{pmatrix}, \quad C_1 = \begin{pmatrix} 0 & 1 \\ 1 & 0 \end{pmatrix}$$

show that closed-loop asymptotic stability cannot be achieved by choosing $K(s) = kI_2$ but that the choice of $K(s) = k\begin{pmatrix} 0 & 1 \\ 1 & 0 \end{pmatrix}$ ensures that the closed-loop system is asymptotically stable if $k > 0$.

Interaction and transient performance: In general, the elements of the $m \times m$ transfer-function matrix $G(s)$ are all nonzero.

$$G(s) = \begin{pmatrix} G_{11}(s) & \cdots & G_{1m}(s) \\ \vdots & & \vdots \\ G_{m1}(s) & \cdots & G_{mm}(s) \end{pmatrix} \qquad (3.1.9)$$

By considering inputs of the form $u(s) = \dfrac{1}{s} e_i$, $1 \leqslant i \leqslant m$, (corresponding to unit step inputs to $u_i(t)$ keeping $u_j(t) \equiv 0, j \neq i$) it is seen that, in general, control inputs to any one loop produce nonzero responses from all outputs due to the presence of nonzero off-diagonal terms in $G(s)$. The phenomenon is a general property of multi-input/multi-output systems ($m \geqslant 2$) and is conventionally termed *open-loop interaction*.

At first sight, it is an appealing idea to attempt a feedback control design by ignoring the interaction terms $G_{ij}(s), j \neq i$. This is not possible in general as it can lead to erroneous predictions for the stability of the closed-loop system.

Exercise 3.1.2
The system

$$\dot{x}(t) = \begin{pmatrix} 0 & 0 \\ 0 & -1 \end{pmatrix} x(t) + \begin{pmatrix} 0 & 1 \\ 1 & 0 \end{pmatrix} u(t)$$

$$y(t) = \begin{pmatrix} 2 & 1 \\ 1 & 2 \end{pmatrix} x(t)$$

has the transfer-function matrix

$$G(s) = \begin{pmatrix} \dfrac{1}{s+1} & \dfrac{2}{s} \\[2ex] \dfrac{2}{s+1} & \dfrac{1}{s} \end{pmatrix}$$

By ·approximating $G(s)$ by $G_A(s) = \text{diag}\left\{\dfrac{1}{s+1}, \dfrac{1}{s}\right\}$ for the purposes of control system design, show that the approximate closed-loop system with $K(s) = I_2$ is stable, but that the actual feedback system is unstable (Hint: calculate $\{I + G_A(s)K(s)\}^{-1}G_A(s)K(s)$ and compare the system pole with the zeros of $|sI - A + BC|$).

In general it is necessary to take account of the interaction terms in the design of multi-input/multi-output control systems as they play an important role in the stability and performance of the closed-loop system. It is also an important concept to grasp at this stage of the text.

The $m \times m$ closed-loop transfer function matrix $H_c(s) = \{I + GK\}^{-1} GK$ will, in general, possess nonzero off-diagonal terms i.e. the closed-loop system possesses interaction effects. The desirability of this interaction will vary with the system concerned and the specified performance objectives e.g. interaction in the closed-loop is of little importance if feedback control is implemented purely to stabilise an open-loop unstable plant. In the multi-input/multi-output servo following however, where it is required that the output response follows the demand signal closely, the magnitude of the interaction effects is an important consideration.

In an analogous manner to the classical approach, closed-loop transient performance is usually assessed in the time-domain in terms of the system response to unit-step changes in the demand signal with zero initial conditions. The multivariable equivalent of the classical concept of a step input is the demand signal $r(s) = s^{-1}\alpha$ where α is a real constant $m \times 1$ vector. The set of all possible α is simply the vector space R^m. It is intuitively obvious that it is impossible to deduce the overall behaviour of the closed-loop system by the response to a single choice of α, but that, if the responses to $r(s) = s^{-1}\alpha_i$, $1 \leqslant i \leqslant m$, are known and α_i, $1 \leqslant i \leqslant m$, are linearly independent, then the response to any input function can be constructed by superposition. Conventionally, the basis vectors $\alpha_i = e_i$, $1 \leqslant i \leqslant m$, are used when the test inputs $r(s) = s^{-1}e_i$, $1 \leqslant i \leqslant m$, are termed *unit-step demands in output i*. To avoid confusion, the demand $r(s) = s^{-1}e_i$ denotes

(a) the demand that a unit-step change occurs in the output $y_i(t)$
(b) the demand that outputs $y_j(t), j \neq i$, are identically zero.

Interaction effects prevents (b) being attained exactly and requirement (a) cannot be achieved exactly due to inertia and other physical effects within the system structure. The conventional performance

criteria taken are hence a relaxation of the demand signal requirements,
(i) the response of $y_i(t)$ to the demand $r(s) = s^{-1} e_i$ should satisfy the
standard classical requirements of suitable rise-time, overshoot, settling
time etc
(ii) the responses $y_j(t), j \neq i$, remain small.
Criterion (ii) is deliberately imprecise as the degree of interaction per-
missible will vary from application to application and the numerical
magnitude of the interaction transients will depend on the physical units
used for the output variables. Unless otherwise stated, it will be assumed
that interaction is acceptable only if the interaction transients have
modulus $\ll 1{\cdot}0$ for all $t > 0$. In this case, the degree of interaction in
response to a unit-step demand in output $y_i(t)$ is defined as a percentage,

$$a_i = 100 \max_{\substack{t \geq 0 \\ }} \max_{\substack{1 \leq j \leq m \\ j \neq i}} |y_j(t)| \qquad (3.1.10)$$

Typically, it will be assumed that closed-loop interaction is acceptable
if $\max_{1 \leq i \leq m} a_i \leq 10\%$.

Steady-state error: If the closed-loop system is stable, the steady-
state response to the step demand $r(s) = \dfrac{1}{s}\alpha$ is easily calculated by
application of the well known final-value theorem to $y(s) = H_c(s) r(s)$

$$y_\infty(\alpha) = \lim_{t \to +\infty} y(t) = \lim_{s \to 0} H_c(s)\alpha \qquad (3.1.11)$$

The corresponding steady-state error is

$$e_\infty(\alpha) = \alpha - y_\infty(\alpha) = \lim_{s \to 0} \{I_m - H_c(s)\}\alpha$$

$$= \lim_{s \to 0} \{I_m + G(s)K(s)\}^{-1}\alpha \qquad (3.1.12)$$

The steady-state response of the system is hence characterised by the
behaviour of the $m \times m$ matrix $H_c(s)$ in the vicinity of $s = 0$ and the
steady-state error by the behaviour of

$$E(s) = \{I_m + G(s)K(s)\}^{-1} \qquad (3.1.13)$$

in the vicinity of $s = 0$ i.e.

$$E_\infty = \lim_{s \to 0} \{I_m + G(s)K(s)\}^{-1} \qquad (3.1.14)$$

where the limit exists as, by assumption, the system is stable. Expressions 3.1.11, 3.1.12 now become

$$y_\infty(\alpha) = \alpha - E_\infty\alpha, \quad e_\infty(\alpha) = E_\infty\alpha \qquad (3.1.15)$$

so that the steady-state error is always zero, if, and only if, $E_\infty = 0$
i.e. $\lim_{s \to 0} H_c(s) = I_m - E_\infty = I_m$.

Exercise 3.1.3

If $|Q(s)| = |G(s)K(s)| \not\equiv 0$, and the closed-loop system is stable, then
the steady-state error is zero for all α (i.e. $E_\infty = 0$) if, and only if,
$\lim_{s \to 0} Q^{-1}(s) = 0$ (Hint: write $H_c(s) = \{I_m + Q^{-1}(s)\}^{-1}$).

Exercise 3.1.4

With the assumption of Exercise 3.1.3 and $K(s) = K_1 + \dfrac{1}{s}K_2$ with
$|K_2| \neq 0$, prove that $E_\infty = 0$ and hence that the steady-state error to
any demand $r(s) = \dfrac{1}{s}\alpha$ is zero. Compare this result with the classical
case of proportional plus integral control.

Exercise 3.1.5

With the assumption of Exercise 3.1.3, $G(0)$ finite and nonsingular and
$K(s) = kK$ (a constant matrix representing proportional control), show
that $\lim_{k \to \infty} E_\infty = 0$ and hence infer that high gain proportional control
reduces the steady-state error.

System integrity: The concept of integrity has been discussed in
Section 2.19. It is an obvious consideration for control systems requiring fail-safe characteristics to satisfy safety standards, but is not required
in many applications.

3.2 Noninteracting control: a motivation

If the suppression of closed-loop interaction in the closed-loop transfer-
function matrix $H_c(s)$ is an important design objective, it is natural to
consider the feasibility of choosing $K(s)$ so that $H_c(s)$ is diagonal. It is
easily shown from eqn. 3.1.6 that

$$Q(s) = H_c(s)(I_m - H_c(s))^{-1} \qquad (3.2.1)$$

so that zero closed-loop interaction requires that $Q(s) = G(s)K(s)$ is diagonal and hence completely noninteracting. If $|G(s)| \neq 0$ and writing,

$$Q(s) = \text{diag}\{q_1(s), \ldots, q_m(s)\} \qquad (3.2.2)$$

then

$$K(s) = G^{-1}(s)\,\text{diag}\{q_1(s), \ldots, q_m(s)\} \qquad (3.2.3)$$

Such a controller is termed a noninteracting controller (not because $K(s)$ is noninteracting, rather because $H_c(s)$ is noninteracting), and is seen to consist of the inverse plant in cascade with a noninteracting system. There are two major practical objections to the use of a noninteracting controller, in many cases,

(a) $K(s)$ has a complex dynamic structure due to the presence of the inverse plant

(b) $K(s)$ may represent an unstable system if $G(s)$ is nonminimum phase, when (Section 2.21) the strictly proper component of the inverse system is unstable.

There are however no theoretical objections, and the interested reader is referred to References 63 and 64 for a detailed analysis of noninteracting control using state-feedback methods. For the purposes of this text, it will be shown that dynamic output feedback-control systems are capable of producing high performance, *low* interaction feedback systems, using, for example, simple multivariable proportional or proportional plus integral control systems (see, for example, Exercises 3.1.4, 3.1.5).

3.3 Level control of a two-vessel liquid storage system

The example discussed in this Section is designed to provide a physical motivation and introduction to the concepts and results used in later chapters and to illustrate how a combination of classical design procedures with the techniques of matrix algebra can yield, in many cases, a simple solution to the multivariable feedback control problem.

Consider the liquid-level system discussed in Section 2.5 and, for simplicity, neglect the disturbance vector $l(s)$. The input-output dynamics are described by the relation $y(s) = G(s)u(s)$, where

$$G(s) = \frac{1}{s\left(s + \dfrac{\beta}{a_1} + \dfrac{\beta}{a_2}\right)} \begin{pmatrix} \left(s + \dfrac{\beta}{a_2}\right)a_1^{-1} & \dfrac{\beta}{a_1 a_2} \\[2ex] \dfrac{\beta}{a_1 a_2} & \left(s + \dfrac{\beta}{a_1}\right)a_2^{-1} \end{pmatrix} \qquad (3.3.1)$$

Note that interaction terms are present and depend explicitly on the intervessel flow parameter β. If $\beta = 0$, open-loop interaction is zero. In all cases the open-loop characteristic polynomial is

$$\rho_0(s) = s\{s + \beta(a_1^{-1} + a_2^{-1})\} \qquad (3.3.2)$$

Consider the case of $a_1 = a_2 = a$ and the choice of unity-negative feedback controller $K(s)$ to produce a highly stable, low interaction response to step demands in liquid level in either vessel. Insight can be gained into the required structure of $K(s)$ by examination of the structure of $G(s)$,

$$G(s) = \begin{pmatrix} G_1(s) & G_2(s) \\ G_2(s) & G_1(s) \end{pmatrix} \qquad (3.3.3)$$

where

$$G_1(s) = \frac{as + \beta}{as(as + 2\beta)}, \quad G_2(s) = \frac{\beta}{as(as + 2\beta)} \qquad (3.3.4)$$

This is highly symmetric which reflects the physical symmetry of the plant (Fig. 2.5.1). A key to the systematic design of the control system is to investigate the eigenvectors and eigenvalues of $G(s)$. It is easily verified that

$$G(s)\begin{pmatrix} 1 \\ 1 \end{pmatrix} = \{G_1(s) + G_2(s)\}\begin{pmatrix} 1 \\ 1 \end{pmatrix}, \quad G(s)\begin{pmatrix} -1 \\ 1 \end{pmatrix} = \{G_1(s) - G_2(s)\}\begin{pmatrix} -1 \\ 1 \end{pmatrix}$$

$$(3.3.5)$$

i.e. the eigenvectors of $G(s)$ are $w_1 = \{1, 1\}^T$ and $w_2 = \{-1, 1\}^T$ with eigenvalues, respectively,

$$g_1(s) = G_1(s) + G_2(s) = \frac{1}{as}$$

$$g_2(s) = G_1(s) - G_2(s) = \frac{1}{as + 2\beta} \qquad (3.3.6)$$

The reader should convince himself that this result is to be expected from physical considerations as,

(i) if $u_1(t) \equiv u_2(t), t \geqslant 0$, then the system response from zero initial conditions takes the form $y_1(t) \equiv y_2(t)$. The intervessel flow $f(t) \equiv 0$ and the two vessels behave as if they are independent i.e. the interaction terms have no effect on the response and the system simply integrates the input flow to give liquid level.

(ii) in a similar manner, if $u_1(t) \equiv -u_2(t)$, the system response from zero initial conditions takes the form $h_1(t) \equiv -h_2(t)$. The intervessel flow in this case is $f(t) = 2\beta h_1(t) \not\equiv 0$ giving rise to the finite time constant in $g_2(s)$.

In effect the relations

$$G(s)w_i = g_i(s)w_i, \qquad i = 1, 2 \tag{3.3.7}$$

indicates that the eigenvectors $w_i, i = 1, 2$ are frequency-independent *modes of the transfer-function matrix*, the dynamics of each mode being described by the characteristic transfer function $g_i(s), i = 1, 2$. As w_1, w_2 are linearly independent, it is easily verified that the output vector can be decomposed

$$y(s) = \begin{pmatrix} y_1(s) \\ y_2(s) \end{pmatrix} = \frac{\{y_1(s) + y_2(s)\}}{2} \begin{pmatrix} 1 \\ 1 \end{pmatrix} + \frac{\{y_2(s) - y_1(s)\}}{2} \begin{pmatrix} -1 \\ 1 \end{pmatrix}$$

$$= \hat{y}_1(s)w_1 + \hat{y}_2(s)w_2 \tag{3.3.8}$$

where $\hat{y}_1(s) = \{y_1(s) + y_2(s)\}/2$, $\hat{y}_2(s) = \{y_2(s) - y_1(s)\}/2$ are the amplitudes of the modes w_1, w_2 in the output vector $y(s)$.

Exercise 3.3.1
Show that the total change in liquid volume of the system is $a(y_1(s) + y_2(s)) = 2\hat{y}_1(s)$ and hence that the mode w_1 represents the total change in liquid volume with dynamics $g_1(s)$. In a similar manner the liquid 'tilt' $y_2(s) - y_1(s) = 2\hat{y}_2(s)$ i.e. the mode w_2 represents the difference in liquid levels. Justify these ideas physically.

The input vector $u(s)$, can, in a similar manner, be decomposed

$$u(s) = \hat{u}_1(s)w_1 + \hat{u}_2(s)w_2 \tag{3.3.9}$$

where $\hat{u}_i(s)$ are the modal-input amplitudes. It is easily verified that

$$y(s) = \hat{y}_1(s)w_1 + \hat{y}_2(s)w_2 = G(s)u(s) = g_1(s)\hat{u}_1(s)w_1 + g_2(s)\hat{u}_2(s)w_2 \tag{3.3.10}$$

and hence that

$$\hat{y}_i(s) = g_i(s)\hat{u}_i(s), \qquad i = 1, 2 \tag{3.3.11}$$

In effect the output amplitude $\hat{y}_i(s)$ is driven by the input amplitude $\hat{u}_i(s)$ $(i = 1, 2)$. Writing the demand and error signals in the form,

$$r(s) = \hat{r}_1(s)w_1 + \hat{r}_2(s)w_2, \quad e(s) = \hat{e}_1(s)w_1 + \hat{e}_2(s)w_2 \tag{3.3.12}$$

it follows directly from the relation $e(s) = r(s) - y(s)$, that

$$\hat{e}_i(s) = \hat{r}_i(s) - \hat{y}_i(s), \qquad i = 1, 2 \qquad (3.3.13)$$

It is important to note that eqns. 3.3.11, 3.3.13 have a single-input/single-output character and that the requirement that $y(s)$ follow $r(s)$ closely can be interpreted as a requirement that $\hat{y}_i(s)$ follow $\hat{r}_i(s)$ closely. It is natural to consider the possibility of choosing a forward-path controller $K(s)$ to retain the classical nature of the problem i.e. a $K(s)$ such that the relation $u(s) = K(s)e(s)$ is equivalent to

$$\hat{u}_i(s) = k_i(s)\hat{e}_i(s), \qquad i = 1, 2 \qquad (3.3.14)$$

for some desired transfer functions $k_i(s)$, $i = 1, 2$. If this is possible then, combining eqns. 3.3.11, 3.3.13 and 3.3.14 gives

$$\hat{y}_i(s) = \frac{g_i(s)k_i(s)}{1 + g_i(s)k_i(s)}\hat{r}_i(s), \qquad i = 1, 2 \qquad (3.3.15)$$

or

$$y(s) = \frac{g_1(s)k_1(s)}{1 + g_1(s)k_1(s)}\hat{r}_1(s)\begin{pmatrix}1\\1\end{pmatrix} + \frac{g_2(s)k_2(s)}{1 + g_2(s)k_2(s)}\hat{r}_2(s)\begin{pmatrix}-1\\1\end{pmatrix} \qquad (3.3.16)$$

and the closed-loop response can be analysed by the analysis and design of the scalar feedback systems (eqn. 3.3.15) and the investigation of their effect on the closed-loop response using eqn. 3.3.16.

Condition 3.3.14 is easily achieved by the choice of $K(s)$ such that

$$K(s)w_i = k_i(s)w_i, \qquad i = 1, 2 \qquad (3.3.17)$$

or, if $T = [w_1, w_2]$ is the eigenvector matrix of $G(s)$, eqns. 3.3.7, 3.3.17 take the form

$$T^{-1}G(s)T = \begin{pmatrix} g_1(s) & 0 \\ 0 & g_2(s) \end{pmatrix}, \quad T^{-1}K(s)T = \begin{pmatrix} k_1(s) & 0 \\ 0 & k_2(s) \end{pmatrix}$$

and

$$T^{-1}y(s) = \begin{pmatrix} \hat{y}_1(s) \\ \hat{y}_2(s) \end{pmatrix}, \quad T^{-1}u(s) = \begin{pmatrix} \hat{u}_1(s) \\ \hat{u}_2(s) \end{pmatrix}$$

$$T^{-1}e(s) = \begin{pmatrix} \hat{e}_1(s) \\ \hat{e}_2(s) \end{pmatrix}, \quad T^{-1}r(s) = \begin{pmatrix} \hat{r}_1(s) \\ \hat{r}_2(s) \end{pmatrix} \qquad (3.3.18)$$

i.e.

$$\begin{pmatrix} \hat{u}_1(s) \\ \hat{u}_2(s) \end{pmatrix} = T^{-1}u(s) = T^{-1}K(s)T\begin{pmatrix} \hat{e}_1(s) \\ \hat{e}_2(s) \end{pmatrix} = \begin{pmatrix} k_1(s)\hat{e}_1(s) \\ k_2(s)\hat{e}_2(s) \end{pmatrix}$$

as required. $\hspace{6cm}$ (3.3.19)

More compactly, the closed-loop transfer-function matrix

$$H_c(s) = TT^{-1}\{I + G(s)K(s)\}^{-1}G(s)K(s)TT^{-1}$$

$$= T\{I + T^{-1}G(s)TT^{-1}K(s)T\}^{-1}T^{-1}G(s)TT^{-1}K(s)TT^{-1}$$

$$= T\begin{pmatrix} \dfrac{g_1(s)k_1(s)}{1 + g_1(s)k_1(s)} & 0 \\ 0 & \dfrac{g_2(s)k_2(s)}{1 + g_2(s)k_2(s)} \end{pmatrix}T^{-1} \qquad (3.3.20)$$

and $y(s) = H_c(s)r(s)$. The return-difference determinant takes the form

$$|T(s)| = |I + G(s)K(s)| = |I + T^{-1}G(s)TT^{-1}K(s)T|$$

$$= (1 + k_1(s)g_1(s))(1 + k_2(s)g_2(s)) \qquad (3.3.21)$$

so that the closed-loop system is stable if, and only if, the scalar feedback systems (eqn. 3.3.15) are stable.

Although the design problem seems to be theoretically solved, the reader should not assume that difficulties will not arise in the application of the above procedure. The main difficulty arises from the general observation that *a stable closed-loop system does not necessarily have low-interaction properties*. Consider, for example, the case of proportional controllers $k_1(s) = k_1$, $k_2(s) = k_2$, when

$$\frac{g_1(s)k_1(s)}{1 + g_1(s)k_1(s)} = \frac{k_1}{as + k_1}, \quad \frac{g_2(s)k_2(s)}{1 + g_2(s)k_2(s)} = \frac{k_2}{as + 2\beta + k_2} \qquad (3.3.22)$$

are simple first-order lags. The closed-loop system is hence asymptotically stable if, and only if, $k_1 > 0$ and $k_2 > -2\beta$. Considering the closed-loop response to a step demand in output $y_1(t)$ with zero initial conditions, then, using eqn. 3.3.20 and the relation $y(t) = \mathcal{L}^{-1}H_c(s)\dfrac{1}{s}e_1$,

$$y_1(t) = \frac{1}{2}\left\{\frac{2(\beta + k_2)}{(2\beta + k_2)} - e^{-k_1 a^{-1}t} - \frac{k_2}{(2\beta + k_2)}e^{-(k_2 + 2\beta)a^{-1}t}\right\} \qquad (3.3.23)$$

$$y_2(t) = \frac{1}{2}\left\{\frac{2\beta}{(2\beta + k_2)} - e^{-k_1 a^{-1}t} + \frac{k_2}{(2\beta + k_2)}e^{-(k_2 + 2\beta)a^{-1}t}\right\}$$

It is easily seen that the system response speed increases as k_1, k_2 are increased and that the steady-state error decreases as k_2 is increased. The steady-state error is independent of k_1 as k_1 acts upon a pure integrator $g_1(s)$ i.e. the steady-state value of $\hat{y}_1(t)$ is independent of both k_1 and k_2. The most interesting aspect of this analysis is a consideration of the effect of relative magnitudes of k_1, k_2 on the closed-loop interaction behaviour. If $k_1 \gg k_2$, then, in the vicinity of $t = 0+$, eqn. 3.3.23 indicates that

$$y(t) \simeq \frac{1}{2}\{1 - e^{-k_1 a^{-1}t}\}\begin{pmatrix}1\\1\end{pmatrix} \qquad (3.3.24)$$

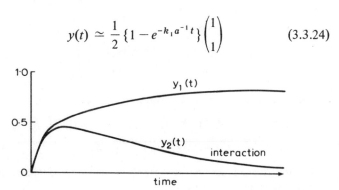

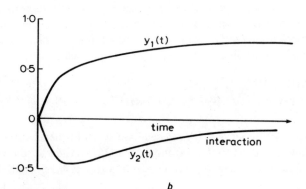

Fig. 3.3.1 Responses to unit-step demands in $y_1(t)$
   $a\ k_1 \gg k_2$
   $b\ k_2 \gg k_1$

so that both liquid levels rise initially at the same rate. If k_1 is sufficiently larger than k_2 then this approximation will be close to its steady state before the pole at $-(k_2 + 2\beta)a^{-1}$ has a significant dynamic effect. Hence, for t large,

$$y(t) \simeq \frac{1}{2}\begin{pmatrix}1\\1\end{pmatrix} - \frac{1}{2}\frac{k_2}{k_2 + 2\beta}\{1 - e^{-(k_2+2\beta)a^{-1}t}\}\begin{pmatrix}-1\\1\end{pmatrix} \qquad (3.3.25)$$

representing the asymptotic movement to the steady-state value. The resulting transient response is shown schematically in Fig. 3.3.1*a*, illustrating the unacceptable level of approximately 50% interaction, despite the fact that the closed-loop system is stable.

Exercise 3.3.2

Using similar considerations to the above, deduce that the closed-loop response to a unit-step demand in output $y_1(t)$, with $k_2 \gg k_1$, takes the form shown schematically in Fig. 3.3.1*b*.

The large interaction effects can be interpreted as the effect of large differences in response speed in the scalar modal feedback systems (eqn. 3.3.15). This is perhaps most easily seen by an examination of eqns. 3.3.22 and assuming that $g_1(s)k_1(s)/(1 + g_1(s)k_1(s) \simeq g_2(s)k_2(s)/(1 + g_2(s)k_2(s))$ over a frequency range of interest i.e. $H_c(s) \simeq g_1(s)k_1(s)/(1 + g_1(s)k_1(s))I_2$ which is a noninteracting system. This leads naturally to the attempt to equalise the response speeds by choosing k_1, k_2 such that the systems (eqns. 3.3.22) have the same time constant i.e. let

$$ak \triangleq k_1 = 2\beta + k_2 \qquad (3.3.26)$$

when, substituting into eqn. 3.3.23,

$$y_1(t) = \frac{ak - \beta}{ak}(1 - e^{-kt})$$

$$y_2(t) = \frac{\beta}{ak}(1 - e^{-kt}) \qquad (3.3.27)$$

indicating that steady-state errors tend to zero as $k \to +\infty$, the response speed can be arbitrarily fast and the interaction effect $y_2(t)$ can be made arbitrarily small. For example, if $ak > 10\beta$, both steady-state errors and interaction effects will be less than 10%. Note however that, if β is large (i.e. the open-loop interaction is large) the 'gain parameter' k must be very large, illustrating the general idea that significant open-loop interaction does lead to limitations in closed-loop performance if the control system gains are limited.

Exercise 3.3.3

Show that the output response to a step demand in output $y_2(t)$ with the controller (eqn. 3.3.26) can be obtained by interchanging the right-hand-sides of eqn. 3.3.27.

To complete the analysis, the forward-path controller

$$K(s) = T \begin{pmatrix} ak & 0 \\ 0 & ak - 2\beta \end{pmatrix} \quad T^{-1} = \begin{pmatrix} ak - \beta & \beta \\ \beta & ak - \beta \end{pmatrix}$$
(3.3.28)

which is a simple proportional output feedback controller. It is of interest to note how the final control structure reflects the required performance (in the form of the pole $-k$) and terms in β required to compensate for the open-loop interaction effects.

Exercise 3.3.4

Check the stability of the final design using the return-difference determinant.

3.4 Feedforward control and inverse systems

The analysis of inverse systems can have great relevance to the regulation of multivariable plant in the presence of disturbances.[2] Consider the $m \times m$ plant $G(s)$ subject to a $p \times 1$ disturbance vector $l(s)$ in the form shown in Fig. 3.4.1a where $L(s)$ is an $m \times p$ transfer-function matrix and $|G(s)| \not\equiv 0$. The input output relationships take the form

$$y(s) = G(s)u(s) + L(s)l(s)$$
(3.4.1)

The feedforward control system is shown in Fig. 3.4.1b where the $m \times p$ feedforward controller $M(s)$ is taken to represent a stable system, and it is assumed that the disturbance can be directly measured,

$$y(s) = \{L(s) + G(s)M(s)\}l(s)$$
(3.4.2)

For perfect feedforward regulation, it is required that $y(s) \equiv 0$, independent of the disturbance i.e.

$$M(s) \equiv -G^{-1}(s)L(s)$$
(3.4.3)

In general, $M(s)$ defined by expr. 3.4.3 is too complicated a structure for implementation and difficulties of stability would arise if $G(s)$ were nonminimum phase when the inverse system has an unstable strictly proper component. This means in practice that $M(s)$ must be set equal

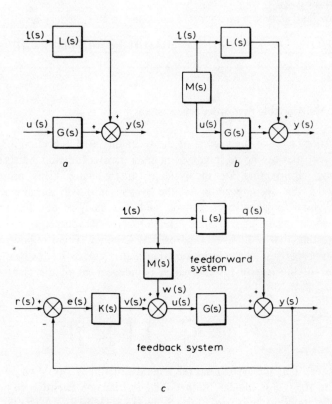

Fig. 3.4.1 Feedforward control systems
   a Plant $G(s)$ subject to disturbance vector
   b Feedforward control system
   c Inclusion of a feedback system

to a stable approximation to $-G^{-1}(s)L(s)$. In this case, perfect regulation of disturbance is not achieved so the system can be augmented by a feedback system as shown in Fig. 3.4.1*c* to offset this effect and the effect of data inaccuracies in the model and time-variation of plant parameters.

Exercise 3.4.1
Show that $L(s) = -G(s)$ for the coupled liquid-level system of Sections 2.5 and 3.3 and hence that perfect feedforward regulation can be

obtained using $M(s) = I_2$. Provide a physical interpretation of this result.

Exercise 3.4.2
Show that, assuming zero initial conditions on all system states,

$$y(s) = \{I_m + G(s)K(s)\}^{-1}\{G(s)K(s)r(s) + (G(s)M(s) + L(s))l(s)\}$$

3.5 Multivariable first-order-type systems

A major factor in the success of the technique used in Section 3.3 was the fact that the liquid level system has a transfer-function matrix $G(s)$ whose eigenvectors are independent of frequency. This property enabled the decomposition of the system into two noninteracting single-input/single-output systems and the analysis of closed-loop behaviour using eqn. 3.3.20. This property disappears if $a_1 \neq a_2$, suggesting that a different approach is required. There is however a basic property of the transfer-function matrix eqn. 3.3.1, expressed in terms of the inverse system, which is independent of the plant data a_1, a_2, β. Writing,

$$G^{-1}(s) \equiv s\begin{pmatrix} a_1 & 0 \\ 0 & a_2 \end{pmatrix} + \begin{pmatrix} \beta & -\beta \\ -\beta & \beta \end{pmatrix} \qquad (3.5.1)$$

it is seen that the system has the general structure $G^{-1}(s) = sA_0 + A_1$, where A_0 is nonsingular. Rather than restrict our attention to liquid level systems, we make use of the following generalisation.[40,42]

Definition 3.5.1: An m-input/m-output strictly proper system described by the $m \times m$ transfer function matrix $G(s)$ is said to be a multivariable first-order-type system (or, more compactly, a multivariable first-order lag) if, and only if, $|G(s)| \not\equiv 0$ and

$$G^{-1}(s) = A_0 s + A_1, \quad |A_0| \neq 0 \qquad (3.5.2)$$

where A_0, A_1 are real constant matrices.

With this definition, the coupled liquid-level system is seen to be a multivariable first-order lag, independent of plant data. The term first-order lag is motivated by the analogy with the classical first-order transfer function defined by $g^{-1}(s) = a_0 s + a_1, a_0 \neq 0$. The similarity will be seen to be more than simply superficial later in the Section.

Writing

$$G(s) = \{A_0 s + A_1\}^{-1} = \{sI_m + A_0^{-1}A_1\}^{-1}A_0^{-1} \qquad (3.5.3)$$

it is seen that $G(s)$ has a state-space realisation specified by $A = -A_0^{-1}A_1$, $B = A_0^{-1}$, $C = I_m$, and $n = m$. In general terms, those readers familiar with realisation theory (Reference 63) should have no difficulty in proving the following result specifying the class of systems satisfying Definition 3.5.1.

Theorem 3.5.1: An m-input/m-output, strictly proper, controllable and observable system specified by the triple (A, B, C) is a multivariable first-order lag, if, and only if, $n = m$ and $|CB| \neq 0$.

Using eqn. 2.16.7, for large values of $|s|$,

$$G(s) = C(sI_n - A)^{-1}B = \frac{1}{s}CB + \frac{1}{s^2}CAB + \frac{1}{s^3}CA^2 B + \dots \qquad (3.5.4)$$

so that

$$I_m = G^{-1}(s)G(s) = \left\{A_0 + \frac{1}{s}A_1\right\}\left\{CB + \frac{1}{s}CAB + \dots\right\} \qquad (3.5.5)$$

and, equating powers of s^{-1}, it follows that

$$A_0 CB = I_m, \quad A_0 = (CB)^{-1} \qquad (3.5.6)$$

$$A_1 CB + A_0 CAB = 0, \quad A_1 = -A_0 CAB A_0 \qquad (3.5.7)$$

providing an easy route to the evaluation of A_0, A_1. An alternative definition of A_1 is obtained directly from eqn. 3.5.2

$$A_1 = \lim_{s \to 0} G^{-1}(s) \qquad (3.5.8)$$

and, recalling Definition 2.20.16,

$$A_0 = (G_\infty^{(1)})^{-1} \qquad (3.5.9)$$

Exercise 3.5.1

Show that the system described by the transfer-function matrix

$$G(s) = \frac{1}{s^2 + 2s - 2}\begin{pmatrix} s+4 & s+2 \\ 3 & s+1 \end{pmatrix}$$

is a multivariable first order lag. Hence find a state-vector realisation of $G(s)$ and check eqns. 3.5.6–3.5.9.

Exercise 3.5.2

Prove that the relations $n = m$, $|G(s)| \not\equiv 0$ imply that $|CB| \neq 0$, and that $|CB| \neq 0$ implies that $|G(s)| \not\equiv 0$, but that n may be greater than m.

As $n = m$, the output vector $y(t)$ is in one-to-one correspondence with the system state $x(t)$ i.e. constant state feedback is, in fact, constant output feedback. Bearing in mind the great flexibility of state feedback for improving system performance, it is anticipated that the feedback control of a multivariable first-order lag is a feasible problem.

Proportional control: Consider a unity-negative feedback control system for the control of an $m \times m$ multivariable first order lag $G(s)$, and the simplest possible case of (constant output feedback) proportional control $K(s) = K$ (a real constant matrix). From the above discussion, it follows that

$$\rho_0(s) = |sI_m + A_0^{-1}A_1| \qquad (3.5.10)$$

A motivation for the following analysis can be obtained by writing $G(s)$ in the form of eqn. 3.5.3, when, if $A_0^{-1}A_1$ has eigenvalues $-\lambda_j$, $1 \leqslant j \leqslant m$, and eigenvector matrix T such that $T^{-1}A_0^{-1}A_1 T = \text{diag}\{-\lambda_1, -\lambda_2, \ldots, -\lambda_m\}$, then

$$G(s) = T \, \text{diag}\{g_1(s), g_2(s), \ldots, g_m(s)\} T^{-1}A_0^{-1} \qquad (3.5.11)$$

where

$$g_j(s) = \frac{1}{s - \lambda_j}, \qquad 1 \leqslant j \leqslant m \qquad (3.5.12)$$

Comparing this relation with eqns. 3.3.17 and 3.3.22 indicates that the only essential differences between the two problems are the possibility that $m \geqslant 2$ and the presence of the term A_0^{-1} in eqn. 3.5.11. The first is a bonus in generality and the second is easily accommodated by defining $K(s)$ by the relation (c.f. eqn. 3.3.18)

$$T^{-1}A_0^{-1}K(s)T = \text{diag}\{k_1, k_2, \ldots, k_m\} \qquad (3.5.13)$$

when the reader can easily verify that

$$T^{-1}G(s)K(s)T = \text{diag}\{g_1(s)k_1, g_2(s)k_2, \ldots, g_m(s)k_m\}$$

$$H_c(s) = \{I_m + G(s)K(s)\}^{-1}G(s)K(s) = T \, \text{diag}\left\{\frac{g_j(s)k_j(s)}{1 + g_j(s)k_j(s)}\right\}_{1 \leqslant j \leqslant m} T^{-1}$$

$$(3.5.14)$$

A comparison with eqn. 3.3.20 suggests that the control analysis can now continue in a similar manner to that of the liquid-level system i.e. to reduce interaction, it is necesssary to use a high gain and to equalise the response of the subsystems in eqn. 3.5.14 by setting

$$k_j = k + \lambda_j, \qquad 1 \leqslant j \leqslant m \qquad (3.5.15)$$

where k is the specified closed-loop pole (identical for each subsystem). Substitution into eqn. 3.5.13 gives the trial proportional controller

$$K(s) = A_0 T \, \text{diag} \{k_1, k_2, \ldots, k_m\} T^{-1} = A_0 T \, \text{diag} \{k + \lambda_j\}_{1 \leqslant j \leqslant m} T^{-1}$$

$$= k A_0 - A_1 \qquad (3.5.16)$$

This controller is, in fact, a good choice even if $A_0^{-1} A_1$ does not have a diagonal canonical form. Evaluating the closed-loop transfer-function matrix

$$H_c(s) = \{I_m + G(s)K\}^{-1} G(s)K = \{G^{-1}(s) + K\}^{-1} K$$

$$= \{sA_0 + A_1 + kA_0 - A_1\}^{-1} \{kA_0 - A_1\}$$

$$= \frac{k}{s+k} \{I_m - k^{-1} A_0^{-1} A_1\} \qquad (3.5.17)$$

and the return-difference is simply

$$|T(s)| = |I_m + G(s)K| = |G(s)| \, |G^{-1}(s) + K|$$

$$= \frac{|A_0 s + A_1 + kA_0 - A_1|}{|sA_0 + A_1|}$$

$$= (s+k)^m / |sI_m + A_0^{-1} A_1| \qquad (3.5.18)$$

and the closed-loop system is asymptotically stable if, and only if, $k > 0$. As k increases, eqn. 3.5.17 implies that the system response speed increases, steady-state error in response to unit-step demands tends to zero as

$$\lim_{s \to 0} H_c(s) = I_m - k^{-1} A_0^{-1} A_1 \to I_m \qquad (k \to +\infty) \quad (3.5.19)$$

and interaction can be made to be arbitrarily small as

$$\mathcal{L}^{-1} H_c(s) \frac{1}{s} = \{1 - e^{-kt}\} \{I_m - k^{-1} A_0^{-1} A_1\} \to \{1 - e^{-kt}\} I_m$$
$$(3.5.20)$$

More precisely, the degree of interaction in response to a unit-step demand in output $y_i(t)$ is

$$a_i = \frac{100}{k} \max_{\substack{1 \leqslant j \leqslant m \\ j \neq i}} |(A_0^{-1} A_1)_{ji}| \qquad (3.5.21)$$

To illustrate the application of the technique, consider the liquid-level system of expr. 3.5.1, where

$$A_0 = \begin{pmatrix} a_1 & 0 \\ 0 & a_2 \end{pmatrix}, \quad A_1 = \begin{pmatrix} \beta & -\beta \\ -\beta & \beta \end{pmatrix} \qquad (3.5.22)$$

giving the controller structure in terms of the parameter k in the form,

$$K = kA_0 - A_1 = \begin{pmatrix} ka_1 - \beta & \beta \\ \beta & ka_2 - \beta \end{pmatrix} \qquad (3.5.23)$$

(Note that eqn. 3.5.23 reduces to eqn. 3.3.28 if $a_1 = a_2 = a$). The closed-loop transfer-function matrix eqn. 3.5.17 is,

$$H_c(s) = \frac{k}{s+k} \begin{pmatrix} 1 - \dfrac{\beta}{ka_1} & \dfrac{\beta}{ka_1} \\ \dfrac{\beta}{ka_2} & 1 - \dfrac{\beta}{ka_2} \end{pmatrix} \qquad (3.5.24)$$

and hence the interaction effects in response to unit-step demands in either output are less than 10% if, and only if, $k > 10\beta \max(a_1^{-1}, a_2^{-1})$ when steady-state errors are less than 10% in all loops.

Exercise 3.5.3
Design a unity-negative proportional feedback control system for the plant of Exercise 3.5.1 to ensure that interaction effects and steady-state errors are less than 10% in all loops in response to unit-step demands.

Proportional plus integral control: Problems could arise in the application of the above technique, if the control gains are limited by engineering considerations. This is of particular relevance if the eigenvalues of $-A_0^{-1}A_1$ (i.e. the poles of the system) have a large spread. Consider the case when $A_0^{-1}A_1$ has a diagonal canonical form, with eigenvector matrix T i.e.

$$H_c(s) = \frac{k}{s+k}\left\{ I_m + T \operatorname{diag}\left\{ \frac{\lambda_1}{k}, \frac{\lambda_2}{k}, \ldots, \frac{\lambda_m}{k} \right\} T^{-1} \right\} \qquad (3.5.25)$$

suggesting that $k \gg \max|\lambda_j|$ is a necessary condition for small closed-loop interaction. If any one pole has a large magnitude, then, in general, the gain parameter k required to produce, say, less than 10% interaction may be too large for the particular system. In this case, large interaction effects may have to be accepted and integral action included in the control system to offset the steady-state errors.

Suppose that a proportional controller (eqn. 3.5.16) has been obtained subject to system constraints and augment the expression by an integral term, expressed in the parametric form,

$$K(s) = \left\{ k + c + \frac{kc}{s} \right\} A_0 - A_1 \qquad (3.5.26)$$

The controller has a state-vector model of the form,

$$\dot{x}_2(t) = e(t)$$

$$u(t) = kcA_0 x_2(t) + \{(k+c)A_0 - A_1\} e(t) \qquad (3.5.27)$$

The open-loop characteristic polynomial is hence

$$\rho_0(s) = s^m \, |sI_m + A_0^{-1} A_1| \qquad (3.5.28)$$

and

$$|T(s)| = |I_m + G(s)K(s)| = |G(s)| \; |G^{-1}(s) + K(s)|$$

$$= \frac{\left| A_0 s + A_1 + \left(k + c + \dfrac{kc}{s}\right) A_0 - A_1 \right|}{|sA_0 + A_1|}$$

$$= (s+k)^m (s+c)^m / s^m \, |sI_m + A_0^{-1} A_1| \qquad (3.5.29)$$

i.e. the closed-loop system is stable if, and only if, $k > 0$ and $c > 0$. The closed-loop transfer-function matrix,

$$H_c(s) = \{I_m + G(s)K(s)\}^{-1} G(s)K(s) = \{G^{-1}(s) + K(s)\}^{-1} K(s)$$

$$= \left\{ sA_0 + A_1 + \left(k + c + \frac{kc}{s}\right) A_0 - A_1 \right\}^{-1} \left\{ \left(k + c + \frac{kc}{s}\right) A_0 - A_1 \right\}$$

$$= \frac{1}{(s+k)(s+c)} \{kcI_m + s((k+c)I_m - A_0^{-1} A_1)\} \qquad (3.5.30)$$

Expressing $H_c(s)$ in pole-residue form,

$$H_c(s) = \frac{k}{(s+k)} M_1(k,c) + \frac{c}{(s+c)} M_2(k,c)$$

$$M_1(k,c) = \frac{k}{k-c} \{I_m - k^{-1} A_0^{-1} A_1\}, \quad M_2(k,c) = \frac{c}{k-c} \{c^{-1} A_0^{-1} A_1 - I_m\}$$

$$(3.5.31)$$

it follows directly that, for $0 < c \ll k$, the closed-loop step responses are similar to those predicted for the proportional control except that the tail of the responses have a time constant c^{-1} producing zero steady-state error in response to unit-step demands, as

$$\lim_{s \to 0} H_c(s) = I_m \qquad (3.5.32)$$

System integrity:[41] The integrity of the closed-loop system can be analysed using exprns. 2.19.13 and 2.19.14. Consider the case of proportional control and closed-loop stability in the presence of a sensor failure in loop j,

$$
\begin{aligned}
e_j^T \{I_m + G(s)K(s)\}^{-1} e_j &= e_j^T \{G^{-1}(s) + K(s)\}^{-1} G^{-1}(s) e_j \\
&= e_j^T \{sA_0 + A_1 + kA_0 - A_1\}^{-1} \{sA_0 + A_1\} e_j \\
&= (s + e_j^T A_0^{-1} A_1 e_j)/(s + k) \qquad (3.5.33)
\end{aligned}
$$

so that the system is stable if, and only if, the jth diagonal term of $A_0^{-1} A_1$ is strictly positive. The situation of an actuator failure in loop j is treated similarly,

$$
\begin{aligned}
e_j^T \{I_m + K(s)G(s)\}^{-1} e_j &= e_j^T G^{-1}(s) \{G^{-1}(s) + K(s)\}^{-1} e_j \\
&= e_j^T \{sA_0 + A_1\} \{sA_0 + A_1 + kA_0 - A_1\}^{-1} e_j \\
&= (s + e_j^T A_1 A_0^{-1} e_j)/(s + k) \qquad (3.5.34)
\end{aligned}
$$

so that the system is stable if, and only if, the jth diagonal term of $A_1 A_0^{-1}$ is strictly positive.

The case of proportional plus integral control yields,

$$
\begin{aligned}
e_j^T \{I_m + G(s)K(s)\}^{-1} e_j &= s(s + e_j^T A_0^{-1} A_1 e_j)/(s + k)(s + c) \\
e_j^T \{I_m + K(s)G(s)\}^{-1} e_j &= s(s + e_j^T A_1 A_0^{-1} e_j)/(s + k)(s + c)
\end{aligned}
\qquad (3.5.35)
$$

so that the failure of a sensor or actuator in any loop releases a pole at the origin.

Exercise 3.5.4
Show that the liquid-level system eqn. 3.5.1 with controller eqn. 3.5.23 $(k > 0)$ is stable in the presence of sensor or actuator failure in any loop.

Exercise 3.5.5
Investigate the integrity of your final design in Exercise 3.5.3.

Exercise 3.5.6
Suggest an intuitive interpretation of the absence of integrity in the presence of integral control action and show that stability in the presence of sensor failure is impossible if $\lim_{s \to 0} Q^{-1}(s) = 0$.

A more general solution: An analysis of eqn. 3.5.20 indicates that the closed-loop system has identical response speeds (with time constant k^{-1}) in response to unit-step demands in any loop. This may not necessarily be a design requirement and could lead to undesirably high control system gains if the eigenvalues of $A_0^{-1}A_1$ have a large spread in modulus (c.f. eqn. 3.5.25). In such cases, the following generalisation may be of some relevance. Replace eqn. 3.5.16 by the more general parametric structure,

$$K(s) = A_0 \text{ diag}\{k_1(s), k_2(s), \ldots, k_m(s)\} - A_1 \qquad (3.5.36)$$

where $k_j(s)$, $1 \leqslant j \leqslant m$, are proper minimum-phase transfer functions. The system return-difference determinant takes the form

$$|T(s)| = |I_m + G(s)K(s)| = |G(s)||G^{-1}(s) + K(s)|$$

$$= |sA_0 + A_1 + A_0 \text{ diag}\{k_1(s), \ldots, k_m(s)\} - A_1| / |sA_0 + A_1|$$

$$= \left\{ \prod_{j=1}^{m} (s + k_j(s)) \right\} / |sI_m + A_0^{-1}A_1|$$

$$= \frac{s^m}{|sI_m + A_0^{-1}A_1|} \times \prod_{j=1}^{m} \left(1 + \frac{1}{s}k_j(s)\right) \qquad (3.5.37)$$

and hence closed-loop stability is governed by the zeros of the classical scalar return-differences $(1 + s^{-1}k_j(s))$, $1 \leqslant j \leqslant m$. The closed-loop transfer-function matrix takes the form

$$H_c(s) = \{G^{-1}(s) + K(s)\}^{-1}K(s)$$

$$= \text{diag}\left\{\frac{1}{s + k_1(s)}, \ldots, \frac{1}{s + k_m(s)}\right\}\{\text{diag}\{k_1(s), \ldots, k_m(s)\}$$
$$- A_0^{-1}A_1\} \qquad (3.5.38)$$

In particular

$$\lim_{s \to 0} H_c(s) = I_m - \lim_{s \to 0} \text{diag}\left\{\frac{1}{k_1(s)}, \ldots, \frac{1}{k_m(s)}\right\}A_0^{-1}A_1 \qquad (3.5.39)$$

so that the steady-state error in output $y_i(t)$ in response to a unit-step demand in $y_j(t)$ is simply

$$(E_\infty)_{ij} = \lim_{s \to 0} \frac{1}{k_i(s)} (A_0^{-1} A_1)_{ij} \qquad (3.5.40)$$

Equivalently, if $k_i(s)$ contains integral action, the steady-state error in $y_i(t)$ in response to step demands is always zero. If $k_i(0)$ is finite, then steady-state errors are reduced by the use of high gains.

The transient performance of eqn. 3.5.38 can be deduced, by noting that, if the control gains of $k_1(s), \ldots, k_m(s)$ are high, the term $A_0^{-1} A_1$ can be neglected to give

$$H_c(s) \simeq \text{diag} \left\{ \frac{k_1(s)}{s + k_1(s)}, \ldots, \frac{k_m(s)}{s + k_m(s)} \right\} \qquad (3.5.41)$$

so that, at high gains, the closed-loop system is approximately noninteracting with the dynamics of the ith loop described by the scalar transfer

function $\dfrac{k_i(s)}{s} \left(1 + \dfrac{k_i(s)}{s} \right)^{-1}, 1 \leqslant i \leqslant m.$

Finally, the integrity of the system is described by the eqns. (eqns. 2.19.13, 2.19.15)

$$e_j^T \{I_m + G(s)K(s)\}^{-1} e_j = e_j^T \{G^{-1}(s) + K(s)\}^{-1} G^{-1}(s) e_j$$

$$= \frac{(s + e_j^T A_0^{-1} A_1 e_j)}{(s + k_j(s))} \qquad (3.5.42)$$

and

$$e_j^T \{I_m + K(s)G(s)\}^{-1} e_j = e_j^T \{sI_m + A_1 A_0^{-1}\} A_0$$

$$\text{diag} \left\{ \frac{1}{s + k_i(s)} \right\}_{1 \leqslant i \leqslant m} A_0^{-1} e_j \qquad (3.5.43)$$

Examining the case of sensor failure in loop j, eqn. 3.5.42 indicates that the closed-loop system is stable if, and only if, the jth diagonal term of $A_0^{-1} A_1$ is strictly positive (c.f. eqn. 3.5.33) and $k_j(s)$ is asymptotically stable. In particular, if $k_j(s)$ includes integral action, stability in the presence of a sensor failure in loop j is impossible. The case of actuator failure in loop j is more complicated if A_0 is not diagonal when stability depends upon all the transfer functions $k_i(s)$, $1 \leqslant i \leqslant m$.

Exercise 3.5.7

Consider the proportional, unity-negative feedback control of a plant with inverse transfer-function matrix,

$$G^{-1}(s) = s\begin{pmatrix} 1 & 1 \\ 0 & 1 \end{pmatrix} + \begin{pmatrix} 21 & 21 \\ 1 & 1 \end{pmatrix}$$

Using the controller $K = kA_0 - A_1$, show that the closed-loop transfer-function matrix takes the form,

$$H_c(s) = \frac{k}{s+k}\left\{I_2 - k^{-1}\begin{pmatrix} 20 & 20 \\ 1 & 1 \end{pmatrix}\right\}$$

and hence that interaction effects, in response to unit-step demands, are less than 10% if, and only if, $k > 200$, and that, if $k = 200$, the controller takes the form

$$K = \begin{pmatrix} 179 & 179 \\ -1 & 199 \end{pmatrix}$$

Considering the more general control structure $K = A_0 \,\text{diag}\,\{k_1, k_2\} - A_1$, the closed-loop transfer-function matrix

$$H_c(s) = \begin{pmatrix} \dfrac{1}{s+k_1} & 0 \\ 0 & \dfrac{1}{s+k_2} \end{pmatrix} \begin{pmatrix} k_1 - 20 & -20 \\ -1 & k_1 - 1 \end{pmatrix}$$

and hence interaction effects are less than 10% if and only if $k_1 > 200$, $k_2 > 10$. If $k_1 = 200$, $k_2 = 10$, then

$$K = \begin{pmatrix} 179 & -11 \\ -1 & 9 \end{pmatrix}$$

indicating an overall lowering of gain in the second loop. Comment on the form of the step responses and the integrity of the closed-loop configuration in both cases.

3.6 Level control of an *m*-vessel liquid storage system

Despite the restricted structure of a multivariable first-order lag, they have an important role to play in theoretical studies[43] and practical applications. The interested reader is referred to Reference 40 for application to gas-turbine control, to Reference 7 for applications to the control of binary distillation columns and liquid-liquid counter-flow heat exchangers and to Reference 58 for possible application to the control of the pressurised flow-box in a Fourdrinier paper-making machine. The conceptual application discussed in this section is a generalisation of the system of Section 2.5 tó *m*-vessels as illustrated in Fig. 3.6.1, and should convince the reader of the simple nature of the results of Section 3.5.

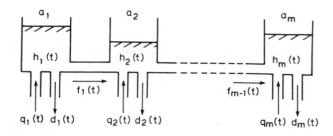

Fig. 3.6.1 M-vessel liquid storage system

Using the notation
- a_i = cross-sectional area of vessel i (assumed to be uniform)
- $h_i(t)$ = height of liquid in vessel i at time t
- $f_i(t)$ = volume flow from vessel i to vessel $i+1$ at time t
- $q_i(t)$ = input volume flow rate to vessel i at time t
- $d_i(t)$ = outlet volume flow rate from vessel i at time t,

then, the system dynamics are represented by

$$a_i \dot{h}_i(t) = q_i(t) - d_i(t) - f_i(t) + f_{i-1}(t), \qquad 1 \leqslant i \leqslant m \quad (3.6.1)$$

where, for notational simplicity, $f_0(t) \equiv f_m(t) \equiv 0$. If $h_{i0}, q_{i0}, d_{i0}, f_{i0}$, $1 \leqslant i \leqslant m$ correspond to a system steady state and defining,

$$h_i(t) = h_{i0} + y_i(t), \qquad 1 \leqslant i \leqslant m$$

$$q_i(t) = q_{i0} + u_i(t), \qquad 1 \leqslant i \leqslant m$$

$$d_i(t) = d_{i0} + l_i(t), \qquad 1 \leqslant i \leqslant m$$

$$f_i(t) \simeq f_{i0} + \beta_i \{y_i(t) - y_{i+1}(t)\}, \qquad 1 \leqslant i \leqslant m - 1$$

$$\beta_i > 0, \qquad 1 \leqslant i \leqslant m \qquad (3.6.2)$$

the following model of perturbation dynamics is obtained:

$$a_i \dot{y}_i(t) = u_i(t) - l_i(t) - \beta_i \{y_i(t) - y_{i+1}(t)\} + \beta_{i-1} \{y_{i-1}(t) - y_i(t)\},$$
$$2 \leqslant i \leqslant m - 1,$$

$$a_1 \dot{y}_1(t) = u_1(t) - l_1(t) - \beta_1 \{y_1(t) - y_2(t)\}$$
$$a_m \dot{y}_m(t) = u_m(t) - l_m(t) + \beta_{m-1} \{y_{m-1}(t) - y_m(t)\} \qquad (3.6.3)$$

Assume, for simplicity, that the disturbance terms $l_i(t)$, $1 \leqslant i \leqslant m$, are zero. Taking Laplace transforms with zero initial conditions and denoting $y(s) = (y_1(s), y_2(s), \ldots, y_m(s))^T$, $u(s) = (u_1(s), \ldots, u_m(s))^T$ yields,

$$\begin{pmatrix} a_1 s + \beta_1 & -\beta_1 & 0 & \cdots \cdots & 0 \\ -\beta_1 & a_2 s + \beta_1 + \beta_2 & -\beta_2 & & \vdots \\ 0 & -\beta_2 & a_3 s + \beta_2 + \beta_3 & & \vdots \\ 0 & 0 & & & 0 \\ \vdots & & & & \\ \vdots & & & & -\beta_{m-1} \\ 0 & & 0 & -\beta_{m-1}, & a_m s + \beta_{m-1} \end{pmatrix} y(s)$$

$$= u(s) \qquad (3.6.4)$$

Comparing this with the relation $y(s) = G(s)u(s)$ indicates that $G^{-1}(s) = A_0 s + A_1$, $|A_0| \neq 0$, where

$$A_0 = \text{diag} \{a_1, a_2, \ldots, a_m\}$$

$$A_1 = \begin{pmatrix} \beta_1 & -\beta_1 & 0 & \cdots \cdots & 0 \\ -\beta_1 & \beta_1 + \beta_2 & -\beta_2 & & \vdots \\ 0 & -\beta_2 & \beta_2 + \beta_3 & & \vdots \\ \vdots & & & & 0 \\ \vdots & & & & -\beta_{m-1} \\ 0 & \cdots \cdots & 0 & -\beta_{m-1} & \beta_{m-1} \end{pmatrix} \qquad (3.6.5)$$

and hence the *m*-vessel system is a multivariable first-order lag. The inverse transfer-function matrix has many zero entries reflecting the nearest-neighbour coupling of the system. This is in contrast to $G(s)$ in which every entry is nonzero, hence motivating the use of the inverse system for purposes of analysis (see later sections and chapters).

Exercise 3.6.1

Calculate $G(s)$ in the case of $m = 3$ and verify that $G_{ij}(s) \not\equiv 0$, $1 \leqslant i$, $j \leqslant 3$. Compare this with the inverse system $G^{-1}(s)$. Justify your conclusions by considering the effect of an impulsive input to vessel *i* and prediction of the steady-state response from physical considerations. (Hint: if a volume v is injected into vessel *i*, show that the steady-state volume change in vessel j, $1 \leqslant j \leqslant m$, is v/m.)

Exercise 3.6.2

Use physical reasoning to deduce that the *m*-vessel system has a pole at the point $s = 0$.

Consider the case of proportional unity-negative feedback control with the controller of eqn. 3.5.16,

$$K(s) = kA_0 - A_1 = \begin{pmatrix} ka_1 - \beta_1 & \beta_1 & 0 \dots \dots \dots 0 \\ \beta_1 & ka_2 - \beta_1 - \beta_2 & \beta_2 & & \vdots \\ 0 & \beta_2 & & & \vdots \\ \vdots & & & & 0 \\ \vdots & & & & \beta_{m-1} \\ 0 \dots \dots \dots \dots 0 & \beta_{m-1} & ka_m - \beta_{m-1} \end{pmatrix}$$

$$(3.6.6)$$

and notice, despite the general complexity of $G(s)$, the control system constructs the input $u_j(t)$ from the error signals $e_{j-1}(t)$, $e_j(t)$, $e_{j+1}(t)$ only, implying a simplicity of implementation.

The closed-loop transfer-function matrix is obtained from eqn. 3.5.17,

$$H_c(s) = \{I_m + G(s)K(s)\}^{-1} G(s)K(s)$$

$$= \frac{k}{s+k} \begin{pmatrix} 1 - \dfrac{\beta_1}{ka_1} & \dfrac{\beta_1}{ka_1} & 0 \; . \; . \; . \; . \; . \; . \; 0 \\[2ex] \dfrac{\beta_1}{ka_2} & 1 - \dfrac{(\beta_1 + \beta_2)}{ka_2} & \dfrac{\beta_2}{ka_2} \; . \; . \; . \; \vdots \\[2ex] \vdots & & \\ 0 \; . \; . \; . \; . \; . \; . \; . \; . \; 0 & \dfrac{\beta_{m-1}}{ka_m} & 1 - \dfrac{\beta_{m-1}}{ka_m} \end{pmatrix}$$

$$(3.6.7)$$

and hence, the closed-loop system has a time constant of k^{-1}, inter-action effects are less than 10% in response to unit-step demands if

$$ka_j \geqslant 10\beta_j, \quad 1 \leqslant j \leqslant m-1, \quad \text{and} \quad ka_j \geqslant 10\beta_{j-1}, \quad 2 \leqslant j \leqslant m$$

$$(3.6.8)$$

and steady-state errors in response to unit-step demands are less than 10% if

$$ka_1 \geqslant \beta_1 10, \quad 10(\beta_{j-1} + \beta_j) \geqslant ka_j, \quad 2 \leqslant j \leqslant m-1,$$

$$\text{and} \quad ka_m \geqslant 10\beta_{m-1} \qquad (3.6.9)$$

Exercise 3.6.3

Show that the closed-loop system is stable in the presence of a sensor failure or an actuator failure in any loop.

3.7 First-order approximation method for feedback design

Bearing in mind the importance of low-order models in classical design applications due to the presence of approximate pole-zero cancellation in the system transfer function, the reader should not be discouraged by the apparent restricted structure of multivariable first order systems (theorem 3.5.1). In particular, they have application to model reduction using state feedback[62] and, in a more general context, as approximate models for feedback-design purposes.[7]

Consider an $m \times m$ minimum-phase transfer-function matrix $G(s)$ of the form (eqn. 2.21.10),

$$G^{-1}(s) = sA_0 + A_1 + H_z(s), \quad |A_0| \neq 0 \qquad (3.7.1)$$

where $H_z(s)$ is stable, and strictly proper. It follows that $H_z(0)$ is finite and, replacing A_1 by $A_1 + H_z(0)$, $H_z(s)$ by $H_z(s) - H_z(0)$, and defining $A_0 H(s) = H_z(s) - H_z(0)$,

$$G^{-1}(s) = sA_0 + A_1 + A_0 H(s), \quad |A_0| \neq 0, \quad H(0) = 0$$
$$(3.7.2)$$

Using eqn. 3.5.4 and the identity $G^{-1}(s) G(s) = I_m$, it is easily verified that $A_0 CB = I_m$ and hence that,

$$|CB| \neq 0, \quad A_0 = (CB)^{-1} \tag{3.7.3}$$

and, quite obviously,

$$A_1 = G^{-1}(s)|_{s=0} \tag{3.7.4}$$

It is intuitively reasonable that, if $H_z(s)$ is 'small' in some sense, that $G(s)$ can be replaced by the approximate first-order model, obtained by neglecting $H(s)$ in eqn. 3.7.2,

$$G_A^{-1}(s) = sA_0 + A_1 \tag{3.7.5}$$

when the results of Section 3.5 could be used to construct a control system $K(s)$.

The precise mathematical justification of these ideas requires a basic knowledge of functional analysis in the form of Banach spaces of analytic functions and the contraction mapping theorem – concepts well outside the scope of this text.[7] For completeness, the essential results can be summarised by defining

$$\|H\| = \max_{s \in D} \ \max_{1 \leqslant i \leqslant m} \ \sum_{j=1}^{m} |H_{ij}(s)| \tag{3.7.6}$$

where D is the contour in the complex plane consisting of the imaginary axis $s = i\omega$, $|\omega| \leqslant R$ and the large semicircle $|s| = R$ in the right-half complex plane. If the controller $K = kA_0 - A_1$ is implemented, then the closed-loop system is stable if

$$\|H\| < k \tag{3.7.7}$$

i.e. in intuitive terms, the closed-loop system $\{I + G(s)K\}^{-1} G(s)K$ is stable over a large range of practical gains k if $H(s)$ is small in the sense that $\|H\|$ is small.

An intuitive insight into the interpretation of the smallness of $H(s)$ can be obtained by a consideration of the scalar transfer function,

$$g(s) = \frac{(s + z)}{(s + p_1)(s + p_2)} \tag{3.7.8}$$

giving the inverse system

$$g^{-1}(s) = s + (p_1 + p_2 - z) + \frac{(z-p_1)(z-p_2)}{s+z} \qquad (3.7.9)$$

and

$$H(s) = \frac{(z-p_1)(z-p_2)}{(s+z)} \qquad (3.7.10)$$

so that

$$\|H\| = \frac{(z-p_1)(z-p_2)}{z} \qquad (3.7.11)$$

The reader can easily verify that $\|H\|$ is small if, and only if, $g(s)$ has approximate pole-zero cancellation, and that, in this case, the frequency response of $g_A(s)$ is a close approximation to that of $g(s)$.

In the multivariable situation, a similar interpretation is taken to be valid and the following design procedure is suggested[7]

Step 1: Calculate A_0 and A_1 from eqns. 3.7.3, 3.7.4 and construct the first-order approximation (eqn. 3.7.5) to the system open-loop dynamics.

Step 2: Compare the open-loop step responses of $G(s)$ and $G_A(s)$ to assess the validity of the approximation.

Step 3: Construct a unity-negative feedback controller $K(s)$ using the analysis of Section 3.5, and check the stability and performance of the closed-loop system $\{I_m + G(s)K(s)\}^{-1}G(s)K(s)$ by simulation of the step responses.

Exercise 3.7.1

Using the approximate first-order model $G_A(s)$ defined by eqn. 3.7.5 and proportional controller $K(s) = kA_0 - A_1$, show that the closed-loop transfer-function matrix

$$H_c(s) = \{I_m + G(s)K(s)\}^{-1}G(s)K(s) = \left\{ I_m + \frac{1}{s+k}H(s) \right\}^{-1}$$

$$\frac{k}{(s+k)}\{I_m - k^{-1}A_0^{-1}A_1\}$$

$$= \left\{ I_m + \frac{1}{s+k}H(s) \right\}^{-1} \{I_m + G_A(s)K(s)\}^{-1}G_A(s)K(s)$$

Noting that,

$$\left\{ I_m + \frac{1}{s+k}H(s) \right\}^{-1} = I_m - \frac{1}{(s+k)}H(s) + \frac{1}{(s+k)^2}(H(s))^2 - \ldots$$

prove that, for $k \gg \|H\|$, the closed-loop transfer-function matrix $H_c(i\omega) \simeq \{I_m + G_A(i\omega)K(i\omega)\}^{-1} G_A(i\omega)K(i\omega)$. Interpret this result in terms of the closed-loop step responses of the exact system $G(s)$ and the system approximation $G_A(s)$.

The interested reader is referred to Edwards and Owens[7] for a description of the application of the technique to a binary distillation column and a liquid-liquid counterflow heat exchanger. One of the important notions to be gained from this analysis is that approximation methods can play an important role in the application of frequency response methods to multivariable feedback design.

3.8 Restricted class of multivariable second-order-type systems

Despite the generalisation provided by the discussion of Section 3.7, multivariable first-order lags do not describe many of the dynamical effects observed in multivariable feedback systems. In particular, it is seen that the control designs suggested in Section 3.5 prevent oscillation in the closed-loop system, independent of the control system gains. A useful vehicle for illustrating oscillation in multivariable feedback systems is the concept of a multivariable second-order-type-system introduced by Owens.[42] A restricted second-order structure is defined by analogy with the second-order inverse transfer function $g^{-1}(s) = s(sa_0 + a_1)$, $a_0 \neq 0$, to be an $m \times m$ invertible system with inverse transfer-function matrix,

$$G^{-1}(s) = s\{sA_0 + A_1\}, \quad |A_0| \neq 0 \qquad (3.8.1)$$

or,

$$G(s) = \frac{1}{s}\{sA_0 + A_1\}^{-1} \qquad (3.8.2)$$

so that the outputs from the plant $G(s)$ are simply integrated outputs from the first-order lag $\{sA_0 + A_1\}^{-1}$. The reader can easily verify, by comparing eqn. 3.8.1 with the relation $G^{-1}(s)y(s) = u(s)$, that the system can be described by a second-order differential equation with matrix coefficients,

$$A_0 \frac{d^2 y(t)}{dt^2} + A_1 \frac{dy(t)}{dt} = u(t), \quad |A_0| \neq 0 \qquad (3.8.3)$$

or, in the form of a state-vector model with state vector $x(t) = (y(t)^T,$

$\dot{y}(t)^T)^T \in R^{2m}$ of the form,

$$\dot{x}(t) = \begin{pmatrix} 0 & I_m \\ 0 & -A_0^{-1}A_1 \end{pmatrix} x(t) + \begin{pmatrix} 0 \\ A_0^{-1} \end{pmatrix} u(t)$$

$$y(t) = (I_m \quad 0)x(t) \tag{3.8.4}$$

Exercise 3.8.1
Show that the state-space model represented by eqn. 3.8.4 is both controllable and observable.

The open-loop characteristic polynomial is seen to be

$$\rho_0(s) = s^m |sI_m + A_0^{-1}A_1| = s^m \prod_{j=1}^{m} (s - \lambda_j) \tag{3.8.5}$$

and hence the system zero polynomial

$$z(s) = \rho_0(s)|G(s)| = \frac{\rho_0(s)}{|G^{-1}(s)|} = |A_0^{-1}| \neq 0 \tag{3.8.6}$$

showing that the system is invertible and has no zeros.

A design for a unity-negative feedback-control system for the plant can proceed in a similar manner to that of Section 3.5. Suppose for simplicity that $A_0^{-1}A_1$ has eigenvalues $-\lambda_j$, $1 \leqslant j \leqslant m$, (i.e. λ_j, $1 \leqslant j \leqslant m$, are a subset of the open-loop poles) with nonsingular eigenvector matrix T,

$$T^{-1}A_0^{-1}A_1 T = \text{diag}\{-\lambda_1, -\lambda_2, \ldots, -\lambda_m\} \tag{3.8.7}$$

and hence that

$$G(s) = \frac{1}{s}\{sI_m + A_0^{-1}A_1\}^{-1}A_0^{-1} = T\frac{1}{s}\text{diag}\left\{\frac{1}{s-\lambda_j}\right\}_{1 \leqslant j \leqslant m} T^{-1}A_0^{-1}$$

$$= T \, \text{diag}\{g_1(s), \ldots, g_m(s)\} T^{-1}A_0^{-1} \tag{3.8.8}$$

where

$$g_j(s) = \frac{1}{s(s-\lambda_j)}, \qquad 1 \leqslant j \leqslant m \tag{3.8.9}$$

are classical type-one, second-order lags. Choosing (c.f. eqn. 3.5.13)

$$K(s) = A_0 T \, \text{diag}\{k_1(s), \ldots, k_m(s)\} T^{-1} \tag{3.8.10}$$

where $k_j(s)$, $1 \leqslant j \leqslant m$ are nonzero proper, minimum-phase transfer functions, then

$$G(s)K(s) = T \, \text{diag}\{g_1(s)k_1(s), \ldots, g_m(s)k_m(s)\} T^{-1} \tag{3.8.11}$$

and hence,

$$H_c(s) = T \operatorname{diag} \left\{ \frac{g_j(s)k_j(s)}{1 + g_j(s)k_j(s)} \right\}_{1 \leqslant j \leqslant m} T^{-1} \qquad (3.8.12)$$

and the return-difference determinant,

$$|T(s)| = |I_m + G(s)K(s)| = |I_m + T^{-1}G(s)K(s)T|$$

$$= \prod_{j=1}^{m} (1 + g_j(s)k_j(s)) \qquad (3.8.13)$$

It is easily verified from eqn. 3.8.13 that the closed-loop system is asymptotically stable if, and only if, the scalar return differences $1 + g_j(s)k_j(s)$, $1 \leqslant j \leqslant m$, satisfy the classical stability criteria. Equivalently, the scalar feedback systems

$$\frac{g_j(s)k_j(s)}{1 + g_j(s)k_j(s)}, \qquad 1 \leqslant j \leqslant m \qquad (3.8.14)$$

must be stable.

The general features of the closed-loop response can be illustrated by writing eqn. 3.8.13 in the form

$$|T(s)| = \prod_{j=1}^{m} \frac{(s(s - \lambda_j) + k_j(s))}{s(s - \lambda_j)} = \frac{\displaystyle\prod_{j=1}^{m} (s(s - \lambda_j) + k_j(s))}{s^m |sI_m + A_0^{-1}A_1|} \qquad (3.8.15)$$

Considering, for simplicity the case of proportional control $k_j(s) = k_j$, $1 \leqslant j \leqslant m$, the stability of the closed-loop system is dictated by the zeros of the polynomial,

$$\prod_{j=1}^{m} (s^2 - \lambda_j s + k_j) \qquad (3.8.16)$$

i.e. if λ_j, $1 \leqslant j \leqslant m$, are real and strictly negative, the closed-loop system is asymptotically stable for all $k_j > 0$, $1 \leqslant j \leqslant m$, but, at high gains, *oscillation* will set in.

The interaction behaviour of the closed-loop system can be studied in terms of the time-responses of the scalar systems represented by eqn. 3.8.14 and the matrix eqn. 3.8.12. In a similar manner to Section 3.3, the closed-loop system will possess small interaction effects to unit-step responses in any output if, and only if, the step responses of eqn. 3.8.14 (or, equivalently the frequency responses) are similar, when

$$H_c(s) \simeq \frac{g_1(s)k_1(s)}{1 + g_1(s)k_1(s)} TT^{-1} = \frac{g_1(s)k_1(s)}{1 + g_1(s)k_1(s)} I_m \quad (3.8.17)$$

which is a noninteracting system.

The integrity of the closed-loop system in the presence of a sensor failure in loop j is described by the rational polynomial

$$e_j^T \{I_m + G(s)K(s)\}^{-1} e_j = e_j^T T \, \mathrm{diag} \left(\frac{1}{1 + \dfrac{k_i(s)}{s(s - \lambda_i)}} \right)_{1 \leqslant i \leqslant m} T^{-1} e_j \quad (3.8.18)$$

so that the numerator polynomial always has a zero at $s = 0$. It is left as an exercise for the reader to show that this is also the case for an actuator failure in loop j and hence that the closed-loop system is unstable in the presence of sensor or actuator failures in any loop.

Exercise 3.8.2
Reconcile this result with that of Exercise 2.19.2.

Exercise 3.8.3
Consider how the above theory must be modified if $A_0^{-1} A_1$ has only a Jordan canonical form.
 Verify eqn. 3.8.13 in this case.

Exercise 3.8.4
If $k_j(s) = k(s - \lambda_j)/(s - \lambda_0)$ and λ_j, $1 \leqslant j \leqslant m$, are real and negative, prove that the closed-loop system is noninteracting (Hint: show that equality holds in eqn. 3.8.17) and asymptotically stable for $k > 0$.

Finally, a useful suggested guideline to the choice of $k_j(s)$, $1 \leqslant j \leqslant m$, to ensure small closed-loop interaction effects is to note that the root-loci of the subsystems (eqn. 3.18.14) possess two important features,
(a) for $k_j > 0$, two unbounded branches running parallel to the imaginary axis
(b) finite cluster points around the zeros of $k_j(s)$.
It follows directly that, at high gains, the approximate pole-zero cancellation in eqn. 3.8.14 requires only that the dominant roots of the root-locus must be similar to ensure low interaction effects. In particular, it is necessary that the intercepts of the root-loci should be almost identical.

3.9 Multivariable second-order-type systems

By analogy with the classical second-order-lag $g^{-1}(s) = a_0 s^2 + a_1 s + a_2$, $a_0 \neq 0$,

Definition 3.9.1 (Owens[42]): An m-input/m-output strictly proper system described by the $m \times m$ transfer function matrix $G(s)$ is said to be a multivariable second-order-type system (or, more compactly, a multivariable second-order lag) if, and only if, $|G(s)| \not\equiv 0$ and

$$G^{-1}(s) = A_0 s^2 + A_1 s + A_2, \quad |A_0| \neq 0 \qquad (3.9.1)$$

where A_0, A_1, A_2 are real, constant matrices.

Note that, if $A_2 = 0$, $G(s)$ takes the form analysed in the previous Section. The system can be described by a second-order differential equation with matrix coefficients,

$$A_0 \frac{d^2 y(t)}{dt^2} + A_1 \frac{dy(t)}{dt} + A_2 y(t) = u(t), \quad |A_0| \neq 0 \quad (3.9.2)$$

or, in a similar manner to eqns. 3.8.4, by a controllable and observable state-vector model of state dimension $n = 2m$,

$$\dot{x}(t) = \begin{pmatrix} 0 & I_m \\ -A_0^{-1} A_2 & -A_0^{-1} A_1 \end{pmatrix} x(t) + \begin{pmatrix} 0 \\ A_0^{-1} \end{pmatrix} u(t)$$

$$y(t) = (I_m \quad 0)x(t) \qquad (3.9.3)$$

Application of Schur's formula gives the system characteristic polynomial,

$$\rho_0(s) = |sI_n - A| = s^m |sI_m + A_0^{-1} A_1 + \frac{1}{s} A_0^{-1} A_2|$$

$$= |s^2 I_m + s A_0^{-1} A_1 + A_0^{-1} A_2| = |A_0^{-1}| |G^{-1}(s)| \quad (3.9.4)$$

and zero polynomial

$$z(s) = \rho_0(s) |G(s)| = |A_0^{-1}| \neq 0 \qquad (3.9.5)$$

i.e. the system is invertible and has no zeros, as expected by analogy with the classical second-order lag.

Exercise 3.9.1
Show that the simple mechanical system of Section 2.6 has inverse transfer-function matrix

$$G^{-1}(s) = s^2 \begin{pmatrix} \dfrac{m_1}{k_1} & 0 \\ 0 & \dfrac{m_2}{k_2} \end{pmatrix} + s \begin{pmatrix} \dfrac{c}{k_1} & \dfrac{-c}{k_1} \\ \dfrac{-c}{k_2} & \dfrac{c}{k_2} \end{pmatrix} + \begin{pmatrix} 1 & 0 \\ 0 & 1 \end{pmatrix}$$

and hence is a multivariable second-order lag. (Is this intuitively obvious?)

Defining, the restricted second-order-type system

$$G_1^{-1}(s) = s(sA_0 + A_1) \tag{3.9.6}$$

then $G^{-1}(s) = G_1^{-1}(s) + A_2$ or, equivalently,

$$G(s) = \{I_m + G_1(s)A_2\}^{-1} G_1(s) \tag{3.9.7}$$

and the plant can be regarded as possessing the feedback structure illustrated in Fig. 3.9.1a, consisting of a forward-path-restricted second-order-type system $G_1(s)$ with input

$$w(t) = u(t) - A_2 y(t) \tag{3.9.8}$$

generated by the input signal $u(t)$ and a constant output-feedback effect. In state-vector terms, using the model eqn. 3.9.3,

$$\dot{x}(t) = \begin{pmatrix} 0 & I_m \\ 0 & -A_0^{-1}A_1 \end{pmatrix} x(t) + \begin{pmatrix} 0 \\ A_0^{-1} \end{pmatrix} w(t)$$

$$w(t) = u(t) - A_2 y(t) = u(t) - (A_2 \quad 0)x(t)$$

$$y(t) = (I_m \quad 0)x(t) \tag{3.9.9}$$

The feedback-control analysis of $G(s)$ can be reduced to the analysis of a unity-negative feedback control configuration for the restricted system $G_1(s)$, by introducing state feedback into the control system, as shown in Fig. 3.9.1b, to cancel out the feedback element A_2. In mathematical terms, the input $u(t)$ to $G(s)$ is replaced by

$$v(t) = u(t) - A_2 y(t) \equiv w(t) \tag{3.9.10}$$

and hence,

$$y(s) = G_1(s)w(s) \equiv G_1(s)v(s) \tag{3.9.11}$$

Let $K_1(s)$ be the $m \times m$ proper controller transfer-function matrix designed for the unity-negative feedback control of $G_1(s)$, then the plant $G(s)$ can be controlled by the system illustrated in Fig. 3.9.2a.

This configuration is a slight generalisation of Fig. 2.18.1 to include the minor-loop element $-A_2$, and has closed-loop transfer-function matrix,

$$H_c(s) = \{I_m + \{I_m - G(s)A_2\}^{-1} G(s)K_1(s)\}^{-1}\{I_m - G(s)A_2\}^{-1} G(s)K_1(s)$$

$$= \{I_m + G_1(s)K_1(s)\}^{-1} G_1(s)K_1(s) \qquad (3.9.12)$$

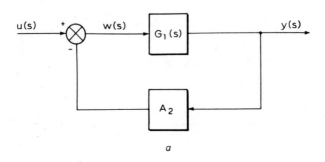

a

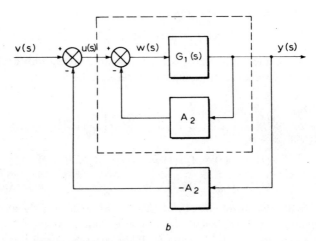

b

Fig. 3.9.1 Feedback control analysis
  a Feedback decomposition of $G(s)$
  b Removal of the feedback loop

If a unity-negative feedback system (Fig. 2.18.1) is required, a suitable forward-path controller $K(s)$ is obtained by examining Fig. 3.9.2*a* with $r(s) \equiv 0$ i.e. $u(s) = -(K_1(s) - A_2)y(s)$, suggesting the choice (see Fig. 3.9.2*b*),

$$K(s) = K_1(s) - A_2 \qquad (3.9.13)$$

The closed-loop transfer-function matrix takes the form,

$$H_c(s) = \{I_m + G(s)K(s)\}^{-1}G(s)K(s) = \{G^{-1}(s) + K(s)\}^{-1}K(s)$$

$$= \{G_1^{-1}(s) + A_2 + K_1(s) - A_2\}^{-1}\{K_1(s) - A_2\}$$

$$= \{I_m + G_1(s)K_1(s)\}^{-1}G_1(s)\{K_1(s) - A_2\} \qquad (3.9.14)$$

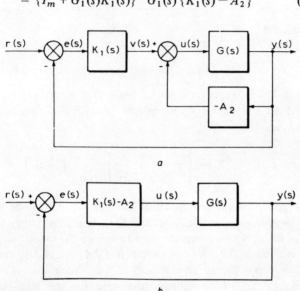

Fig. 3.9.2 Control configurations for a second-order lag
  a Unity-negative feedback with minor-loop element
  b Unity-negative feedback

A comparison with eqn. 3.9.12 indicates that the two expressions can be regarded as approximately equal if the gains of the control element $K_1(s)$ are large (see Section 3.8). More precisely, if eqn. 3.9.12 is a low-interaction system, then eqn. 3.9.14 is a low-interaction system if the control-systems gains are large. The stability of the two configurations can be examined using the identity,

$$|T(s)| = |I_m + G(s)K(s)| = |G(s)||G^{-1}(s) + K(s)|$$

$$= |G(s)||G_1^{-1}(s) + K_1(s)|$$

$$= \frac{|G_1^{-1}(s)|}{|G^{-1}(s)|}|I_m + G_1(s)K_1(s)| \qquad (3.9.15)$$

Noting eqns. 3.9.4, 3.8.6, it is easily verified that the closed-loop characteristic polynomials of the two configurations are identical and hence the systems have identical stability characteristics.

Exercise 3.9.2
Verify the stability predictions for both configurations using state-vector representations of $G(s), G_1(s), K(s)$.

Exercise 3.9.3
Suppose that $T^{-1}A_0^{-1}A_1 T = \text{diag}\{-\lambda_1, -\lambda_2, \ldots, -\lambda_m\}$ and write

$$G_1^{-1}(s) = s^2 A_0 + s A_1 + A_0 T \text{diag}\{\omega_1^2, \omega_2^2, \ldots, \omega_m^2\} T^{-1}$$

where ω_i^2, $1 \leq i \leq m$, are real scalars. Show that the decompositions of Fig. 3.9.1 are still valid if A_2 is replaced by $A_2 - A_0 T \text{diag}\{\omega_1^2, \ldots, \omega_m^2\} T^{-1}$, and that

$$G_1(s) = T \text{diag}\left\{\frac{1}{s^2 - \lambda_j s + \omega_j^2}\right\}_{1 \leq j \leq m} T^{-1} A_0^{-1}$$

Hence suggest how the techniques of Sections 3.8, 3.9 can be generalised to provide a design for $K_1(s)$ and $K(s)$. In general terms, suitable choice of ω_i^2, $1 \leq i \leq m$, may be used to reduce the magnitude of the 'error' term in eqn. 3.9.14. For example, if $A_0^{-1}A_1$ and $A_0^{-1}A_2$ commute it is always possible to choose $\omega_1^2, \ldots, \omega_n^2$ such that $A_2 = A_0 T \text{diag}\{\omega_1^2, \ldots, \omega_m^2\} T^{-1}$ removing the need for the minor-loop in Fig. 3.9.2a.

As a final point in the Section, examination of eqns. 3.8.9 and 3.8.12 indicates that the techniques suggested for the designs may hit problems if any of the eigenvalues λ_j have positive real parts. In the case of a restricted second-order-type system, eqn. 3.8.5, this corresponds to the situation of an open-loop unstable plant and, in the case of a general second-order lag, to the situation where $G_1(s)$ is unstable. In such cases, adequate control action requires the inclusion of minor-loop rate feedback,

$$u(s) = v(s) - H(s)y(s) \qquad (3.9.16)$$

where

$$H(s) = H_1 s + H_2 \qquad (3.9.17)$$

Noting that $x(t) = (y(t)^T, \dot{y}(t)^T)^T$ in eqn. 3.9.3 and assuming zero initial conditions, it is easily verified that

$$u(t) = v(t) - (H_2, H_1)x(t) \qquad (3.9.18)$$

and hence that eqns. 3.9.16, 3.9.17 are equivalent to a state feedback loop. The transfer-function matrix relating $y(s)$ to $v(s)$ is simply

$$\{I_m + G(s)H(s)\}^{-1} G(s) = \{G^{-1}(s) + H(s)\}^{-1}$$

$$= \{s^2 A_0 + s A_1 + A_2 + s H_1 + H_2\}^{-1}$$

(3.9.19)

Choosing $H_2 = -A_2$ gives $y(s) = G_1(s)v(s)$ where

$$G_1^{-1}(s) = s(s A_0 + A_1 + H_1) \qquad (3.9.20)$$

is a restricted second-order-type system. The control configuration now takes the form shown in Fig. 3.9.3 where the forward-path element $K_1(s)$ can be designed using the technique of Section 3.8. Note that the

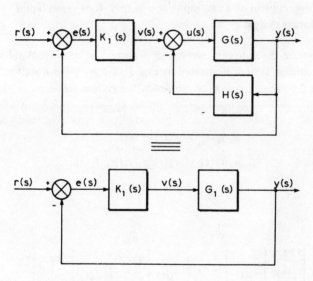

Fig. 3.9.3 Control configuration with minor-loop feedback and equivalent system

degrees of freedom available in H_1 can be used to ensure that the eigenvalues of $A_0^{-1}(A_1 + H_1)$ have strictly positive real parts. For example, choosing

$$H_1 = A_0 \operatorname{diag}\{\mu_1, \mu_2, \dots, \mu_m\} - A_1 \qquad (3.9.21)$$

gives $A_0^{-1}(A_1 + H_1) = \operatorname{diag}\{\mu_1, \mu_2, \dots, \mu_m\}$ where μ_i, $1 \leqslant i \leqslant m$, can be specified as real, positive scalars. Alternatively, choosing

$$H_1 = A_0 T \operatorname{diag}\{\mu_1, \mu_2, \dots, \mu_m\} T^{-1} \qquad (3.9.22)$$

where T is the eigenvector matrix of $A_0^{-1} A_1$, gives $A_0^{-1}(A_1 + H_1) = T \operatorname{diag}\{\mu_1 - \lambda_1, \dots, \mu_m - \lambda_m\} T^{-1}$ and the analysis can proceed as in Section 3.8 choosing μ_i, $1 \leqslant i \leqslant m$, such that $\mu_i - \lambda_i$ has positive real part, $1 \leqslant i \leqslant m$. The only constraint in the choice of μ_i is that H_1 should be real. This is readily ensured by choosing $\mu_i = \bar{\mu}_j$ whenever $\lambda_i = \bar{\lambda}_j$.

Exercise 3.9.4

Extend Exercise 3.9.3 to cope with rate feedback by using $H_2 = A_0 T$ diag$\{\omega_1^2, \ldots, \omega_m^2\} T^{-1} - A_2$ where T is the eigenvector matrix of $A_0^{-1}(A_1 + H_1)$.

3.10 Level control of a two-input/two-output, four-vessel liquid storage system

To illustrate the concepts evolved in Section 3.9, consider the 4-vessel liquid storage system illustrated in Fig. 3.10.1 with the notation as in Section 2.5. The equations of motion of the system are

$$a_1 \dot{h}_1(t) = u_1(t) - f_1(t)$$
$$a_2 \dot{h}_2(t) = f_1(t) - f_2(t) - l_1(t)$$
$$a_3 \dot{h}_3(t) = f_2(t) - f_3(t) - l_2(t)$$
$$a_4 \dot{h}_4(t) = f_3(t) + u_2(t) \qquad\qquad (3.10.1)$$

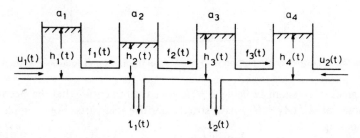

Fig. 3.10.1 Two-input/two-output, four-vessel system

with inputs $u_1(t), u_2(t)$, outputs $y_1(t) = h_2(t), y_2(t) = h_3(t)$ and disturbances $l_1(t), l_2(t)$. Replacing all variables by perturbation variables about some system steady state, and taking the linear approximation

$$f_i(t) = \beta_i(h_i(t) - h_{i+1}(t)), \quad \beta_i > 0, \qquad i = 1, 2, 3 \quad (3.10.2)$$

for the intervessel flow terms, the reader can verify that the system is a multivariable second-order lag. In the particular case of interest we neglect the disturbance $l_1(t), l_2(t)$ and take the data $a_1 = a_2 = a_3 = a_4 = 1, \beta_1 = \beta_3 = 1, \ \beta_2 = \beta > 0$ when the system has inverse transfer-function matrix,

$$G^{-1}(s) = s^2 \begin{pmatrix} 1 & 0 \\ 0 & 1 \end{pmatrix} + s \begin{pmatrix} 2 + \beta & -\beta \\ -\beta & 2 + \beta \end{pmatrix} + \begin{pmatrix} \beta & -\beta \\ -\beta & \beta \end{pmatrix}$$

(3.10.3)

giving

$$A_0 = \begin{pmatrix} 1 & 0 \\ 0 & 1 \end{pmatrix}, \quad A_1 = \begin{pmatrix} 2 + \beta & -\beta \\ -\beta & 2 + \beta \end{pmatrix}, \quad A_2 = \begin{pmatrix} \beta & -\beta \\ -\beta & \beta \end{pmatrix}$$

(3.10.4)

$$z(s) \equiv 1, \quad \rho_0(s) = (s^2 + (2 + \beta)s + \beta)^2 - \beta^2(s+1)^2 \quad (3.10.5)$$

Considering initially the configuration of Fig. 3.9.2a, the minor loop element is well defined by the plant data of eqn. 3.10.4. It remains to choose $K_1(s)$ by the design of a unity-negative feedback system for the plant $G_1(s)$ (eqn. 3.9.6),

$$G_1^{-1}(s) = s \left\{ s \begin{pmatrix} 1 & 0 \\ 0 & 1 \end{pmatrix} + \begin{pmatrix} 2 + \beta & -\beta \\ -\beta & 2 + \beta \end{pmatrix} \right\}$$

(3.10.6)

The reader will note that $A_0^{-1} A_1 = A_1$, having eigenvalues and eigenvector matrix,

$$-\lambda_1 = 2, \quad -\lambda_2 = 2 + 2\beta$$

$$T = \begin{pmatrix} 1 & -1 \\ 1 & 1 \end{pmatrix}$$

(3.10.7)

giving

$$g_1(s) = \frac{1}{s(s - \lambda_1)} = \frac{1}{s(s + 2)}, \quad g_2(s) = \frac{1}{s(s - \lambda_2)} = \frac{1}{s(s + 2(1 + \beta))}$$

(3.10.8)

It is worthwhile noting at this point that the intervessel flow parameter β is a physical measure of system interaction. In particular, if $\beta \ll 1 = \beta_1 = \beta_3$, interaction is small and the dynamics of the subsystems $g_1(s)$ and $g_2(s)$ are essentially identical, implying that $k_1(s) \equiv k_2(s) = k(s)$ will be adequate to ensure that the dynamics of expr. 3.8.14 are essentially identical and hence that the closed-loop system will possess small interaction. The forward-path controller $K_1(s)$ takes the form

$$K_1(s) = A_0 T \operatorname{diag}\{k_1(s), k_2(s)\} T^{-1} = k(s)\begin{pmatrix} 1 & 0 \\ 0 & 1 \end{pmatrix} \quad (3.10.9)$$

indicating that the control system $G_1(s)$ is noninteracting, each loop of $G_1(s)$ being controlled independently. The corresponding controller of Fig. 3.9.2b is,

$$K(s) = K_1(s) - A_2 = \begin{pmatrix} k(s) - \beta & \beta \\ \beta & k(s) - \beta \end{pmatrix} \simeq K_1(s) \quad (3.10.10)$$

for $\beta \ll 1$, and the use of a high gain controller $k(s)$.

In the more general situation, the response speeds of $g_1(s)$ and $g_2(s)$ differ greatly implying that phase compensation must be introduced into $g_1(s)$ if the subsystems (expr. 3.8.14) are to have similar dynamics ensuring small closed-loop interaction effects. For the purposes of this Section, the control possibilities can be illustrated by the choice of

$$k_1(s) = \frac{k(s+2)}{(s+2(1+\beta))}, \quad k_2(s) = k \quad (3.10.11)$$

where k is a positive scalar gain constant. The closed-loop transfer-function matrix takes the form

$$H_c(s) = \{I_m + G_1(s)K_1(s)\}^{-1} G_1(s)K_1(s)$$

$$= T \operatorname{diag}\left\{\frac{g_i(s)k_i(s)}{1 + g_i(s)k_i(s)}\right\}_{i=1,2} T^{-1}$$

$$= \frac{k}{s^2 + 2(1+\beta)s + k}\begin{pmatrix} 1 & 0 \\ 0 & 1 \end{pmatrix} \quad (3.10.12)$$

which is a noninteracting system, with closed-loop dynamics dominated by the choice of gain k. Note in all cases, the system steady-state errors in response to unit-step demands are zero in all loops. The forward-path controller takes the form,

$$K_1(s) = \begin{pmatrix} 1 & -1 \\ 1 & 1 \end{pmatrix} \frac{k}{2} \begin{pmatrix} \dfrac{(s+2)}{s+2(1+\beta)} & 0 \\ 0 & 1 \end{pmatrix} \begin{pmatrix} 1 & 1 \\ -1 & 1 \end{pmatrix} \quad (3.10.13)$$

which is easily realised in terms of phase-compensation elements and summing/differencing junctions. Finally, the dynamics of unity-negative feedback system of Fig. 3.9.2b are obtained from the controller $K(s) = K_1(s) - A_2$, giving closed-loop transfer-function matrix eqn. 3.9.14,

$$H_c(s) = \frac{k}{(s^2 + 2(1+\beta)s + k)}\begin{pmatrix} 1 & 0 \\ 0 & 1 \end{pmatrix} - \{I_2 + G_1(s)K_1(s)\}^{-1} G_1(s)A_2$$

$$(3.10.14)$$

differing from eqn. 3.10.12 owing to the second term,

$$\{I_2 + G_1(s)K_1(s)\}^{-1} G_1(s)A_2 = T\,\mathrm{diag}\left\{\frac{g_i(s)}{1 + g_i(s)k_i(s)}\right\}_{i=1,2} T^{-1}\,A_0^{-1}A_2$$

$$= \frac{k}{s^2 + 2(1+\beta)s + k}\begin{pmatrix} 1 & -1 \\ -1 & 1 \end{pmatrix}\frac{\beta}{k}$$

$$(3.10.15)$$

The effect of this term can be deduced from the step responses of eqn. 3.10.12. In particular, considering the response to unit-step demands in either loop, the steady-state-error matrix (eqn. 3.1.14) takes the form

$$E_\infty = \frac{\beta}{k}\begin{pmatrix} 1 & -1 \\ -1 & 1 \end{pmatrix}$$

$$(3.10.16)$$

and the degree of interaction eqn. 3.1.10 is

$$a_1 = a_2 = \frac{\beta}{k}\,100\max_{t\geqslant 0}\left|\mathcal{L}^{-1}\frac{k}{s(s^2 + 2(1+\beta)s + k)}\right|$$

$$= \frac{100\beta}{k}\{1 + \exp(-(1+\beta)\,\pi/\sqrt{k - (1+\beta)^2})\}$$

$$\leqslant \frac{200\beta}{k}$$

$$(3.10.17)$$

if eqn. 3.10.12 is underdamped. For example, choosing k such that the damping ratio of eqn. 3.10.12 is $1/\sqrt{2}$, gives

$$\frac{\beta}{k} = \frac{\beta}{2(1+\beta)^2}, \quad a_1 = a_2 = \frac{100\beta}{k}\{1 + e^{-\pi}\} \quad (3.10.18)$$

and the performance data,

(i) $\beta = 0\cdot1, \quad \dfrac{\beta}{k} = 0\cdot041, \quad a_1 = a_2 = 4\cdot5\%$

(ii) $\beta = 1\cdot0$, $\dfrac{\beta}{k} = 0\cdot125$, $a_1 = a_2 = 13\cdot9\%$

(iii) $\beta = 9\cdot0$, $\dfrac{\beta}{k} = 0\cdot045$, $a_1 = a_2 = 5\cdot0\%$

If β is very large ($\beta \gg 1$) then the phase-compensation requirement for $k_1(s)$ is excessive, implying control difficulties if the inner vessels are strongly coupled.

Exercise 3.10.1
Repeat the analysis with $k_1(s) = k(s+2)/(s+p)$, $k_2(s) = k(s+2(1+\beta))/(s+p)$ where $p > 0$. Show that the structure of eqns. 3.10.12, 3.10.15 remains essentially the same but that the closed-loop performance can be improved.

Exercise 3.10.2
Show that $K_1(s)$ is a noninteracting controller for $G_1(s)$ but that $K(s)$ is not a noninteracting controller for $G(s)$.

Exercise 3.10.3
Show that
$$K_1(s) = \frac{k}{(s+2(1+\beta))}\begin{pmatrix} s+2+\beta & -\beta \\ -\beta & s+2+\beta \end{pmatrix}$$
and discuss the relative merits of realising $K_1(s)$ element by element or by direct construction of the factors in eqn. 3.10.13.

3.11 Simple harmonic motion: multivariable-style

To illustrate the fact that adequate closed-loop control may be impossible without the inclusion of minor-loop rate feedback, consider the multivariable generalisation of the transfer function $g^{-1}(s) = a_0 s^2 + a_2$, namely an $m \times m$ strictly proper system with inverse transfer-function matrix
$$G^{-1}(s) = s^2 A_0 + A_2, \quad |A_0| \neq 0 \qquad (3.11.1)$$
i.e. a multivariable second-order lag with $A_1 = 0$, with
$$z(s) \equiv |A_0^{-1}|, \quad \rho_0(s) = |s^2 I_m + A_0^{-1} A_2| \qquad (3.11.2)$$

A physical example of such a system is illustrated in Fig. 3.11.1 consisting of two masses m_1, m_2 on a friction-free surface, connected by springs of stiffness constants k_1, k_2, k_3. If $y_1(t), y_2(t)$ represent the

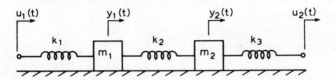

Fig. 3.11.1 Oscillatory mechanical system

displacements of masses m_1, m_2, respectively, from an equilibrium position and $u_1(t), u_2(t)$ represent similar displacements of the ends of the outer springs, the equations of motion of the system for small perturbations take the form

$$m_1\ddot{y}_1(t) = k_1(u_1(t) - y_1(t)) + k_2(y_2(t) - y_1(t))$$
$$m_2\ddot{y}_2(t) = k_2(y_1(t) - y_2(t)) + k_3(u_2(t) - y_2(t)) \quad (3.11.3)$$

giving the inverse transfer-function matrix,

$$G^{-1}(s) = s^2 \begin{pmatrix} \dfrac{m_1}{k_1} & 0 \\ 0 & \dfrac{m_2}{k_3} \end{pmatrix} + \begin{pmatrix} 1 + \dfrac{k_2}{k_1} & \dfrac{-k_2}{k_1} \\ \dfrac{-k_2}{k_3} & 1 + \dfrac{k_2}{k_3} \end{pmatrix} \quad (3.11.4)$$

The major control problem with a system of this type can be illustrated by noting that, under unity-negative feedback with forward-path controller $K(s) = K$ (a constant proportional controller),

$$|T(s)| = |I_m + G(s)K(s)| = \frac{|G^{-1}(s) + K(s)|}{|G^{-1}(s)|}$$

$$= |s^2 I_m + A_0^{-1}(A_2 + K)| / |s^2 I_m + A_0^{-1} A_2| \quad (3.11.5)$$

In particular, the closed-loop system is unstable if $A_0^{-1}(A_2 + K)$ has complex or real, strictly negative eigenvalues and marginally stable (i.e. closed-loop poles on the imaginary axis of the complex plane) if $A_0^{-1}(A_2 + K)$ has real, positive eigenvalues. In general terms, the closed-loop system cannot be stabilised using constant output feedback. This result is also valid for the configuration of Fig. 3.9.2a with $K_1(s)$ a proportional controller. For example, noting that (eqn. 3.9.6)

$$G_1(s) = \frac{1}{s^2} A_0^{-1} \qquad (3.11.6)$$

and using the controller $K_1(s) = A_0 \, \mathrm{diag}\{k_1, \ldots, k_m\}$ where $k_1, \ldots, k_m$ are real positive constants, the closed-loop transfer-function matrix takes the form,

$$\{I_m + G_1(s)K_1(s)\}^{-1} G_1(s)K_1(s) = \mathrm{diag}\left\{\frac{k_i}{s^2 + k_i}\right\}_{1 \leqslant i \leqslant m}$$

$$(3.11.7)$$

which is noninteracting but has zero damping.

A solution to the control problem can be obtained using the rate feedback configuration of Fig. 3.9.3 with $H(s)$ of the form defined by eqn. 3.9.17. Choosing

$$H_2 = -A_2, \quad H_1 = A_0 \, \mathrm{diag}\{\alpha_1, \alpha_2, \ldots, \alpha_m\} \quad (3.11.8)$$

where α_i, $1 \leqslant i \leqslant m$, are real, strictly positive scalars, gives

$$G_1(s) = \mathrm{diag}\left\{\frac{1}{s(s + \alpha_j)}\right\}_{1 \leqslant j \leqslant m} A_0^{-1} \qquad (3.11.9)$$

and hence, with $K_1(s)$ as above, the closed-loop transfer-function matrix takes the form,

$$\{I_m + G_1(s)K_1(s)\}^{-1} G_1(s)K_1(s) = \mathrm{diag}\left\{\frac{k_j}{s^2 + \alpha_j s + k_j}\right\}_{1 \leqslant j \leqslant m}$$

$$(3.11.10)$$

and is asymptotically stable if $\alpha_j > 0$, $k_j > 0$, $1 \leqslant j \leqslant m$, and also noninteracting.

Exercise 3.11.1

Using the data $m_1 = 1, m_2 = 2, k_1 = 1, k_2 = 2$, and k_3 unspecified in eqn. 3.11.4, use the above technique to design a control configuration with minor-loop feedback generating a closed-loop system with damping equal to 0·7 in both loops.

Exercise 3.11.2

If there exists a nonsingular transformation T such that $T^{-1} A_0^{-1} A_2 T = \mathrm{diag}\{-\lambda_1, \ldots, -\lambda_m\}$ show that the transfer-function matrix eqn. 3.11.1 takes the form

$$G(s) = T \operatorname{diag}\left\{\frac{1}{s^2 - \lambda_j}\right\}_{1 \leqslant j \leqslant m} T^{-1} A_0^{-1}$$

Using the configuration of Fig. 3.9.3 with rate-feedback and forward-path elements

$$H(s) = s A_0 T \operatorname{diag}\{\alpha_1, \ldots, \alpha_m\} T^{-1},$$

$$K_1(s) = A_0 T \operatorname{diag}\{k_1(s), \ldots, k_m(s)\} T^{-1},$$

show that the closed-loop transfer-function matrix takes the form

$$T \operatorname{diag}\left\{\frac{k_i(s)}{s^2 + \alpha_i s + k_i(s) - \lambda_i}\right\}_{1 \leqslant i \leqslant m} T^{-1}$$

Hence, generalise the results of Section 3.8 to produce a design technique for $H(s)$ and $K_1(s)$.

3.12 Multivariable kth-order-type systems

Multivariable systems can also exhibit kth-order types of behaviour.[42] By analogy with the classical kth-order lag $g^{-1}(s) = a_0 s^k + a_1 s^{k-1} + \ldots + a_k$,

Definition 3.12.1: An m-input/m-output strictly proper system described by the $m \times m$ transfer-function matrix $G(s)$ is said to be a multivariable kth-order-type system (or, more compactly, a multivariable kth-order lag) if, and only if $|G(s)| \not\equiv 0$ and

$$G^{-1}(s) = A_0 s^k + A_1 s^{k-1} + \ldots + A_{k-1} s + A_k, \quad |A_0| \neq 0$$
(3.12.1)

where $A_0, \ldots, A_k$ are real, constant matrices.

Equivalently, the system can be described by a kth-order differential equation with matrix coefficients,

$$A_0 \frac{d^k y(t)}{dt^k} + A_1 \frac{d^{k-1}}{dt^{k-1}} y(t) + \ldots + A_k y(t) = u(t) \quad (3.12.2)$$

or, defining the state vector $x(t) = (y(t)^T, \frac{dy(t)^T}{dt}, \ldots, \frac{d^{k-1}}{dt^{k-1}} y(t)^T)^T$,

by the controllable and observable state-vector model of dimension $n = km$,

$$\dot{x}(t) = \begin{pmatrix} 0 & I_m & 0 \dots \dots 0 \\ 0 & 0 & I_m & & \vdots \\ \vdots & & & 0 & \\ \vdots & & & & \\ 0 \dots \dots \dots \dots \dots 0 & I_m \\ -A_0^{-1}A_k & -A_0^{-1}A_{k-1} \dots \dots & -A_0^{-1}A_1 \end{pmatrix} x(t) + \begin{pmatrix} 0 \\ \vdots \\ \vdots \\ \vdots \\ 0 \\ A_0^{-1} \end{pmatrix} u(t)$$

$$y(t) = (I_m \quad 0 \quad \dots \quad 0)x(t) \tag{3.12.3}$$

It is left as an exercise for the reader to prove (using induction on k and Schur's formula) that the system characteristic polynomial is

$$\rho_0(s) = |s^k I_m + s^{k-1}A_0^{-1}A_1 + \dots + A_0^{-1}A_k|$$
$$= |A_0^{-1}| \, |G^{-1}(s)| \tag{3.12.4}$$

and hence that the system has no zeros, with zero polynomial,

$$z(s) \equiv |A_0^{-1}| \neq 0 \tag{3.12.5}$$

There is no known exact analytical method for the design of a unity-negative feedback system for a kth-order lag. For our purposes however, it is possible to demonstrate control possibilities using a combination of minor-loop state feedback and dynamic output feedback. Consider the state feedback control law,

$$u(t) = v(t) - Fx(t), \quad F = (H_k, \dots, H_1) \tag{3.12.6}$$

where H_i, $1 \leqslant i \leqslant k$, are constant $m \times m$ matrices. Taking Laplace transforms of eqn. 3.12.6 with zero initial conditions, and noting the definition of the state vector, gives

$$u(s) = v(s) - H(s)y(s) \tag{3.12.7}$$

where

$$H(s) = s^{k-1}H_1 + \dots + sH_{k-1} + H_k \tag{3.12.8}$$

Consider the control configuration of Fig. 3.9.3, with

$$G_1(s) = \{I_m + G(s)H(s)\}^{-1}G(s) = \{G^{-1}(s) + H(s)\}^{-1} \tag{3.12.9}$$

Choosing, $1 \leqslant i \leqslant k$,

$$H_i = A_0 \, \text{diag} \, \{d_{i1}, d_{i2}, \dots, d_{im}\} - A_i \tag{3.12.10}$$

leads to the identity,

$$G_1(s) = \text{diag} \, \{g_1(s), g_2(s), \dots, g_m(s)\} A_0^{-1} \tag{3.12.11}$$

where, $1 \leqslant i \leqslant m$,

$$g_i(s) = \frac{1}{s^k + d_{1i}s^{k-1} + \ldots + d_{ki}} \qquad (3.12.12)$$

are classical kth-order lags. Finally, setting the forward-path controller

$$K_1(s) = A_0 \operatorname{diag}\{k_1(s), \ldots, k_m(s)\} \qquad (3.12.13)$$

where $k_i(s)$, $1 \leqslant i \leqslant m$, are proper minimum-phase scalar transfer functions, leads to the expression for the closed-loop transfer-function matrix

$$H_c(s) = \operatorname{diag}\left\{\frac{g_i(s)k_i(s)}{1 + g_i(s)k_i(s)}\right\}_{1 \leqslant i \leqslant m} \qquad (3.12.14)$$

which is a noninteracting system. Note that the properties of the subsystems $g_i(s)$, $1 \leqslant i \leqslant m$, can be specified by the state-feedback parameters d_{ij}, $1 \leqslant i \leqslant k$, $1 \leqslant j \leqslant m$ and the design completed by the choice of compensation elements $k_i(s)$ to produce the desired closed-loop responses to unit-step demands.

If $k \geqslant 2$, and $A_0^{-1}A_1$ has a complete set of eigenvectors generating the eigenvector matrix T,

$$T^{-1}A_0^{-1}A_1 T = \operatorname{diag}\{-\lambda_1, -\lambda_2, \ldots, -\lambda_m\} \qquad (3.12.15)$$

then an alternative solution to the control problem can be derived requiring only the derivatives $y(t), \dfrac{dy(t)}{dt}, \ldots, \dfrac{d^{k-2}y(t)}{dt^{k-2}}$ (c.f. eqn. 3.12.8). Choosing

$$H_1 = 0$$
$$H_i = A_0 T \operatorname{diag}\{d_{i1}, d_{i2}, \ldots, d_{im}\} T^{-1} - A_i, \qquad 2 \leqslant i \leqslant k$$
$$\qquad (3.12.16)$$

gives

$$G_1(s) = \{G^{-1}(s) + H_1(s)\}^{-1} = T \operatorname{diag}\{g_1(s), \ldots, g_m(s)\} T^{-1} A_0^{-1} \qquad (3.12.17)$$

where
$$g_i(s) = \frac{1}{s^k - \lambda_i s^{k-1} + d_{2i}s^{k-2} + \ldots + d_{ki}}, \qquad 1 \leqslant i \leqslant m \qquad (3.12.18)$$

If the forward-path controller takes the form

$$K_1(s) = A_0 T \operatorname{diag}\{k_1(s), \ldots, k_m(s)\} T^{-1} \qquad (3.12.19)$$

the reader should verify that the closed-loop transfer-function matrix takes the form

$$H_c(s) = T \operatorname{diag}\left\{\frac{g_i(s)k_i(s)}{1 + g_i(s)k_i(s)}\right\}_{1 \leqslant i \leqslant m} T^{-1} \qquad (3.12.20)$$

The state-feedback parameters d_{ij}, $2 \leqslant i \leqslant k$, $1 \leqslant j \leqslant m$ can be used to partially structure the pole distribution of the subsystems $g_i(s)$, $1 \leqslant i \leqslant m$, and the design completed by the choice of phase-compensation networks $k_i(s)$, $1 \leqslant i \leqslant m$. Closed-loop interaction can be manipulated using the technique suggested in Section 3.8.

Exercise 3.12.1

Consider the application of the above techniques to the second-order lag,

$$G^{-1}(s) = s^2 \begin{pmatrix} 1 & 1 \\ 0 & 1 \end{pmatrix} + s \begin{pmatrix} 3 & 3 \\ 1 & 2 \end{pmatrix} + \begin{pmatrix} 0 & 0 \\ 1 & 0 \end{pmatrix}$$

3.13 Mixed-type multivariable structures

Multi-input/multi-output systems can exhibit more complex dynamic structures than those discussed in the previous sections. In particular, the systems considered have no zeros and an important assumption throughout the analysis is that A_0 is nonsingular. It is this second restriction that is of interest in this Section, where it will be shown that multivariable systems can exhibit first and second order behaviours simultaneously (or, in more general terms, dynamics of several orders (see Chapter 6)).

Definition 3.13.1: An m-input/m-output strictly proper system described by the $m \times m$ transfer function matrix $G(s)$ is said to be a mixed first- and second-order-type system (or, more compactly, a $(1, 2)$ lag if, and only if, $|G(s)| \not\equiv 0$ and (c.f. eqn. 3.9.1)

$$G^{-1}(s) = s^2 A_0 + s A_1 + A_2, \quad |A_0| = 0, \quad A_0 \neq 0 \tag{3.13.1}$$

where A_0, A_1, A_2 are real, constant matrices.

Equivalently, the system dynamics can be described by the second-order differential equation with matrix coefficients,

$$A_0 \frac{d^2 y(t)}{dt^2} + A_1 \frac{dy(t)}{dt} + A_2 y(t) = u(t) \tag{3.13.2}$$

As in previous sections, the key to the control analysis of $G(s)$ is the investigation of the structure of the system. The following theorem is of importance in this context:

Theorem 3.13.1: If $G(s)$ is an $m \times m$ invertible, strictly proper transfer-function matrix with a decomposition,

$$G^{-1}(s) = G_1(s) + G_2(s)$$

where $\lim_{|s| \to \infty} G(s)G_2(s) = 0$, then $|G_1(s)| \not\equiv 0$ and $G_1^{-1}(s)$ is strictly proper.

Proof: The identity $G^{-1} = G_1 + G_2$ implies that $I_m = GG^{-1} = GG_1 + GG_2$ and hence $\lim_{|s| \to \infty} G(s)G_1(s) = I_m$. It follows directly that $|G_1(s)| \not\equiv 0$ and $\lim_{|s| \to \infty} G_1^{-1}(s)G^{-1}(s) = I_m = \lim_{|s| \to \infty} \{I_m + G_1^{-1}(s)G_2(s)\}$, so that $\lim_{|s| \to \infty} G_1^{-1}(s)G_2(s) = 0$. The identity $G = \{G_1 + G_2\}^{-1} = \{I_m + G_1^{-1}G_2\}^{-1}G_1^{-1}$ implies immediately that $G_1^{-1}(s)$ is strictly proper, completing the proof of the result.

Exercise 3.13.1
Show that k^* (Section 2.20) is the same for both $G(s)$ and $G_1^{-1}(s)$.

Applying theorem 3.13.1 to the identity eqn. 3.13.1 with $G_1(s) = s^2 A_0 + sA_1$, $G_2(s) = A_2$ implies immediately that $|s\{sA_0 + A_1\}| \not\equiv 0$ and $s\{sA_0 + A_1\}$ has a strictly proper inverse.

Theorem 3.13.2: Defining $r = \mathrm{rank}\ A_0$, there exists nonsingular $m \times m$ matrices P_1, P_2 such that

$$P_2\{s^2 A_0 + sA_1\}P_1 = \begin{pmatrix} sA_0^{(1)} & 0 \\ 0 & s^2 A_0^{(2)} + sA_1^{(2)} \end{pmatrix}$$

where $A_0^{(1)}$ has dimension $(m-r) \times (m-r)$, $A_0^{(2)}$ and $A_1^{(2)}$ have dimension $r \times r$ and $|A_0^{(i)}| \neq 0$, $i = 1, 2$.

Proof: We need only consider $sA_0 + A_1$ and note that $|sA_0 + A_1| \not\equiv 0$ from the above discussion. Writing $sA_0 + A_1 = (s - \alpha)A_0 + \alpha A_0 + A_1$ where α is a real scalar, it is hence possible to choose α such that $|\alpha A_0 + A_1| \neq 0$. Without loss of generality, take $\alpha = 0$ and $|A_1| \neq 0$ so that

$$\{sA_0 + A_1\}A_1^{-1} = sA_0 A_1^{-1} + I_m \qquad (3.13.3)$$

There exists a transformation T such that

$$T^{-1}A_0 A_1^{-1} T = \begin{pmatrix} J(0) & 0 \\ 0 & A_0^{(2)} \end{pmatrix} \qquad (3.13.4)$$

where $A_0^{(2)}$ is square and nonsingular and $J(0)$ consists of Jordan blocks corresponding to the zero eigenvalues of $A_0 A_1^{-1}$. Write $P_2 = T^{-1}$, $P_1 = A_1^{-1} T$, then

$$P_2 \{s^2 A_0 + s A_1\} P_1 = s I_m + s^2 \begin{pmatrix} J(0) & 0 \\ 0 & A_0^{(2)} \end{pmatrix} \qquad (3.13.5)$$

which is block diagonal in form, and has a strictly proper inverse. This in fact proves the result as $J(0)$ must be a zero matrix e.g. if $J(0)$ contains an $l \times l$ nonzero Jordan block, eqn. 3.13.5 has a block diagonal entry of the form

$$s \begin{pmatrix} 1 & s & 0 & \dots & 0 \\ 0 & 1 & s & & \vdots \\ \vdots & & & & 0 \\ \vdots & & & & s \\ 0 & \dots & \dots & 0 & 1 \end{pmatrix}$$

with inverse

$$\frac{1}{s} \begin{pmatrix} 1 & -s & s^2 & \dots & (-1)^{l-1} s^{l-1} \\ 0 & 1 & & & \\ \vdots & & & & -s \\ 0 & \dots & \dots & 0 & 1 \end{pmatrix}$$

which is not strictly proper.

Writing

$$P_2 A_2 P_1 = \begin{pmatrix} A_1^{(1)} & A_{12} \\ A_{21} & A_2^{(2)} \end{pmatrix} \qquad (3.13.6)$$

gives

$$P_2 G^{-1}(s) P_1 = \begin{pmatrix} s A_0^{(1)} + A_1^{(1)} & A_{12} \\ A_{21} & s^2 A_0^{(2)} + s A_1^{(2)} + A_2^{(2)} \end{pmatrix} \qquad (3.13.7)$$

Considering the block diagonal entries defined by

$$G_1^{-1}(s) = s A_0^{(1)} + A_1^{(1)}, \quad |A_0^{(1)}| \neq 0$$

$$G_2^{-1}(s) = s^2 A_0^{(2)} + s A_1^{(2)} + A_2^{(2)}, \quad |A_0^{(2)}| \neq 0 \qquad (3.13.8)$$

it should be noted that $G_1(s)$ and $G_2(s)$ are first- and second-order lags of dimension $(m - r) \times (m - r)$ and $r \times r$, respectively. Defining

$$y(t) = P_1 \begin{pmatrix} \tilde{y}_1(t) \\ \tilde{y}_2(t) \end{pmatrix}, \quad \begin{pmatrix} \tilde{u}_1(t) \\ \tilde{u}_2(t) \end{pmatrix} = P_2 u(t) \qquad (3.13.9)$$

then eqn. 3.13.2 can be written in the form,

$$A_0^{(1)} \frac{d\tilde{y}_1(t)}{dt} + A_1^{(1)}\tilde{y}_1(t) + A_{12}\tilde{y}_2(t) = \tilde{u}_1(t)$$

$$A_0^{(2)} \frac{d^2\tilde{y}_2(t)}{dt^2} + A_1^{(2)} \frac{d\tilde{y}_2(t)}{dt} + A_2^{(2)}\tilde{y}_2(t) + A_{21}\tilde{y}_1(t) = \tilde{u}_2(t)$$

$$(3.13.10)$$

which has a controllable and observable state-vector representation, of state dimension $(m - r) + 2r = m + r$,

$$x(t) = \left(\tilde{y}_1(t)^T, \tilde{y}_2(t)^T, \frac{d\tilde{y}_2(t)^T}{dt} \right)^T$$

$$\dot{x}(t) = \begin{pmatrix} -(A_0^{(1)})^{-1}A_1^{(1)} & -(A_0^{(1)})^{-1}A_{12} & 0 \\ 0 & 0 & I_r \\ -(A_0^{(2)})^{-1}A_{21} & -(A_0^{(2)})^{-1}A_2^{(2)} & -(A_0^{(2)})^{-1}A_1^{(2)} \end{pmatrix}$$

$$x(t) + \begin{pmatrix} (A_0^{(1)})^{-1} & 0 \\ 0 & 0 \\ 0 & (A_0^{(2)})^{-1} \end{pmatrix} \begin{pmatrix} \tilde{u}_1(t) \\ \tilde{u}_2(t) \end{pmatrix}$$

$$\begin{pmatrix} \tilde{y}_1(t) \\ \tilde{y}_2(t) \end{pmatrix} = \begin{pmatrix} I_{m-r} & 0 & 0 \\ 0 & I_r & 0 \end{pmatrix} x(t) \qquad (3.13.11)$$

It is left as an exercise for the reader to show that the system has no zeros with zero polynomial

$$z(s) = |(A_0^{(1)})^{-1}| \, |(A_0^{(2)})^{-1}| \neq 0 \qquad (3.13.12)$$

and hence a characteristic polynomial,

$$\rho_0(s) = |P_2 G^{-1}(s)P_1| z(s) = |P_2 P_1| \, |(A_0^{(1)}A_0^{(2)})^{-1}| \, |s^2 A_0 + sA_1 + A_2| \qquad (3.13.13)$$

A more compact representation is obtained from eqn. 3.13.10 by taking Laplace transforms with zero initial conditions

$$\tilde{y}_1(s) = G_1(s)\{\tilde{u}_1(s) - A_{12}\tilde{y}_2(s)\}$$
$$\tilde{y}_2(s) = G_2(s)\{\tilde{u}_2(s) - A_{21}\tilde{y}_1(s)\} \qquad (3.13.14)$$

yielding the structure illustrated in Fig. 3.13.1, consisting of first- and second-order lags coupled by output feedback elements A_{12}, A_{21}.

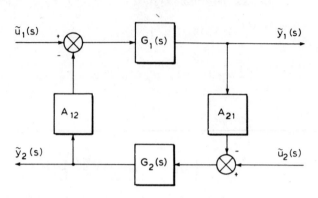

Fig. 3.13.1 Internal structure of a mixed first- and second-order lag

An approach to the design of a control system for the plant $G(s)$ can proceed in many ways. The most obvious approach is a parallel to the techniques suggested in Section 3.9, by choosing a minor-loop element to remove the interaction terms A_{12}, A_{21}. This is accomplished by the minor-loop feedback

$$u(s) = v(s) - P_2^{-1}\begin{pmatrix} 0 & -A_{12} \\ -A_{21} & 0 \end{pmatrix} P_1^{-1} y(s) \qquad (3.13.15)$$

when the transfer-function matrix relating $y(s)$ to $v(s)$ is given by

$$G_0(s) = \left\{ G^{-1}(s) + P_2^{-1}\begin{pmatrix} 0 & -A_{12} \\ -A_{21} & 0 \end{pmatrix} P_1^{-1} \right\}^{-1}$$

$$= P_1 \begin{pmatrix} G_1(s) & 0 \\ 0 & G_2(s) \end{pmatrix} P_2 \qquad (3.13.16)$$

Exercise 3.13.2
Verify that eqn. 3.13.15 is a state feedback law equivalent to the relations,

$$\tilde{u}_1(t) = \tilde{v}_1(t) + A_{12}\tilde{y}_2(t), \quad \tilde{u}_2(t) = v_2(t) + A_{21}\tilde{y}_1(t),$$

$$v(t) = P_2^{-1}\begin{pmatrix} \tilde{v}_1(t) \\ \tilde{v}_2(t) \end{pmatrix}$$

cancelling out the loops A_{12}, A_{21} in Fig. 3.13.1.

Consider a unity-negative feedback system for the control of $G_0(s)$,

$$y(s) = G_0(s)v(s), \quad v(s) = K_0(s)e(s), \quad e(s) = r(s) - y(s)$$
$$(3.13.17)$$

and set

$$K_0(s) = P_2^{-1}\begin{pmatrix} K_1(s) & 0 \\ 0 & K_2(s) \end{pmatrix}P_1^{-1} \qquad (3.13.18)$$

where $K_1(s)$ $(m-r) \times (m-r)$ and $K_2(s)$ $(r \times r)$ are proper controller transfer-function matrices. The reader can verify that

$$G_0(s)K_0(s) = P_1\begin{pmatrix} G_1(s)K_1(s) & 0 \\ 0 & G_2(s)K_2(s) \end{pmatrix}P_1^{-1} \qquad (3.13.19)$$

and hence that the closed-loop transfer-function matrix

$$H_c(s) = \{I_m + G_0(s)K_0(s)\}^{-1}G_0(s)K_0(s)$$

$$= P_1\begin{pmatrix} \{I_{m-r} + G_1(s)K_1(s)\}^{-1}G_1(s)K_1(s) \\ 0 \end{pmatrix}$$

$$\begin{pmatrix} 0 \\ \{I_r + G_2(s)K_2(s)\}^{-1}G_2(s)K_2(s) \end{pmatrix}P_1^{-1}$$
$$(3.13.20)$$

with return-difference determinant,

$$|T(s)| = |I_m + G_0(s)K_0(s)| = |I_{m-r} + G_1(s)K_1(s)| \, |I_r + G_2(s)K_2(s)|$$
$$(3.13.21)$$

Equivalently, using the controller structure eqn. 3.13.15 and eqn. 3.13.18, the design analysis reduces to the analysis of unity-negative feedback systems for the first-order lag $G_1(s)$ and the second-order lag $G_2(s)$, using, for example, the analysis of Sections 3.5 and 3.9, followed by an investigation of the closed-loop performance using eqn. 3.13.20. In particular, if $m = 2, r = 1$, the closed-loop system will have a small degree of interaction in response to unit-step demands if the transfer functions $\{1 + G_i(s)K_i(s)\}^{-1}G_i(s)K_i(s), i = 1, 2$, have similar response characteristics over the frequency range of interest.

Finally, if a unity-negative feedback system is required for $G(s)$, consider the forward-path controller

$$K(s) = K_0(s) + P_2^{-1}\begin{pmatrix} 0 & -A_{12} \\ -A_{21} & 0 \end{pmatrix} P_1^{-1} \qquad (3.13.22)$$

generating the closed-loop transfer-function matrix

$$H_c(s) = \{I_m + G(s)K(s)\}^{-1}G(s)K(s) = \{G^{-1}(s) + K(s)\}^{-1}K(s)$$

$$= P_1 \text{ block diag} \left(\{I + G_i(s)K_i(s)\}^{-1}G_i(s)K_i(s)\right)_{i=1,2} P_1^{-1}$$

$$- P_1 \text{ block diag} \left(\{I + G_i(s)K_i(s)\}^{-1}G_i(s)\right)_{i=1,2}\begin{pmatrix} 0 & A_{12} \\ A_{21} & 0 \end{pmatrix} P_1^{-1}$$

$$(3.13.23)$$

which is essentially identical to eqn. 3.13.20 if the control systems gains are high.

Exercise 3.13.2
The above analysis can be extended to include the possibility of minor-loop compensation along the lines suggested in Sections 3.8, 3.9, 3.11, 3.12. For example, if eqn. 3.13.15 is replaced by the form

$$u(s) = v(s) - P_2^{-1}\begin{pmatrix} H^{(1)}(s) & -A_{12} \\ -A_{21} & H^{(2)}(s) \end{pmatrix} P_1^{-1}, \qquad (3.13.24)$$

then $G_0(s)$ takes the form

$$G_0(s) = P_1 \begin{pmatrix} \{I_{m-r} + G_1(s)H^{(1)}(s)\}^{-1}G_1(s) & \\ & 0 \\ & \\ 0 & \\ & \{I_r + G_2(s)H^{(2)}(s)\}^{-1}G_2(s) \end{pmatrix} P_2$$

$$(3.13.25)$$

The reader should verify this and also prove that eqn. 3.13.24 is equivalent to the relations (Exercise 3.13.2)

$$\tilde{u}_1(s) = \tilde{v}_1(s) - H^{(1)}(s)\tilde{y}_1(s) + A_{12}\tilde{y}_2(s)$$
$$\tilde{u}_2(s) = \tilde{v}_2(s) - H^{(2)}(s)\tilde{y}_2(s) + A_{21}\tilde{y}_1(s)$$

3.14 Level control of a two-input/two-output three vessel liquid storage system

Consider the three-vessel system shown in Fig. 3.14.1 and the application of the techniques of Section 3.13 to the design of a configuration

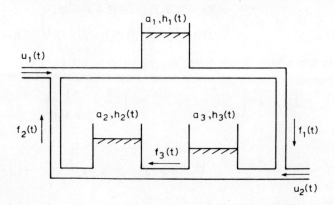

Fig. 3.14.1 Two-input/two-output three-vessel liquid storage system

for the control of the deviations $h_1(t)$, $h_2(t)$ of the heights of the levels in vessels one and two from some equilibrium position. The equations of motion of the system take the form,

$$a_1\dot{h}_1(t) = u_1(t) + f_2(t) - f_1(t)$$
$$a_2\dot{h}_2(t) = f_3(t) - f_2(t)$$
$$a_3\dot{h}_3(t) = f_1(t) + u_2(t) - f_3(t) \qquad (3.14.1)$$

Considering the data $a_1 = a_2 = a_3 = 1$, and taking the linear approximation to the intervessel flows

$$f_1(t) = h_1(t) - h_3(t)$$
$$f_2(t) = h_2(t) - h_1(t)$$
$$f_3(t) = \beta(h_3(t) - h_2(t)), \qquad \beta > 0 \qquad (3.14.2)$$

the system has a state-vector model of the form

$$x(t) = (h_1(t), h_2(t), h_3(t))^T, \quad u(t) = (u_1(t), u_2(t))^T$$

$$\dot{x}(t) = \begin{pmatrix} -2 & 1 & 1 \\ 1 & -(1+\beta) & \beta \\ 1 & \beta & -(1+\beta) \end{pmatrix} x(t) + \begin{pmatrix} 1 & 0 \\ 0 & 0 \\ 0 & 1 \end{pmatrix} u(t)$$

$$y(t) = \begin{pmatrix} h_1(t) \\ h_2(t) \end{pmatrix} = \begin{pmatrix} 1 & 0 & 0 \\ 0 & 1 & 0 \end{pmatrix} x(t) \qquad (3.14.3)$$

and an inverse transfer-function matrix

$$G^{-1}(s) = \beta^{-1} \begin{pmatrix} \beta(s+2)+1 & -(s+1+2\beta) \\ -(s+1+2\beta) & (s+1+\beta)^2 - \beta^2 \end{pmatrix} \qquad (3.14.4)$$

The system is hence a mixed-type structure with $m = 2, r = 1$ and

$$A_0 = \beta^{-1} \begin{pmatrix} 0 & 0 \\ 0 & 1 \end{pmatrix}, \quad A_1 = \beta^{-1} \begin{pmatrix} \beta & -1 \\ -1 & 2(1+\beta) \end{pmatrix},$$

$$A_2 = \beta^{-1} \begin{pmatrix} 2\beta+1 & -(2\beta+1) \\ -(2\beta+1) & (2\beta+1) \end{pmatrix} \qquad (3.14.5)$$

The first step in the control analysis is the decomposition (eqn. 3.13.7) of $G^{-1}(s)$ obtained by writing $P_2 = T^{-1}, P_1 = A_1^{-1} T$ where T is the eigenvector matrix of $A_0 A_1^{-1}$,

$$A_0 A_1^{-1} = \begin{pmatrix} 0 & 0 \\ 1 & \beta \end{pmatrix} \frac{1}{2\beta(\beta+1)-1}, \quad T = \begin{pmatrix} \beta & 0 \\ -1 & 1 \end{pmatrix} \qquad (3.14.6)$$

giving

$$P_2 = \beta^{-1} \begin{pmatrix} 1 & 0 \\ 1 & \beta \end{pmatrix}$$

$$P_1 = \frac{\beta}{2\beta(\beta+1)-1} \begin{pmatrix} 2\beta(\beta+1)-1 & 1 \\ 0 & \beta \end{pmatrix} \qquad (3.14.7)$$

and

$$P_2 G^{-1}(s)P_1 = s^2 \begin{pmatrix} 0 & 0 \\ 0 & \dfrac{\beta}{2\beta(\beta+1)-1} \end{pmatrix} + s \begin{pmatrix} 1 & 0 \\ 0 & 1 \end{pmatrix}$$

$$+ \frac{(2\beta+1)}{\beta(2\beta(\beta+1)-1)} \begin{pmatrix} 2\beta(\beta+1)-1 & 1-\beta \\ (1-\beta)(2\beta(\beta+1)-1) & (1-\beta)^2 \end{pmatrix}$$

$$(3.14.8)$$

More conveniently, the coefficient matrix of s^2 can be simplified by scaling the columns and rows of P_1 and P_2, respectively,

$$P_1 = \begin{pmatrix} 1 & 1 \\ 0 & \beta \end{pmatrix}, \quad P_2 = \begin{pmatrix} 1 & 0 \\ 1 & \beta \end{pmatrix} \qquad (3.14.9)$$

giving,

$$P_2 G^{-1}(s)P_1 = s^2 \begin{pmatrix} 0 & 0 \\ 0 & \beta \end{pmatrix} + s \begin{pmatrix} 1 & 0 \\ 0 & 2\beta^2 + 2\beta - 1 \end{pmatrix}$$

$$+ \frac{(2\beta+1)}{\beta} \begin{pmatrix} 1 & 1-\beta \\ 1-\beta & (1-\beta)^2 \end{pmatrix} \qquad (3.14.10)$$

from which,

$$G_1^{-1}(s) = s + \frac{(2\beta+1)}{\beta}, \quad G_2^{-1}(s) = \beta s^2 + (2\beta^2 + 2\beta - 1)s$$

$$+ \frac{(2\beta+1)(1-\beta)^2}{\beta}$$

$$A_{12} = A_{21} = \frac{(2\beta+1)(1-\beta)}{\beta} \qquad (3.14.11)$$

Note that $G_1(s)$ is a stable first-order lag for all $\beta > 0$ and $G_2(s)$ is a stable second-order lag if, and only if, $\beta > (\sqrt{3}-1)/2 = 0.35$. In physical terms, if the coupling between vessels 2 and 3 is small, control difficulties will arise (as expected intuitively) requiring minor-loop compensation to offset the small damping ratio of this subsystem. On the other hand, if the coupling is large enough, vessels 2 and 3 will move essentially in phase and the system will behave as if it consisted of two vessels of area $a_1 = 1$ and $a_2 + a_3 = 2$. The control problems in this case are easily surmounted (see Section 3.3).

The next step is to choose forward-path elements $K_1(s), K_2(s)$ by the analysis of unity-negative feedback systems for $G_1(s), G_2(s)$, respectively. Using the data $\beta = 2$, and considering the second-order lag $G_2(s)$,

$$G_2^{-1} = 2s^2 + 11s + 2\cdot5$$

$$= 2(s + 0\cdot24)(s + 5\cdot26) \qquad (3.14.12)$$

so that the system is overdamped. The first-order lag takes the form

$$G_1^{-1}(s) = s + 2\cdot5 \qquad (3.14.13)$$

To ensure small closed-loop interaction effects the response characteristics of the scalar feedback systems $(1 + G_iK_i)^{-1}G_iK_i$ must be similar. However, choosing $K_1(s) = K_1$ (proportional control), it is easily verified that steady-state errors in response to unit-step demands on $(1 + G_1K_1)^{-1}G_1K_1$ are less than 10% if, and only if, $K_1 > 22\cdot5$ when the closed-loop time constant is less than $0\cdot04$. If also $K_2(s)$ is a proportional controller, the subsystem $(1 + G_2K_2)^{-1}G_2K_2$ has a response time of the order of $0\cdot4$ unless excessive oscillation can be tolerated, implying that phase compensation must be introduced into $K_2(s)$ to increase closed-loop response speeds. Choosing, for simplicity,

$$K_2(s) = k_2 \frac{(s + 5\cdot0)}{(s + 19\cdot5)}, \quad k_2 > 0 \qquad (3.14.14)$$

and $k_2 = 390\cdot0$ to produce a damping ratio of $0\cdot7$, the closed-loop system will have a response time of the order of $1\cdot0/$(intercept of the root-locus plot) $= 0\cdot1$. For small closed-loop interaction try the time constant $(K_1 + 2\cdot5)^{-1} = 0\cdot1$ i.e. $K_1 = 7\cdot5$, and eqn. 3.13.18

$$K_0(s) = \begin{pmatrix} 1 & 0 \\ -0\cdot5 & 0\cdot5 \end{pmatrix} \operatorname{diag}\left\{7\cdot5, \ 390\cdot0 \frac{(s + 5\cdot0)}{(s + 19\cdot5)}\right\} \begin{pmatrix} 1 & -0\cdot5 \\ 0 & 0\cdot5 \end{pmatrix}$$

$$(3.14.15)$$

generating the unity-negative feedback system with forward-path controller (eqn. 3.13.22),

$$K(s) = \begin{pmatrix} 1 & 0 \\ -0\cdot5 & 0\cdot5 \end{pmatrix} \begin{pmatrix} 7\cdot5 & 2\cdot5 \\ 2\cdot5 & 390\cdot0 \dfrac{(s + 5\cdot0)}{(s + 19\cdot5)} \end{pmatrix} \begin{pmatrix} 1 & -0\cdot5 \\ 0 & 0\cdot5 \end{pmatrix}$$

$$(3.14.16)$$

The system closed-loop responses to unit-step demands are illustrated in Fig. 3.14.2, with maximum steady-state errors and interaction effects of approximately 22%. The large steady-state errors are expected from the small value of gain K_1 and can be offset by the inclusion of integral control action in both $K_1(s)$ and $K_2(s)$. The large interaction effects are due partly to the low gains used, but primarily arise from the essentially

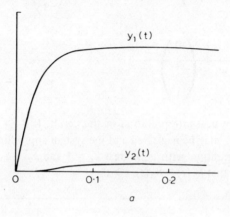

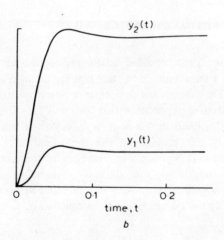

Fig. 3.14.2 System responses
    a Response to unit-step demand in $y_1(t)$
    b Response to unit-step demand in $y_2(t)$

different dynamic character of $G_1(s)$ and $G_2(s)$. This can be partly compensated for by the inclusion of rate feedback loops, or by increasing the phase advance in $K_2(s)$.

Exercise 3.14.1
Verify that the open-loop plant eqn. 3.14.3 has eigenvalues and eigenvectors,

$$\lambda_1 = 0, \quad w_1 = \begin{pmatrix} 1 \\ 1 \\ 1 \end{pmatrix}, \quad \lambda_2 = -3, \quad w_2 = \begin{pmatrix} 2 \\ -1 \\ -1 \end{pmatrix}, \quad \lambda_3 = -(1+2\beta),$$

$$w_3 = \begin{pmatrix} 0 \\ -1 \\ 1 \end{pmatrix}$$

Provide a physical interpretation of this result. If $\beta \gg 1$, suggest why the mode w_3 may be neglected and the system approximated by a two-vessel configuration with tank areas $a_1 = 1$ and $a_2 + a_3 = 2$, obtained by assuming that $h_2(t) \equiv h_3(t), t > 0$.

3.15 Systems with one zero and $|CB| \neq 0$

Neglecting the computer-aided-design techniques of the remaining chapters, it is a fair comment to state that the detailed effect of system zeros on feedback design and performance is only partially understood, despite the intuitive expectation that they will play an important role. The analysis described in this Section takes only a small step towards the solution of this problem at the theoretical level, but illustrates several principles. It represents an extension of the work described by Owens[40] by considering the class of m-input/m-output invertible minimum-phase systems possessing one zero and where CB is nonsingular. Equivalently the system satisfies the constraints,

$$|CB| \neq 0, \quad n = m+1, \quad z(s) = b_0 s + b_1, \quad b_0 \neq 0, \quad z = \frac{b_1}{b_0} > 0$$
$$(3.15.1)$$

and has an inverse,

$$G^{-1}(s) = sA_0 + \tilde{A}_1 + \frac{1}{s+z}\tilde{\alpha}_1\alpha_2^T, \quad |A_0| \neq 0 \quad (3.15.2)$$

where

$$A_0 = (CB)^{-1} \quad (3.15.3)$$

and $\tilde{\alpha}_1$, α_2 are real $m \times 1$ vectors. Defining

$$A_1 = \tilde{A}_1 + z^{-1}\tilde{\alpha}_1\alpha_2^T = \lim_{s \to 0} G^{-1}(s)$$

$$\alpha_1 = -z^{-1}A_0^{-1}\tilde{\alpha}_1 \qquad (3.15.4)$$

$G^{-1}(s)$ can be written in the form of eqn. 3.7.2

$$G^{-1}(s) = sA_0 + A_1 + A_0 \frac{s}{s+z}\alpha_1\alpha_2^T \qquad (3.15.5)$$

Application of the approximation technique of Section 3.7, a sufficient condition for the unity-negative feedback system with forward-path controller

$$K(s) = kA_0 - A_1 \qquad (3.15.6)$$

to be asymptotically stable is (eqn. 3.7.7) that

$$\|H\| = \left\{\max_{1 \leqslant i \leqslant m} |(\alpha_1)_i|\right\}\sum_{j=1}^{m} |(\alpha_2)_j| < k \qquad (3.15.7)$$

In this special case, however, a more detailed analysis is possible.

Proportional control: Following the methods of Section 3.7, approximate $G(s)$ by the first-order model

$$G_A^{-1}(s) = sA_0 + A_1 \qquad (3.15.8)$$

when, using the forward-path controller eqn. 3.15.6,

$$|I_m + G_A(s)K(s)| = \frac{(s+k)^m}{|sI_m + A_0^{-1}A_1|} \qquad (3.15.9)$$

and

$$\{I_m + G_A(s)K(s)\}^{-1}G_A(s)K(s) = \frac{k}{s+k}\{I_m - k^{-1}A_0^{-1}A_1\} \qquad (3.15.10)$$

Consider now the application of $K(s)$ to the original plant $G(s)$,

$$\frac{\rho_c(s)}{\rho_0(s)} = |I_m + G(s)K(s)| = |G(s)||G^{-1}(s) + K(s)|$$

$$= \frac{z(s)}{\rho_0(s)}\left|A_0s + A_1 + A_0\frac{s}{(s+z)}\alpha_1\alpha_2^T + kA_0 - A_1\right| \qquad (3.15.11)$$

giving

$$\rho_c(s) = b_0 |A_0| (s+z) \left| (s+k)I_m + \frac{s}{(s+z)} \alpha_1 \alpha_2^T \right|$$

$$= b_0 |A_0| (s+z)(s+k)^m \left| I_m + \frac{s}{(s+k)(s+z)} \alpha_1 \alpha_2^T \right|$$

$$= b_0 |A_0| (s+z)(s+k)^m \left\{ 1 + \frac{s}{(s+k)(s+z)} \alpha_2^T \alpha_1 \right\}$$

$$= b_0 |A_0| (s+k)^{m-1} \{(s+k)(s+z) + s\alpha_2^T \alpha_1\} \quad (3.15.12)$$

Noting that the coefficient of s^{m+1} is unity, we must have

$$b_0 = |A_0^{-1}|$$

so that

$$\rho_c(s) = (s+k)^{m-1} \{s^2 + s(k+z+\alpha_2^T\alpha_1) + kz\} \quad (3.15.13)$$

implying that the closed-loop system is stable if, and only if,

$$k > 0, \quad k + z + \alpha_2^T \alpha_1 > 0 \quad (3.15.14)$$

(Note: the reader should compare this result with eqn. 3.15.7.) The closed-loop system hence has $m-1$ poles at $s_i = -k$, $1 \leqslant i \leqslant m-1$, plus two poles satisfying

$$s_m(k) = -(k + \alpha_2^T \alpha_1) + \epsilon_1(k)$$

$$s_{m+1}(k) = -z + \epsilon_2(k) \quad (3.15.15)$$

where

$$\lim_{k \to \infty} \epsilon_i(k) = 0, \quad i = 1, 2 \quad (3.15.16)$$

Note that the closed-loop system can always be stabilised by the choice of high enough gains k, and that one closed-loop pole $s_{m+1}(k)$ is attracted to the system zero $-z$ (this is a special case of a more general result noted by Kouvaritakis and Shaked[14] and provides a justification of the definition of system zeros used in Section 2.21. See also the discussion in Chapter 6).

An insight into the performance of the closed-loop system can be obtained by examination of the closed-loop transfer-function matrix at high gains k,

$$H_c(s) = \{I_m + G(s)K(s)\}^{-1}G(s)K(s) = \{G^{-1}(s) + K(s)\}^{-1}K(s)$$

$$= \left\{ sA_0 + A_1 + A_0\frac{s}{(s+z)}\alpha_1\alpha_2^T + kA_0 - A_1 \right\}^{-1}\{kA_0 - A_1\}$$

$$= \frac{k}{s+k}\left\{ I_m + \frac{s}{(s+k)(s+z)}\alpha_1\alpha_2^T \right\}^{-1}\{I_m - k^{-1}A_0^{-1}A_1\} \quad (3.15.17)$$

Noting that,

$$\left\{ I_m + \frac{s}{(s+k)(s+z)}\alpha_1\alpha_2^T \right\}^{-1}$$

$$= I_m - \frac{s}{(s - s_m(k))(s - s_{m+1}(k))}\alpha_1\alpha_2^T \quad (3.15.18)$$

then

$$H_c(s) = \frac{k}{s+k}\left\{ I_m - \frac{s}{(s - s_m(k))(s - s_{m+1}(k))}\alpha_1\alpha_2^T \right\}$$

$$\{I_m - k^{-1}A_0^{-1}A_1\} \quad (3.15.19)$$

Assuming, for simplicity, that $\alpha_2^T\alpha_1 \neq 0$ and writing $H_c(s)$ as a partial-fraction expansion

$$H_c(s) = \frac{k}{(s+k)}M_1(k) + \frac{k}{s - s_m(k)}M_2(k)$$

$$+ \frac{1}{s - s_{m+1}(k)}M_3(k) \quad (3.15.20)$$

then

$$M_1(k) = \lim_{s \to -k} k^{-1}(s+k)H_c(s)$$

$$= \left\{ I_m + \frac{k}{(k + s_m(k))(k + s_{m+1}(k))}\alpha_1\alpha_2^T \right\}\{I_m - k^{-1}A_0^{-1}A_1\}$$

$$\to I_m - \frac{\alpha_1\alpha_2^T}{\alpha_2^T\alpha_1} \quad (\text{as } k \to +\infty) \quad (3.15.21)$$

In a similar manner,

$$M_2(k) = \frac{(-1)}{(k + s_m(k))} \frac{s_m(k)}{(s_m(k) - s_{m+1}(k))} \alpha_1 \alpha_2^T \{I_m - k^{-1} A_0^{-1} A_1\}$$

$$\rightarrow \frac{\alpha_1 \alpha_2^T}{\alpha_2^T \alpha_1} \qquad (\text{as } k \rightarrow +\infty) \tag{3.15.22}$$

and

$$M_3(k) = \frac{k}{k + s_{m+1}(k)} (-1) \frac{s_{m+1}(k)}{s_{m+1}(k) - s_m(k)} \alpha_1 \alpha_2^T$$

$$\{I_m - k^{-1} A_0^{-1} A_1\}$$

$$\rightarrow 0 \qquad (\text{as } k \rightarrow +\infty) \tag{3.15.23}$$

In effect the pole $s_{m+1}(k)$ makes a negligible contribution to the closed-loop performance at high gains, when

$$H_c(s) \simeq \frac{k}{s + k} \left\{ I_m - \frac{\alpha_1 \alpha_2^T}{\alpha_2^T \alpha_1} \right\} + \frac{k}{(s - s_m(k))} \frac{\alpha_1 \alpha_2^T}{\alpha_2^T \alpha_1} \tag{3.15.24}$$

Noting (eqn. 3.15.15) that the time constants of the two terms are essentially identical, it follows that $H_c(s) \simeq \dfrac{k}{s + k} I_m$ indicating a small degree of closed-loop interaction and small steady-state errors. In particular, the dynamics of the closed-loop system (eqn. 3.15.17) are essentially identical to the dynamics of the approximate system (eqn. 3.15.10), providing some confidence in the suggested approximation procedure.

Proportional plus integral control: The above results can be extended to include an integral component in the controller of the form suggested in Section 3.5,

$$K(s) = \left\{ k + c + \frac{kc}{s} \right\} A_0 - A_1 \tag{3.15.25}$$

when

$$|I_m + G(s)K(s)| = |G(s)||G^{-1}(s) + K(s)|$$

$$= |G(s)||A_0| \left| \left(s + k + c + \frac{kc}{s} \right) I_m + \frac{s}{(s + z)} \alpha_1 \alpha_2^T \right|$$

$$= |G(s)||A_0| \frac{(s + k)^m (s + c)^m}{s^m} \left| I_m + \frac{s^2}{(s + k)(s + c)(s + z)} \alpha_1 \alpha_2^T \right|$$

$$\tag{3.15.26}$$

Noting that $|G(s)| \|A_0\|/s^m = (s+z)/\rho_0(s)$, it is easily verified that the closed-loop characteristic polynomial takes the form

$$\rho_c(s) = (s+z)(s+k)^m(s+c)^m \left\{ 1 + \frac{s^2}{(s+k)(s+c)(s+z)} \alpha_2^T \alpha_1 \right\}$$

$$= (s+k)^{m-1}(s+c)^{m-1}\{(s+k)(s+c)(s+z) + s^2 \alpha_2^T \alpha_1\}$$

$$(3.15.27)$$

and hence that the closed-loop system has $m-1$ poles at $s = -k$, $m-1$ poles at $s = -c$ plus three poles equal to the roots of the polynomial

$$s^3 + (k+c+z+\alpha_2^T\alpha_1)s^2 + (kc+kz+cz)s + kcz \quad (3.15.28)$$

Application of the Routh-Hurwitz stability criterion indicates closed-loop stability if, and only if,

$$k > 0, \quad k+c+z+\alpha_2^T\alpha_1 > 0, \quad c > 0 \quad (3.15.29)$$

and

$$(k+c+z+\alpha_2^T\alpha_1)(kc+kz+cz) - kcz > 0 \quad (3.15.30)$$

Expressions 3.15.29 are valid if $c > 0$ and the proportional control system (obtained by setting $c = 0$) is stable. In this case,

$$(k+c+z+\alpha_2^T\alpha_1)(kc+kz+cz) - kcz$$

$$> (k+c+z+\alpha_2^T\alpha_1)kz - kcz$$

$$= (k+z+\alpha_2^T\alpha_1)kz > 0 \quad (3.15.31)$$

so that the closed-loop system is stable for all $c > 0$.

The above results can be viewed either as a design technique for the restricted class of systems considered or as a justification of the techniques suggested in Section 3.7. In either case, it would seem that a useful controller design can be generated using the restricted plant data $A_0^{-1} = CB$ (representing the initial derivatives in response to unit-step demands (see problem 13 in Chapter 2)) and the steady-state data $A_1 = \lim_{s \to 0} G^{-1}(s)$. It is reassuring that control design can be a simple procedure but the reader should note that the analysis will not deal with many situations of practical interest. For example, CB may be singular (see Sections 3.8, 3.9, 3.11–3.13) and the position of the zero and the magnitude of $\alpha_1 \alpha_2^T$ in eqns. 3.15.5 may be such that the asymptotic results obtained in this Section may not be valid over the range of gains considered in practice e.g. consider the transfer function $(m = 1)$

$$g(s) = \frac{(s+20)}{s(s+1)} \quad (3.15.31)$$

which, over a reasonable range of gains, behaves as a second-order lag!

Exercise 3.15.1
Suppose, in Section 3.14, the outputs are replaced by $y_1(t) = h_1(t)$, $y_2(t) = h_2(t) + h_3(t) =$ total change in volume in vessels 2 and 3 i.e. in eqns. 3.14.3, replace the output equation by

$$y(t) = \begin{pmatrix} 1 & 0 & 0 \\ 0 & 1 & 1 \end{pmatrix} x(t)$$

Show that the system has a zero at the position $s = -(1 + 2\beta)$ and an inverse of the form of eqn. 3.15.2 with $\tilde{\alpha}_1 \alpha_2^T = 0$. Note that the approximation (eqn. 3.15.8) is exact in this case, the system behaving as a first-order lag. Provide a physical interpretation of this result by using Exercise 3.14.1 and a consideration of the observability of the system.

3.16 Dyadic transfer-function matrices

A conceptually appealing and practical result providing a partial generalisation of many of the techniques of previous sections can be obtained by a consideration of *dyadic transfer-function matrices.*[37]

Definition 3.16.1: An $m \times m$ transfer-function matrix is said to be *dyadic* if, and only if, $|G(s)| \not\equiv 0$ and there exists constant $m \times m$ matrices P_1, P_2 and transfer functions $g_1(s), \ldots, g_m(s)$ such that

$$G(s) = P_1 \, \text{diag} \{g_1(s), g_2(s), \ldots, g_m(s)\} P_2 \qquad (3.16.1)$$

It is left as an exercise for the reader to show that the liquid-level system (eqn. 3.3.18), the first-order lag (eqn. 3.5.11), the second-order lag (eqn. 3.8.8), the oscillatory system of Exercise 3.11.2, the compensated mixed-type system (eqn. 3.13.16) with $m = 2$, $r = 1$ and the example of Section 3.14 with $\beta = 1$ are all dyadic transfer-function matrices. In this Section, these results are generalised by allowing $g_i(s)$, $1 \leqslant i \leqslant m$, to take a totally general form subject only to the restriction that they are strictly proper. In particular, $G(s)$ may possess more than one zero.

The physical structure of a dyadic transfer-function matrix can be revealed by defining subsystems with input output relations,

$$\tilde{y}_i(s) = g_i(s)\tilde{u}_i(s), \qquad 1 \leqslant i \leqslant m \qquad (3.16.2)$$

and setting

$$y(s) = P_1\begin{pmatrix}\tilde{y}_1(s) \\ \cdot \\ \cdot \\ \tilde{y}_m(s)\end{pmatrix}, \qquad \begin{pmatrix}\tilde{u}_1(s) \\ \cdot \\ \cdot \\ \tilde{u}_m(s)\end{pmatrix} = P_2 u(s) \qquad (3.16.3)$$

It is easily verified that the system takes the form shown in Fig. 3.16.1, consisting of a noninteracting system 'sandwiched' between input and output transformations P_2, P_1, respectively. The matrices P_1, P_2 are the sole source of interaction in the system and arise from the practical decision to measure $y_1(t), \ldots, y_m(t)$ (rather than the subsystem outputs $\tilde{y}_1(t), \ldots, \tilde{y}_m(t)$) and to control these outputs by direct action using $u_1(t), \ldots, u_m(t)$ (rather than the subsystem inputs $\tilde{u}_1(t), \ldots, \tilde{u}_m(t)$).

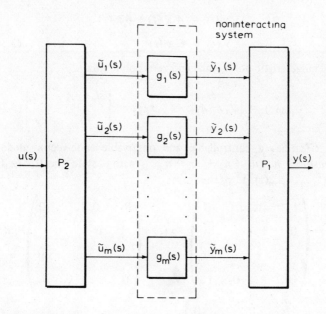

Fig. 3.16.1 Decomposition of a dyadic system $G(s)$

The structure of the matrix $G(s)$ is revealed by writing

$$P_1 = (\alpha_1, \alpha_2, \ldots, \alpha_m), \qquad P_2 = \begin{pmatrix}\beta_1^T \\ \cdot \\ \cdot \\ \beta_m^T\end{pmatrix} \qquad (3.16.4)$$

when

$$y(s) = P_1 \begin{pmatrix} \tilde{y}_1(s) \\ \cdot \\ \cdot \\ \tilde{y}_m(s) \end{pmatrix} = \sum_{i=1}^{m} \tilde{y}_i(s)\alpha_i = \sum_{i=1}^{m} g_i(s)\tilde{u}_i(s)\alpha_i$$

(3.16.5)

$$= \sum_{i=1}^{m} g_i(s)\alpha_i\beta_i^T u(s) \equiv G(s)u(s)$$

That is,

$$G(s) = \sum_{j=1}^{m} g_j(s)\alpha_j\beta_j^T \qquad (3.16.6)$$

consisting of a linear combination of the transfer functions $g_j(s)$, $1 \leqslant j \leqslant m$, and the dyads (unity-rank matrices) $\alpha_j\beta_j^T$, $1 \leqslant j \leqslant m$.

In state-vector terms, suppose that $g_j(s)$ is generated by a controllable and observable model of state dimension n_j,

$$\dot{x}_j(t) = A_j x_j(t) + B_j \tilde{u}_j(t)$$
$$\tilde{y}_j(t) = C_j x_j(t) \qquad (3.16.7)$$

with characteristic polynomial and zero polynomial

$$\rho_{0j}(s) = |sI_{n_j} - A_j|, \qquad z_j(s) = \begin{vmatrix} sI_{n_j} - A & -B_j \\ C_j & 0 \end{vmatrix} \quad (3.16.8)$$

then $G(s)$ has a controllable and observable state-vector model of dimension $n = n_1 + n_2 + \ldots + n_m$, with state $x(t) = (x_1(t)^T, x_2(t)^T, \ldots, x_m(t)^T)^T$ of the form

$$\dot{x}(t) = \begin{pmatrix} A_1 & 0 & \cdots & 0 \\ 0 & A_2 & & \vdots \\ \vdots & & 0 & \\ 0 & \cdots & 0 & A_m \end{pmatrix} x(t) + \begin{pmatrix} B_1 & 0 & \cdots & 0 \\ \vdots & B_2 & & \vdots \\ \vdots & & & \dot{0} \\ 0 & \cdots & 0 & B_m \end{pmatrix} P_2 u(t)$$

$$y(t) = P_1 \begin{pmatrix} C_1 & 0 & \cdots & 0 \\ 0 & C_2 & & \vdots \\ \vdots & & 0 & \\ \dot{0} & \cdots & 0 & C_m \end{pmatrix} x(t) \qquad (3.16.9)$$

with characteristic polynomial and zero polynomial

$$\rho_0(s) = \rho_{01}(s) \ldots \rho_{0m}(s), \quad z(s) = z_1(s) \ldots z_m(s)|P_1 P_2| \quad (3.16.10)$$

The modal structure of $G(s)$ (c.f. Section 3.3) is revealed by noting that the following definition is equivalent to Definition 3.16.1.

Definition 3.16.2: An $m \times m$ transfer-function matrix $G(s)$ is dyadic if, and only if, $|G(s)| \not\equiv 0$ and there exists a nonsingular constant $m \times m$ matrix K_1 such that $G(s)K_1$ has m linearly independent *constant* eigenvectors α_j, $1 \leqslant j \leqslant m$,

$$G(s)K_1\alpha_j = g_j(s)\alpha_j \tag{3.16.11}$$

where $g_j(s)$, $1 \leqslant j \leqslant m$, are rational transfer functions.

Exercise 3.16.2
Use eqns. 3.16.11 and 3.16.6 to prove that $\beta_i^T K_1 \alpha_j = \delta_{ij}$ (the Kronecker delta). Hence show that an input of the form $\tilde{u}_i(s)\alpha_i$ to the composite system $G(s)K_1$ generates an output $y(s) = \tilde{y}_i(s)\alpha_i = g_i(s)\tilde{u}_i(s)\alpha_i$. Provide a modal interpretation of this result.

Exercise 3.16.3
Prove that it is always possible to choose $K_1 = P_2^{-1}P_1^{-1}$. Note that P_1, P_2 are not unique but, in general, are defined uniquely within scalar multiples of columns and rows, respectively.

Consider, for example, the transfer-function matrix[59]

$$G(s) = \frac{1}{(s+1)^2}\begin{pmatrix} 1-s & 2-s \\ \frac{1}{3}-s & 1-s \end{pmatrix} \tag{3.16.12}$$

Although it is not obvious by inspection, the reader should verify that

$$G(s) = \begin{pmatrix} 1 & 3 \\ 1 & 2 \end{pmatrix}\begin{pmatrix} \dfrac{1}{(s+1)} & 0 \\ 0 & \dfrac{1}{(s+1)^2} \end{pmatrix}\begin{pmatrix} -1 & -1 \\ \frac{2}{3} & 1 \end{pmatrix} \tag{3.16.13}$$

and hence that $G(s)$ is a dyadic transfer-function matrix. It is important to note that, despite the complex nonminimum-phase nature of the elements of $G(s)$, the subsystems

$$g_1(s) = \frac{1}{(s+1)}, \quad g_2(s) = \frac{1}{(s+1)^2} \tag{3.16.14}$$

have a simple structure and the system has no zeros. The decomposition is hence a simplification of the system dynamic structure and can be expected to be of importance in the design process. A convenient computational approach to the calculation of the decomposition (eqn. 3.16.1) is specified by the following step-by-step method:

Step 1: Choose a real number $\hat{s}$ such that $z(\hat{s}) \neq 0$ (i.e. $|G(\hat{s})| \neq 0$) and compute $G^{-1}(\hat{s})$. In many cases the choice of $\hat{s} = 0$ is sufficient.

Step 2: Calculate

$G(s)G^{-1}(\hat{s})$

$$= P_1 \, \text{diag}\,\{g_1(s), \ldots, g_m(s)\} P_2 P_2^{-1} \, \text{diag}\left\{\frac{1}{g_1(\hat{s})}, \ldots, \frac{1}{g_m(\hat{s})}\right\} P_1^{-1}$$

$$= P_1 \, \text{diag}\left\{\frac{g_1(s)}{g_1(\hat{s})}, \ldots, \frac{g_m(s)}{g_m(\hat{s})}\right\} P_1^{-1} \qquad (3.16.15)$$

Step 3: The eigenvectors of $G(s)G^{-1}(\hat{s})$ are simply $\alpha_1, \ldots, \alpha_m$ and P_1 is defined as in eqn. 3.16.4. The simplest approach is to evaluate the eigenvectors for a specific real $s_1 \neq \hat{s}$. If the $g_i(s)$, $1 \leqslant i \leqslant m$, are distinct, a trial and error choice of s_1 ensures that $g_i(s_1) \neq g_j(s_1)$, $i \neq j$, hence defining the eigenvectors uniquely to within a scalar multiple.

Step 4: Write $P_2 = P_1^{-1}G(\hat{s})$, and evaluate $g_i(s)$, $1 \leqslant i \leqslant m$, from the formula

$$P_1^{-1}G(s)P_2^{-1} = \text{diag}\left\{\frac{g_1(s)}{g_1(\hat{s})}, \ldots, \frac{g_m(s)}{g_m(\hat{s})}\right\} \qquad (3.16.16)$$

taking $g_i(\hat{s}) = 1$, $1 \leqslant i \leqslant m$, without loss of generality.

Exercise 3.16.4
Given an *arbitrary* $m \times m$ invertible $G(s)$ the above procedure can be used to evaluate matrices P_1, P_2. Show that $G(s)$ is a dyadic transfer-function matrix if, and only if, $P_1^{-1}G(s)P_2^{-1}$ is diagonal at all frequencies.

Exercise 3.16.5
Verify eqn. 3.16.13 using the above technique with $\hat{s} = 0, s_1 = 1$.

Consider the design of a unity-negative feedback system for the dyadic plant $G(s)$. From Fig. 3.16.1 and eqn. 3.16.2, it is noted that control is a simple matter if it is possible to control $\tilde{y}_i(s)$ using $\tilde{u}_i(s)$,

$$\tilde{y}_i(s) = g_i(s)\tilde{u}_i(s), \quad \tilde{u}_i(s) = k_i(s)\tilde{e}_i(s),$$

$$\tilde{e}_i(s) = \tilde{r}_i(s) - \tilde{y}_i(s) \qquad (3.16.17)$$

This conceptual scheme can be used to define the forward-path controller

$$K(s) = P_2^{-1} \, \text{diag} \, \{k_1(s), \dots, k_m(s)\} P_1^{-1} \qquad (3.16.18)$$

producing a return-difference determinant

$$|I_m + G(s)K(s)| = |I_m + P_1 \, \text{diag} \, \{g_1(s)k_1(s), \dots, g_m(s)k_m(s)\} P_1^{-1}|$$

$$= \prod_{j=1}^{m} (1 + g_j(s)k_j(s)) \qquad (3.16.19)$$

and closed-loop transfer-function matrix

$$H_c(s) = \{I_m + G(s)K(s)\}^{-1} G(s)K(s)$$

$$= P_1 P_1^{-1} \{I_m + G(s)K(s)\}^{-1} G(s)K(s) P_1 P_1^{-1}$$

$$= P_1 \, \text{diag} \left\{ \frac{g_i(s)k_i(s)}{1 + g_i(s)k_i(s)} \right\}_{1 \leqslant i \leqslant m} P_1^{-1} \qquad (3.16.20)$$

It is seen that the stability and performance of the closed-loop system is governed by the stability and performance of the scalar feedback systems (eqn. 3.16.17) and the output transformation P_1. The feedback system retains the overall modal structure of $G(s)$ i.e. $H_c(s)$ is a dyadic transfer-function matrix and it is easily verified that

$$H_c(s)\alpha_j = \frac{g_j(s)k_j(s)}{1 + g_j(s)k_j(s)} \alpha_j, \qquad 1 \leqslant j \leqslant m \quad (3.16.21)$$

Steady-state error: Eqn. 3.16.20 implies that the steady-state errors in response to unit-step demands are small if, and only if, the scalar-feedback systems have small steady-state errors.

Interaction effects: In a similar manner to the analysis of Section 3.8, interaction effects are small if the scalar feedback systems have similar dynamic characteristics or if the output matrix P_1 is nearly diagonal.

System integrity: Considering the case of sensor failure in loop j,

$$e_j^T \{I_m + G(s)K(s)\}^{-1} = e_j^T P_1 P_1^{-1} \{I_m + G(s)K(s)\}^{-1} P_1 P_1^{-1} e_j$$

$$= e_j^T P_1 \, \text{diag} \left\{ \frac{1}{1 + g_i(s)k_i(s)} \right\}_{1 \leqslant i \leqslant m} P_1^{-1} e_j$$

$$= \sum_{i=1}^{m} \frac{1}{1 + g_i(s)k_i(s)} (e_j^T P_1 e_i)(e_i^T P_1^{-1} e_j)$$

$$(3.16.22)$$

For the case of actuator failure in loop j,

$$e_j^T\{I_m + K(s)G(s)\}^{-1}e_j = e_j^T P_2^{-1} P_2 \{I_m + K(s)G(s)\}^{-1} P_2^{-1} P_2 e_j$$

$$= e_j^T P_2^{-1} \text{ diag}\left\{\frac{1}{1 + g_i(s)k_i(s)}\right\}_{1 \leqslant i \leqslant m} P_2 e_j$$

$$= \sum_{i=1}^{m} \frac{1}{1 + g_i(s)k_i(s)} (e_j^T P_2^{-1} e_i)(e_i^T P_2 e_j) \quad (3.16.23)$$

Alternatively,

$$e_j^T\{I_m + G(s)K(s)\}^{-1}e_j = 1 - \sum_{i=1}^{m} \frac{g_i(s)k_i(s)}{1 + g_i(s)k_i(s)} (e_j^T P_1 e_i)(e_i^T P_1^{-1} e_j)$$

$$e_j^T\{I_m + K(s)G(s)\}^{-1}e_j = 1 - \sum_{i=1}^{m} \frac{g_i(s)k_i(s)}{1 + g_i(s)k_i(s)} (e_j^T P_2^{-1} e_i)(e_i^T P_2 e_j)$$

$$(3.16.24)$$

These expressions can be analysed using the well known techniques of the Nyquist diagram and counting encirclements. For example, if the closed-loop system is asymptotically stable, then the system is stable in the presence of a sensor failure in loop j if, and only if, the Nyquist plot of

$$(-1) \sum_{i=1}^{m} \frac{g_i(s)k_i(s)}{1 + g_i(s)k_i(s)} (e_j^T P_1 e_i)(e_i^T P_1^{-1} e_j) \quad (3.16.25)$$

does not encircle, or intersect, the $(-1, 0)$ point of the complex plane. In a similar manner, the system is stable in the presence of an actuator failure in loop j if, and only if, the Nyquist plot of

$$(-1) \sum_{i=1}^{m} \frac{g_i(s)k_i(s)}{1 + g_i(s)k_i(s)} (e_j^T P_2^{-1} e_i)(e_i^T P_2 e_j) \quad (3.16.26)$$

does not encircle, or intersect, the $(-1, 0)$ point of the complex plane. It should be noted that the relevant frequency responses depend explicitly on the scalar feedback systems $g_i k_i/(1 + g_i k_i)$ and the input-output matrices P_2, P_1. In particular, if the system is found to be unstable in the presence of a sensor or actuator failure, examination of the contributions of the subsystems to the frequency response exprns. 3.16.25 and 3.16.26 may indicate the source of instability and suggest modifications to the compensating networks $k_1(s), \ldots, k_m(s)$.

To illustrate the application of the technique, consider the dyadic system (eqn. 3.16.12) with

$$P_1 = \begin{pmatrix} 1 & 3 \\ 1 & 2 \end{pmatrix}, \quad P_2 = \begin{pmatrix} -1 & -1 \\ \frac{2}{3} & 1 \end{pmatrix},$$

$$g_1(s) = \frac{1}{(s+1)} \quad g_2(s) = \frac{1}{(s+1)^2} \tag{3.16.27}$$

and forward-path controller

$$K(s) = P_2^{-1} \begin{pmatrix} k_1(s) & 0 \\ 0 & k_2(s) \end{pmatrix} P_1^{-1}$$

$$= \begin{pmatrix} -3 & -3 \\ 2 & 3 \end{pmatrix} \begin{pmatrix} k_1(s) & 0 \\ 0 & k_2(s) \end{pmatrix} \begin{pmatrix} -2 & 3 \\ 1 & -1 \end{pmatrix} \tag{3.16.28}$$

Initially, suppose that proportional-control action is required with $k_1(s) = k_1$, $k_2(s) = k_2$. Using eqn. 3.16.20, the closed-loop transfer-function matrix takes the form

$$H_c(s) = \begin{pmatrix} 1 & 3 \\ 1 & 2 \end{pmatrix} \begin{pmatrix} \dfrac{k_1}{s+1+k_1} & 0 \\ 0 & \dfrac{k_2}{s^2+2s+1+k_2} \end{pmatrix} \begin{pmatrix} -2 & 3 \\ 1 & -1 \end{pmatrix} \tag{3.16.28}$$

so that the system is stable for $k_1 + 1 > 0$, $k_2 + 1 > 0$. Consider the response to a unit-step demand in $y_1(t)$,

$$y(s) = H_c(s) \frac{1}{s} \begin{pmatrix} 1 \\ 0 \end{pmatrix} = \frac{-2k_1}{s(s+1+k_1)} \begin{pmatrix} 1 \\ 1 \end{pmatrix} + \frac{k_2}{s(s^2+2s+1+k_2)} \begin{pmatrix} 3 \\ 2 \end{pmatrix}$$

$$\tag{3.16.29}$$

It is easily verified that steady-state errors are small only if both k_1 and k_2 are large. Although closed-loop stability places no constraint on the relative magnitudes of k_1 and k_2, the design requirement of low closed-loop interaction places quite severe restrictions (see Section 3.3). Consider, for example, the case of $k_1 \gg 1$ (required for small steady-state errors), then, independent of the choice of $k_2 > 0$, the first term in eqn. 3.16.29 will respond more rapidly than the second giving

$$y(t) \simeq \frac{-2k_1}{k_1+1}(1 - e^{-(k_1+1)t}) \begin{pmatrix} 1 \\ 1 \end{pmatrix}, \quad 0 \leqslant t \ll 1 \tag{3.16.30}$$

indicating a large degree of interaction in the vicinity of $t = 0+$. For

$t \gg k_1^{-1}$, the first term in eqn. 3.16.29 will have reached its steady state, giving

$$y(t) \simeq \frac{-2k_1}{k_1 + 1}\begin{pmatrix}1\\1\end{pmatrix} + \frac{k_2}{k_2 + 1}(1 - e^{-t}\psi(t))\begin{pmatrix}3\\2\end{pmatrix} \quad (3.16.31)$$

where $\psi(t)$ is a periodic function. The overall response is illustrated schematically in Fig. 3.16.2.

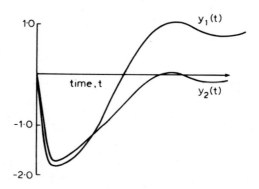

Fig. 3.16.2 Response for $k_1 \gg 1$ to a unit-step demand in $y_1(t)$

Exercise 3.16.6
Obtain similar expressions to eqns. 3.16.30 and 3.16.31 for the output response to a unit-step demand in output $y_2(t)$ with $k_1 \gg 1$. Sketch your results and note that the system has approximately 300% interaction.

An examination of eqn. 3.16.29 indicates that the problem lies in the difference in rank of the transfer functions in eqn. 3.16.28. The first term represents a first-order-lag type response with time constant $(k_1 + 1)^{-1}$ whilst the second term has second-order dynamics tending to its steady-state value at a rate proportional to e^{-t}, independent of the value of k_2. In effect, the use of proportional control generates a conflict situation requiring high gains to reduce steady-state errors yet simultaneously requiring low gains to reduce closed-loop interaction effects. If it is accepted that a high gain k_1 is required to reduce steady-state errors, it is necessary to introduce phase advance into $g_2(s)$ to increase its response speed. Choosing, for simplicity,

$$k_2(s) = k_2 \frac{(s+1)}{(s+p)}, \quad p > 0 \qquad (3.16.32)$$

then eqn. 3.16.29 becomes

$$y(s) = \frac{-2k_1}{s(s+1+k_1)} \binom{1}{1} + \frac{k_2}{s(s^2+(p+1)s+p+k_2)} \binom{3}{2} \qquad (3.16.33)$$

The first term has a first-order type of response $e^{-(k_1+1)t}$, the second having a second-order response with envelope decaying as $e^{-1/2(p+1)t}$. This suggests that a reasonable attempt at equalising the subsystem response speeds can be obtained by setting

$$k_1 + 1 = \tfrac{1}{2}(p+1) \qquad (3.16.34)$$

With this assumption, it is easily seen that an increase in phase advance makes possible a reduction in steady-state error. For simplicity, take $p = 9$ so that $k_1 = 4$ and choose $k_2 = 41 \cdot 0$ to produce a damping ratio of $0 \cdot 7$. The resulting responses to unit-step demands are shown in Fig. 3.16.3 where it is seen that the system responds rapidly with relatively small steady-state error. Note also that interaction effects are approximately 70% but are confined to only a small time interval. The responses could be improved by optimisation of the parameters k_1 and k_2, but it is likely that the improvement will be only marginal owing to the essential incompatibility of dynamic behaviour of $g_1(s)$ and $g_2(s)$.

Exercise 3.16.7
Consider the minor-loop compensation scheme,

$$y(s) = G(s)u(s), u(s) = v(s) - H(s)y(s),$$

$$v(s) = K(s)e(s), e(s) = r(s) - y(s)$$

with $K(s)$ as in eqn. 3.16.18 and $H(s) = P_2^{-1} \text{diag}\, \{h_1(s), \ldots, h_m(s)\} P_1^{-1}$. Show that the closed-loop transfer-function matrix takes the form

$$H_c(s) = P_1 \text{diag} \left\{ \frac{\tilde{g}_i(s)k_i(s)}{1 + \tilde{g}_i(s)k_i(s)} \right\}_{1 \leqslant i \leqslant m} P_1^{-1}$$

where

$$\tilde{g}_i(s) = g_i(s)/(1 + g_i(s)h_i(s)), \qquad 1 \leqslant i \leqslant m$$

Suggest how rate feedback elements in $h_2(s)$ may be used to improve the closed-loop response in the example discussed above.

Finally consider the integrity of the closed-loop system with $k_1(s) = k_1$ and $k_2(s)$ as defined in eqn. 3.16.32. For the case of sensor failure in loop one, (eqn. 3.16.22)

$$e_1^T(I + GK)^{-1}e_1 = \frac{(-2)(s+1)}{s+1+k_1} + \frac{3(s+1)(s+p)}{s^2 + (1+p)s + p + k_2}$$

$$= \frac{(s+1)(s^2 + s(p+1+3k_1) + p(1+3k_1) - 2k_2)}{(s+1+k_1)(s^2 + (1+p)s + p + k_2)}$$

$$(3.16.35)$$

indicating stability if, and only if,

$$p + 1 + 3k_1 > 0, \quad p(1 + 3k_1) - 2k_2 > 0 \qquad (3.16.36)$$

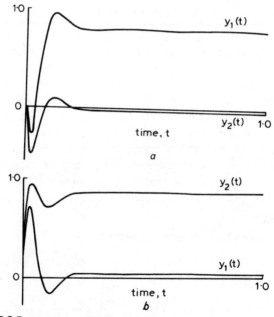

Fig. 3.16.3 Responses to unit-step demands
  a Responses to a unit-step demand in output one
  b Responses to a unit-step demand in output two

For the case of sensor failure in loop two,

$$e_2^T(I + GK)^{-1}e_2 = \frac{3(s+1)}{(s+1+k_1)} + \frac{(-2)(s+1)(s+p)}{s^2 + (1+p)s + p + k_2}$$

$$= \frac{(s+1)(s^2 + s(1+p-2k_1) + p + 3k_2 - 2k_1p)}{(s+1+k_1)(s^2 + (1+p)s + p + k_2)}$$

$$(3.16.37)$$

indicating stability if, and only if,

$$1 + p - 2k_1 > 0, \quad p + 3k_2 - 2k_1p > 0 \qquad (3.16.38)$$

Regarding the case of proportional control as generated by $p = 1$, expr. 3.16.38 indicates that it is necessary that $k_1 < 1$ – an extreme constraint on the system performance, alleviated by choosing $p > 1$. In particular, for the given design ($k_1 = 4$, $p = 9$, $k_2 = 41 \cdot 0$) it is easily verified that the closed-loop system is stable in the presence of sensor failure in either loop.

Exercise 3.16.8
Investigate, in a similar manner, the stability in the presence of actuator failures.

3.17 On the effect of symmetry

The reader will have observed that, in almost all the preceding sections, an important part of the control analysis is an investigation of structural decompositions of $G(s)$. In many cases, such decompositions can be given an important physical interpretation in terms of physical properties of the systems considered. This Section considers an important aspect of system structure encountered in situations where the plant possesses spatial symmetry (see, for example, References 29 and 35).

Reflection symmetry: The simplest case represents a generalisation of the analysis of Section 3.3. Consider a two-input/two-output system of the form shown in Fig. 3.17.1a consisting of two identical subsystems with symmetric interaction effects (for simplicity we regard each subsystem as a vessel, interaction being termed the intervessel flow of power, material etc). An immediate consequence of the physical symmetry is that $G(s)$ is invariant under interchange of input and output subscripts i.e.

$$\begin{pmatrix} y_1(s) \\ y_2(s) \end{pmatrix} = G(s) \begin{pmatrix} u_1(s) \\ u_2(s) \end{pmatrix} \qquad (3.17.1)$$

and

$$\begin{pmatrix} y_2(s) \\ y_1(s) \end{pmatrix} = G(s) \begin{pmatrix} u_2(s) \\ u_1(s) \end{pmatrix} \tag{3.17.2}$$

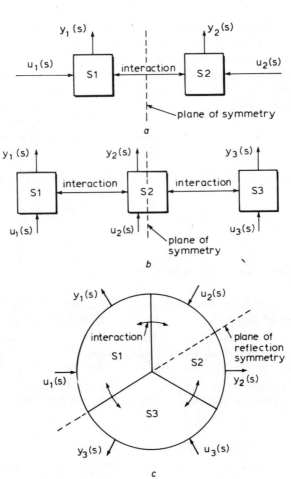

Fig. 3.17.1 Symmetrical configurations
    a Two-input/two-output system
    b Identical vessels with symmetric interaction effects
    c Identical zones with identical interaction dynamics

A compact way of representing these relations is to write

$$\begin{pmatrix} 0 & 1 \\ 1 & 0 \end{pmatrix} G(s) = G(s) \begin{pmatrix} 0 & 1 \\ 1 & 0 \end{pmatrix} \tag{3.17.3}$$

so that $G(s)$ takes the intuitively obvious form, (c.f. Section 3.3)

$$G(s) = \begin{pmatrix} G_1(s) & G_2(s) \\ G_2(s) & G_1(s) \end{pmatrix} \tag{3.17.4}$$

It is an interesting observation that this structure is independent of the detailed dynamic modelling of the plant and is a consequence solely of the physical symmetry of the system. In particular, it follows that $G(s)$ has frequency independent eigenvectors

$$w_1 = \begin{pmatrix} 1 \\ 1 \end{pmatrix}, \quad w_2 = \begin{pmatrix} -1 \\ 1 \end{pmatrix} \tag{3.17.5}$$

with corresponding eigenvalues

$$g_1(s) = G_1(s) + G_2(s), \quad g_2(s) = G_1(s) - G_2(s) \tag{3.17.6}$$

and if $T = [w_1, w_2]$,

$$T^{-1}G(s)T = \text{diag}\{g_1(s), g_2(s)\} \tag{3.17.7}$$

That is, $G(s)$ is a dyadic transfer-function matrix and control design can be approached using the techniques of Section 3.16.

A more complex situation is illustrated in Fig. 3.17.1*b* consisting of three identical vessels with symmetric interaction effects. Note that $G(s)$ will be invariant under interchange of vessels $S1$ and $S3$ i.e.

$$\begin{pmatrix} 0 & 0 & 1 \\ 0 & 1 & 0 \\ 1 & 0 & 0 \end{pmatrix} G(s) = G(s) \begin{pmatrix} 0 & 0 & 1 \\ 0 & 1 & 0 \\ 1 & 0 & 0 \end{pmatrix} \tag{3.17.8}$$

from which

$$G(s) = \begin{pmatrix} G_1(s) & G_2(s) & G_3(s) \\ G_4(s) & G_5(s) & G_4(s) \\ G_3(s) & G_2(s) & G_1(s) \end{pmatrix} \tag{3.17.9}$$

The most convenient approach to analysis is to examine the relation $G^{-1}(s)y(s) = u(s)$ and note that $y_i(s)$ depends physically on $u_i(s)$, $y_{i+1}(s)$ and $y_{i-1}(s)$ e.g. suppose that

$$G^{-1}(s) = \begin{pmatrix} \hat{G}_1(s) & \hat{G}_2(s) & 0 \\ \hat{G}_2(s) & \hat{G}_1(s) & \hat{G}_2(s) \\ 0 & \hat{G}_2(s) & \hat{G}_1(s) \end{pmatrix} \tag{3.17.10}$$

with frequency-independent eigenvectors,

$$w_1 = \begin{pmatrix} 1 \\ \sqrt{2} \\ 1 \end{pmatrix}, \quad w_2 = \begin{pmatrix} 1 \\ 0 \\ -1 \end{pmatrix}, \quad w_3 = \begin{pmatrix} 1 \\ -\sqrt{2} \\ 1 \end{pmatrix}$$

and corresponding eigenvalues

$$g_1(s) = \hat{G}_1(s) + \sqrt{2}\hat{G}_2(s), \quad g_2(s) = \hat{G}_1(s),$$
$$g_3(s) = \hat{G}_1(s) - \sqrt{2}\hat{G}_2(s) \tag{3.17.11}$$

Defining $T = [w_1, w_2, w_3]$, then

$$T^{-1}G^{-1}(s)T = \text{diag}\{g_1(s), g_2(s), g_3(s)\} \tag{3.17.12}$$

from which it is easily verified that $G(s)$ is a dyadic transfer-function matrix.

Reflection plus rotation symmetry: A form of symmetry found in spatially distributed systems such as nuclear reactors[35] is illustrated in Fig. 3.17.1c where the system consists of three dynamically identical zones with identical interaction dynamics. In this case $G(s)$ is invariant under interchange of $S1$ and $S3$ and also invariant under rotation through $2\pi/3$ i.e. $G(s)$ satisfies eqn. 3.17.8 and also

$$\begin{pmatrix} 0 & 0 & 1 \\ 1 & 0 & 0 \\ 0 & 1 & 0 \end{pmatrix} G(s) = G(s) \begin{pmatrix} 0 & 0 & 1 \\ 1 & 0 & 0 \\ 0 & 1 & 0 \end{pmatrix} \tag{3.17.13}$$

so that,

$$G(s) = \begin{pmatrix} G_1(s) & G_2(s) & G_2(s) \\ G_2(s) & G_1(s) & G_2(s) \\ G_2(s) & G_2(s) & G_1(s) \end{pmatrix} \tag{3.17.14}$$

with frequency-independent eigenvectors,

$$w_1 = \begin{pmatrix} 1 \\ 1 \\ 1 \end{pmatrix}, \quad w_2 = \begin{pmatrix} 0 \\ 1 \\ -1 \end{pmatrix}, \quad w_3 = \begin{pmatrix} 1 \\ -1 \\ 0 \end{pmatrix} \tag{3.17.15}$$

and eigenvalues

$$g_1(s) = G_1(s) + 2G_2(s), \quad g_2(s) = G_1(s) - G_2(s) = g_3(s) \tag{3.17.16}$$

If $T = [w_1, w_2, w_3]$, then

$$T^{-1}G(s)T = \text{diag}\{g_1(s), g_2(s), g_3(s)\} \qquad (3.17.17)$$

so that $G(s)$ is a dyadic transfer-function matrix.

Exercise 3.17.1

Suggest physical interpretations of the eigenvectors of $G(s)$ in the above examples.

A more detailed analysis of spatial symmetry is best put in the context of matrix representations of finite groups (Reference 35). This is beyond the scope of this text so we content ourselves with the observation that systems with a degree of spatial symmetry tend to exhibit dyadic properties.

3.18 Summary

Perhaps the most important observation on the contents of this chapter is the overriding theme of system decomposition (in the form of decomposition of $G(s)$) into a modal type of structure by the use of transformation techniques and, possibly, suitable choice of minor-loop compensation elements. The system can then be represented in a pseudoclassical form characterised, in general, by constant input and output transformation matrices P_1, P_2 and a set of m subsystems $g_i(s)$, $1 \leqslant i \leqslant m$, characterising the dynamic behaviour of the overall system. The control structures derived retain sufficient degrees of freedom to enable high performance control systems to be designed in a straightforward manner. The material has both strong and weak points:

(a) it is assumed that the structure of the forward-path controller $K(s)$ is unconstrained in the sense that every element is available as a design parameter. This means that if, for example, $K(s)$ is constrained by practical considerations to be a diagonal controller (as may be the case if the multivariable analysis is to be used to tune an existing control configuration), the analysis cannot be applied. In such cases, multivariable theory is unlikely to be of any help

(b) the system structures discussed in this chapter quite obviously only represent a small class of all possible mathematical structures. The reader should not dismiss the material out of hand as they represent a useful introduction to principles and, as illustrated in Sections 3.7, it is known that many physical systems can usefully be approximated by such models

(c) the control structures suggested are in harmony with the structure of $G(s)$ in the sense that they enable the separate compensation of the subsystem dynamics $g_i(s)$, $1 \leqslant i \leqslant m$, by individual subsystems within the controller structure, and provide heuristic but highly effective techniques for ensuring that the closed-loop system has a small degree of interaction.

3.19 Problems and exercises

1 Show that the system described by the transfer-function matrix

$$G(s) = \frac{1}{(s+1)(s+\alpha)} \begin{pmatrix} s+1 & s+1 \\ -1 & s+\alpha-1 \end{pmatrix}$$

is a multivariable first-order lag. Calculate a controllable and observable state-vector model for the process and verify that the system has open-loop poles $s = -1$ and $s = -\alpha$. By considering a unity-negative feedback system with forward-path proportional controller $K = kA_0 - A_1$, show that the closed-loop system has interaction effects and steady-state errors of less than 10% in response to unit-step demands if, and only if, $k > 10 \max(1, \alpha)$. Alternatively, if $K = A_0 \operatorname{diag}\{k_1, k_2\} - A_1$, show that the design requirement is achieved if, and only if, $k_1 > 10 \max(1, \alpha)$ and $k_2 > 10$. In particular, if $\alpha \gg 1$, the required gain in loop two is considerably reduced.

2 Apply the technique of Section 3.7 to the system

$$\dot{x}(t) = \begin{pmatrix} -2 & 1 & 0.2 \\ 1 & -2 & 0.1 \\ 1 & 2 & -2 \end{pmatrix} x(t) + \begin{pmatrix} 1 & 0 \\ 0 & 1 \\ 0 & 0 \end{pmatrix} u(t)$$

$$y(t) = \begin{pmatrix} 1 & 0 & 0 \\ 0 & 1 & 0 \end{pmatrix} x(t)$$

by writing $G^{-1}(s) = sA_0 + A_1 + A_0 H(s)$, where

$$H(s) = \frac{s}{2(s+2)} \begin{pmatrix} 0.2 \\ 0.1 \end{pmatrix} \begin{bmatrix} 1 & 2 \end{bmatrix}$$

Hence show that the closed-loop system is stable with $K(s) = kA_0 - A_1$

if $k > \|H\| = 0.3$. Investigate the exact structure of the closed-loop system using the analysis of Section 3.15.

3 Show that the two-degree-of-freedom gyro discussed by Briggs[4] is a second-order lag of the restricted type analysed in Section 3.8.

4 Extend your results for problem 1 to show that the system

$$G(s) = \frac{1}{s(s+1)(s+\alpha)} \begin{pmatrix} s+1 & s+1 \\ -1 & s+\alpha-1 \end{pmatrix}$$

is a multivariable second order-type system. If $\alpha = 2$, use the techniques of Section 3.8 to design a unity-negative feedback system possessing fast response speeds, a damping ratio of approximately 0.7 in both loops and small interaction effects. Comment on the difficulties encountered if $\alpha \to 0+$ and show how they can be removed by the use of minor-loop rate feedback (Hint: investigate the damping of the subsystems $g_1(s), g_2(s)$).

5 Consider the design of a unity-negative feedback system for the control of the second-order lag

$$G^{-1}(s) = s^2 \begin{pmatrix} 2 & 0 \\ 0 & 1 \end{pmatrix} + s \begin{pmatrix} 2(1+\alpha) & 2 \\ 1 & 1+\alpha \end{pmatrix} + \begin{pmatrix} 2 & 2 \\ 1 & 2 \end{pmatrix}$$

using the techniques of Section 3.9 and $\alpha = 10, 1$ and 0, respectively. In the case of $\alpha = 0$, show that rate feedback is required to introduce damping into an oscillating subsystem. Suggest a physical reason why control difficulties are reduced as α increases (Hint: look at the damping of the subsystems $g_1(s), g_2(s)$ and the criterion for small closed-loop interaction).

6 Show that the system

$$G(s) = \frac{1}{(s+1)^3 - 1} \begin{pmatrix} 1 & s^2 + 2s + 1 \\ s+1 & 1 \end{pmatrix}$$

is a mixed-type system. Use the analysis of Section 3.13 to design a unity-negative feedback configuration for $G(s)$ taking care to ensure that the closed-loop system exhibits small steady-state errors and interaction effects in response to unit-step demands.

7 Consider an $m \times m$ system

$$G(s) = \frac{1}{p(s)} \{L_1 + sL_2\}, \quad |G(s)| \neq 0$$

with $p(s)$ a scalar polynomial and L_1, L_2 constant $m \times m$ matrices.

Show that there exists a real scalar α such that $|L_1 + \alpha L_2| \neq 0$ and that $G(s)$ is a dyadic transfer-function matrix if $L_2\{L_1 + \alpha L_2\}^{-1}$ has a diagonal canonical form. Apply the result to the liquid-level system of Section 3.3 and problem 1.

8 Prove that the $m \times m$ invertible system $G(s)$ is dyadic if, and only if, $G^{-1}(s)$ is dyadic. Hence show that, if the second-order system eqn. 3.9.1 is such that $A_0^{-1}A_1$ had distinct eigenvalues, then $G(s)$ is dyadic if, and only if, $A_0^{-1}A_1 A_0^{-1}A_2 = A_0^{-1}A_2 A_0^{-1}A_1$. Apply the result to the mechanical system of Exercise 3.9.1 with the data $m_1 k_2 = m_2 k_1$, and check the result directly.

9 If $G_i(s)$, $1 \leq i \leq k$, are $m \times m$ first-order lags, show that $G(s) = G_1(s)G_2(s) \ldots G_k(s)$ is a multivariable kth-order lag.

10 Let $G(s)$ be an $m \times m$ invertible system satisfying the invariance relation

$$P_1 G(s) P_2 = G(s) P_2 P_1$$

where P_1, P_2 are constant nonsingular matrices. If P_1 has distinct eigenvalues, prove that $G(s)$ is a dyadic transfer-function matrix (Hint: show that $G(s)P_2$ has the same eigenvectors as P_1). Apply the result to the transfer-function matrix

$$G(s) = \begin{pmatrix} \dfrac{1}{s} & \dfrac{2s+1}{s(s+1)} \\ \dfrac{1}{s+1} & \dfrac{2s+1}{s(s+1)} \end{pmatrix}$$

with

$$P_1 = \begin{pmatrix} 0 & 1 \\ 1 & 0 \end{pmatrix}, \quad P_2 = \begin{pmatrix} 1 & -1 \\ 0 & 1 \end{pmatrix}$$

to show that

$$G(s) = \begin{pmatrix} 1 & -1 \\ 1 & 1 \end{pmatrix} \begin{pmatrix} \dfrac{2s+1}{s(s+1)} & 0 \\ 0 & \dfrac{1}{s(s+1)} \end{pmatrix} \begin{pmatrix} 0.5 & 1 \\ -0.5 & 0 \end{pmatrix}$$

Hence design a unity-negative feedback system for $G(s)$.

11 Given an $m \times m$ invertible transfer-function matrix $G(s)$ satisfying

$$P_2 G^{-1}(s) P_1 = \text{diag}\{g_1^{-1}(s), g_2^{-1}(s), \ldots, g_m^{-1}(s)\} - P_3$$

where P_1, P_2, P_3 are constant $m \times m$ matrices with $|P_1 P_2| \neq 0$ and $g_1(s), \ldots, g_m(s)$ are scalar transfer functions, show that the use of the minor-loop feedback

$$u(s) = v(s) - P_2^{-1}P_3P_1^{-1}y(s)$$

generates a relation of the form $y(s) = G_0(s)v(s)$ where $G_0(s)$ is a dyadic transfer-function matrix. Relate this result to the analysis of Section 3.13 with $m = 2, r = 1$ by using a forward-path controller $K_0(s)$

$$v(s) = K_0(s)e(s), \quad e(s) = r(s) - y(s)$$

$$K_0(s) = P_2^{-1} \operatorname{diag} \{k_1(s), k_2(s), \ldots, k_m(s)\} P_1^{-1}.$$

generating a closed-loop transfer-function matrix

$$H_c(s) = P_1 \operatorname{diag} \left\{ \frac{g_i(s)k_i(s)}{1 + g_i(s)k_i(s)} \right\}_{1 \leqslant i \leqslant m} P_1^{-1}$$

If the minor-loop element is removed, investigate the effect on closed-loop performance of using the forward-path controller $K(s) = K_0(s) + P_2^{-1}P_3P_1^{-1}$.

12 Suppose, after completion of a design, the closed-loop transfer-function matrix takes the form

$$H_c(s) = P_1 \begin{pmatrix} \dfrac{20}{s + 21} & 0 \\ 0 & \dfrac{20}{s + 20} \end{pmatrix} P_1^{-1}$$

where

$$P_1 = \begin{pmatrix} 1 & \beta \\ 1 & 1 \end{pmatrix}, \quad \beta \neq 1$$

The arguments used in this chapter suggest that the closed-loop system possesses small steady-state error and interaction effects in response to unit-step demands will be small as the subsystem dynamics are virtually identical. This result depends on the structure of P_1 (in this simple example represented as the parameter β), as is illustrated by computing the steady-state matrix

$$H_c(0) = \begin{pmatrix} 1 & 0 \\ 0 & 1 \end{pmatrix} - \frac{1}{21(1 - \beta)} \begin{pmatrix} 1 \\ 1 \end{pmatrix} (1 \quad -\beta)$$

indicating that steady-state errors can be large if $\beta \simeq 1$ (i.e. P_1 is 'almost singular' or, equivalently, if the columns of P_1 are almost colinear). Representing the overall steady-state error in terms of the sum of the moduli-squared of the elements of $I - H_c(0)$

$$\frac{4}{(21)^2}\left\{\frac{1}{(1-\beta)^2} + \frac{\beta^2}{(1-\beta)^2}\right\}$$

it is seen that the overall steady-state error is a minimum when $\beta = -1$ i.e. when the columns of P_1 are orthogonal. Suggest a physical argument extending the result to the general case of the $m \times m$ system

$$H_c(s) = P_1 \text{ diag } \{q_1(s), \ldots, q_m(s)\}P_1^{-1}$$

where $q_i(s)$, $1 \leqslant i \leqslant m$, represent 'almost identical' dynamics. Show that the response of the example system to a unit-step demand in $y_1(t)$ is

$$y(s) = H_c(s)\frac{1}{s}\binom{1}{0} = \frac{20}{s(s+21)}\binom{1}{1}\frac{1}{(1-\beta)} - \frac{20}{s(s+20)}\binom{\beta}{1}\frac{1}{(1-\beta)}$$

and investigate the effect of the structural parameter β on the inter-action effects. In particular, show that interaction effects are small if $\beta = -1$.

13 Show that a multivariable first-order lag $G^{-1}(s) = sA_0 + A_1$, $|A_0| \neq 0$ subjected to unity-negative feedback control with $K(s) = kA_0 - A_1$ is stable with respect to sensor failure in loop j if, and only if, the steady-state error in output $y_j(t)$ in response to a unit-step demand in $y_j(t)$ is strictly positive (Reference 41).

Chapter 4

Eigenvalue-type methods
in feedback design

Given the transfer-function matrix description of input-output dynamics, it is a natural first step to consider the use and interpretation of the eigenvalues and eigenvectors of $G(s)$ for the purposes of feedback design (Section 3.3). This approach will be seen to be an important conceptual tool in the analysis of feedback dynamics making possible a practical generalisation of the ideas discussed in chapter three to cope with the systematic design of a unity-negative feedback system for a general form of $m \times m$, invertible strictly proper system $G(s)$. It is worthwhile noting at this stage that it is unnecessarily restrictive to consider eigenvector transformations alone. The general form of transformation used can be represented as

$$G(s) = P_1(s)H(s)P_2(s)$$

where $P_1(s)$, $H(s)$, $P_2(s)$ are $m \times m$ matrix functions of the complex variable s and, by assumption, $H(s)$ is taken to possess useful structural properties so constructed as to simplify the design procedure. The two main structures considered are:

(a) $P_1(s)P_2(s) = I_m$ and $H(s) = \text{diag}\{g_1(s), \dots, g_2(s)\}$ when $P_1(s)$ is the eigenvector matrix of $G(s)$ and $g_i(s)$, $1 \leq i \leq m$, are the eigenvalues of $G(s)$

(b) $P_1(s)$ and $P_2(s)$ are constant nonsingular matrices and $H(s)$ is 'approximately diagonal' over a frequency range of interest. For example, if $G(s)$ is dyadic it is possible to choose P_1, P_2 such that $H(s)$ is diagonal at all frequencies

4.1 Commutative-controller design technique

The lesson to be learned from Chapter 3 is that the key to the feedback-control analysis of the $m \times m$ strictly proper, invertible system $G(s)$ is the analysis of its structure. The concept of structure is elusive, ranging from the ideas of mathematical structures, physical dynamic structure to simple ideas of spatial configurations. The ideas used in this Section are based on the simple structural concepts introduced by MacFarlane[18] using eigenanalysis of $G(s)$. The reader may be interested to compare the following general development with the simple analysis of Section 3.3.

Suppose that $G(s)$ has m eigenvalues $g_j(s)$, $1 \leqslant j \leqslant m$, and linearly independent eigenvectors $w_j(s)$, $1 \leqslant j \leqslant m$,

$$G(s)w_j(s) = g_j(s)w_j(s), \qquad 1 \leqslant j \leqslant m \qquad (4.1.1)$$

Following the analysis of Section 3.3, it is instructive to interpret $w_j(s)$, $1 \leqslant j \leqslant m$, as modal types of behaviour in the sense that an input of the form $u(s) = w_j(s)$ generates an output $y(s) = g_j(s)w_j(s)$, unchanged in direction but modified in magnitude by the frequency-dependent scalar $g_j(s)$. A more convenient form of eqn. 4.1.1 is obtained by defining the eigenvector matrix

$$W(s) = [w_1(s), \ldots, w_m(s)] \qquad (4.1.2)$$

when

$$V(s)G(s)W(s) = \mathrm{diag}\,\{g_1(s), \ldots, g_m(s)\} \qquad (4.1.3)$$

where $V(s) = W^{-1}(s)$. Consider the design of a unity-negative feedback system for the plant $G(s)$, with forward-path controller

$$K(s) = W(s)\,\mathrm{diag}\,\{k_1(s), \ldots, k_m(s)\}V(s) \qquad (4.1.4)$$

It is easily verified that $K(s)$ has eigenvectors $w_j(s)$ with eigenvalues equal to the proper scalar transfer functions $k_j(s)$, $1 \leqslant j \leqslant m$ i.e.

$$K(s)w_j(s) = k_j(s)w_j(s) \qquad (4.1.5)$$

and the controller $K(s)$ retains the 'modal' structure of the plant $G(s)$. MacFarlane terms the controller $K(s)$ a *commutative controller* due to the property,

$$G(s)K(s) = W(s)\,\mathrm{diag}\,\{g_j(s)\}_{1 \leqslant j \leqslant m}V(s)\,W(s)\,\mathrm{diag}\,\{k_j(s)\}_{1 \leqslant j \leqslant m}V(s)$$

$$= K(s)G(s) \qquad (4.1.6)$$

The closed-loop transfer-function matrix takes the form

$$H_c(s) = \{I_m + G(s)K(s)\}^{-1}G(s)K(s)$$

$$= W(s)\,\mathrm{diag}\,\left\{\frac{g_j(s)k_j(s)}{1 + g_j(s)k_j(s)}\right\}_{1 \leqslant j \leqslant m} V(s) \qquad (4.1.7)$$

indicating that the closed-loop performance is governed by the scalar feedback systems

$$\frac{g_j(s)k_j(s)}{1 + g_j(s)k_j(s)}, \qquad 1 \leqslant j \leqslant m \qquad (4.1.8)$$

and the structure of the eigenvector-transformation matrix $W(s)$. Note that $W(s)$ is the eigenvector matrix of $H_c(s)$, and is, in general, frequency-dependent.

Exercise 4.1.1
If $G(s) = P_1 \text{ diag } \{g_1(s), \ldots, g_m(s)\}P_2$ with $P_1 P_2 = I_m$, show that the commutative-controller technique reduces to the methods outlined in Section 3.16. Apply the result to the examples of Section 3.17.

The commutative-controller design method does contain many of the important basic concepts used for system design using eigenvalue-type methods but should be regarded primarily as an introduction to the general techniques described in this Chapter. The disadvantages of the technique provide useful indications of what to avoid in the development of feedback-design methods,
(a) In contrast to the examples of Sections 3.3 and 3.17, the eigenvectors of $G(s)$ are, in general, frequency-dependent and the eigenvalues are not rational transfer functions in the sense that they cannot be expressed as the ratio of two polynomials in the complex variable s. For example, the system

$$G_1(s) = \begin{pmatrix} 0 & -\dfrac{1}{s} \\ \dfrac{1}{s+1} & 0 \end{pmatrix} \qquad (4.1.9)$$

has eigenvalues

$$\pm \sqrt{\frac{-1}{s(s+1)}} \qquad (4.1.10)$$

These properties can lead to difficulties in the application of the standard stability criterion and make it difficult to deduce the closed-loop characteristics from eqn. 4.1.7.
(b) In general, the commutative controller $K(s)$ has a highly complex dynamic structure, induced by the frequency-dependence of $W(s)$. For example, if $k_j(s)$, $1 \leqslant j \leqslant m$, are simple proportional controls, the forward-path controller $K(s) = W(s) \text{ diag } \{k_1, k_2, \ldots, k_m\}V(s)$ is not necessarily a constant output-feedback controller.
(c) An implicit assumption in the technique is that the eigenvectors of $G(s)$ are fundamental to the physical dynamic behaviour of the plant

and should be retained as eigenvectors of the closed-loop system $H_c(s)$. In fact the eigenvectors are highly sensitive to the ordering of inputs in $u(s)$ and to the physical units used in the state-vector model and can be modified with advantages in the design process. For example, if the inputs are interchanged in eqn. 4.1.9, the following transfer-function matrix is obtained

$$G_2(s) = G_1(s)\begin{pmatrix} 0 & 1 \\ 1 & 0 \end{pmatrix} = \begin{pmatrix} -\dfrac{1}{s} & 0 \\ 0 & \dfrac{1}{s+1} \end{pmatrix}$$

The reader can easily verify that $G_2(s)$ has eigenvector matrix $W(s) = I_2$, eigenvalues $g_1(s) = -s^{-1}$, $g_2(s) = (s+1)^{-1}$, and is a noninteracting system.

It seems, therefore, that the commutative-controller analysis uses only superficially useful structural concepts. In general terms it will be seen that a deeper analysis of the structure of $G(s)$ is of great importance in the choice of $K(s)$ although it is the eigenstructure of $Q(s) = G(s)K(s)$ that dictates closed-loop dynamics. The eigenstructure of $G(s)$ alone has little significance unless (see Sections 3.3, 3.17) they are independent of frequency.

Exercise 4.1.2
Show that eqn. 4.1.9 is a first-order lag. Calculate the decomposition eqn. 4.1.3 and note that the first-order nature of $G_1(s)$ is not reflected in the eigenvector decomposition.

Exercise 4.1.3
Apply the commutative controller method to the examples of Sections 3.3 and 3.10 (when the eigenvectors of $G(s)$ are frequency-independent).

Exercise 4.1.4
Show that the dyadic transfer-function matrix eqn. 3.16.12 has frequency-dependent eigenvectors, but that $G(s)P_2^{-1}P_1^{-1}$ has a frequency-independent eigenvector matrix $W(s) = P_1$. In general terms, if $G(s) = P_1 \operatorname{diag}\{g_1(s), \ldots, g_m(s)\}P_2$ is dyadic and $K(s) = P_2^{-1}\operatorname{diag}\{k_1(s), \ldots, k_m(s)\}P_1^{-1}$ prove that $P_1P_2K(s)$ is a commutative controller for $G(s)P_2^{-1}P_1^{-1}$.

4.2 Characteristic transfer functions and characteristic directions

Consider a unity-negative feedback system for the control of an $m \times m$ strictly proper, invertible system $G(s)$ using the $m \times m$ proper forward-path controller $K(s)$. Using the notation $Q(s) = G(s)K(s)$, the closed-loop transfer-function matrix takes the form

$$H_c(s) = \{I_m + Q(s)\}^{-1} Q(s) \qquad (4.2.1)$$

Suppose that $Q(s)$ has m eigenvalues $q_i(s)$, $1 \leqslant i \leqslant m$, with corresponding linearly independent eigenvectors $w_i(s)$, $1 \leqslant i \leqslant m$. The complex-valued functions $q_i(s)$, $1 \leqslant i \leqslant m$, are termed the *characteristic transfer functions* of the forward path system and the eigenvectors $w_i(s)$, $1 \leqslant i \leqslant m$, are termed the *characteristic directions* of $Q(s)$,

$$Q(s)w_i(s) = q_i(s)w_i(s), \qquad 1 \leqslant i \leqslant m \qquad (4.2.2)$$

Defining the frequency-dependent eigenvector matrix,

$$W(s) = [w_1(s), w_2(s), \ldots, w_m(s)], \quad V(s) = W^{-1}(s) \quad (4.2.3)$$

then eqn. 4.2.2 is replaced by the relation

$$V(s)Q(s)W(s) = \text{diag}\{q_1(s), \ldots, q_m(s)\} \qquad (4.2.4)$$

from which eqn. 4.2.1 takes the form,

$$H_c(s) = W(s) \, \text{diag}\left\{\frac{q_i(s)}{1 + q_i(s)}\right\}_{1 \leqslant i \leqslant m} V(s) \qquad (4.2.5)$$

Note that this analysis makes no assumptions on the relative structure of $G(s)$ and $K(s)$, other than that $Q(s)$ has a complete set of eigenvectors. In this sense, although quite obviously similar to the analysis of Section 4.1, the above development represents a quite general situation. In particular, it is not assumed that $G(s)$ and $K(s)$ commute.

In a similar manner to eqn. 4.1.1, eqn. 4.2.2 indicates that the characteristic directions and characteristic transfer functions describe a form of modal behaviour in the forward-path system. Moreover, eqn. 4.2.5 indicates that the eigenvectors of $H_c(s)$ are identical to the eigenvectors of $Q(s)$, with eigenvalues (characteristic transfer functions) $q_i(s)/(1 + q_i(s))$, $1 \leqslant i \leqslant m$ i.e.

$$H_c(s)w_i(s) = \frac{q_i(s)}{1 + q_i(s)} w_i(s), \qquad 1 \leqslant i \leqslant m \qquad (4.2.6)$$

It is instructive to consider the response of the closed-loop system to a demand signal $r(s)$,

$$y(s) = H_c(s)r(s) = W(s) \text{ diag} \left\{ \frac{q_i(s)}{1 + q_i(s)} \right\}_{1 \leqslant i \leqslant m} V(s)r(s)$$

$$= W(s) \sum_{j=1}^{m} \frac{q_j(s)}{1 + q_j(s)} e_j e_j^T V(s)r(s)$$

$$= \sum_{j=1}^{m} w_j(s) \frac{q_j(s)}{1 + q_j(s)} \{e_j^T V(s)r(s)\} \qquad (4.2.7)$$

where e_j, $1 \leqslant j \leqslant m$, is the unit-column vector consisting of zero elements everywhere with the exception of a unit element in the jth position. The physical interpretation of the decomposition eqn. 4.2.7 is expressed by noting that the system output can be constructed as a linear combination of the characteristic directions, scaled by complex-valued functions

$$\hat{y}_j(s) = \frac{q_j(s)}{1 + q_j(s)} \{e_j^T V(s)r(s)\} \qquad (4.2.8)$$

The 'characteristic outputs' $\hat{y}_j(s)$, $1 \leqslant j \leqslant m$, are seen to be the response of scalar feedback systems $q_j(s)/(1 + q_j(s))$, $1 \leqslant j \leqslant m$, (defined by the characteristic transfer functions) to the demand signals

$$\hat{r}_j(s) = e_j^T V(s)r(s), \qquad 1 \leqslant j \leqslant m \qquad (4.2.9)$$

(The reader is advised to compare this analysis with that of Section 3.3). In this sense, it is seen that the characteristic transfer functions and characteristic directions form a complete description of both the open-loop dynamics $Q(s)$ and the closed-loop dynamics $H_c(s)$.

The analysis and manipulation of characteristic transfer functions and directions has been suggested[21-23] as a basis for the design of high-performance feedback systems by choosing $K(s)$ to produce 'acceptable' eigenproperties of $Q(s)$. The essential elements of the technique can be illustrated by considering the impact of $q_j(s)$ and $w_j(s)$, $1 \leqslant j \leqslant m$, on the closed-loop performance.

4.3 Closed-loop stability and characteristic loci

The stability of the closed-loop system is described by the return-difference determinant

$$\frac{\rho_c(s)}{\rho_0(s)} = |T(s)| = |I_m + Q(s)| \qquad (4.3.1)$$

where $\rho_c(s)$ and $\rho_0(s)$ are the closed-loop and open-loop characteristic polynomials, respectively. The stability of the system could be analysed by application of (say) the Routh-Hurwitz criterion to the numerator of $|T(s)|$. To obtain a relationship between closed-loop stability and the characteristic transfer functions, it is necessary to move into the realm of a multivariable equivalent to the Nyquist stability criterion.

Definition 4.3.1: The symbol D will be used to denote the usual (Nyquist) contour in the complex plane consisting of the imaginary axis $s = i\omega$, $|\omega| \leqslant R$ and the semicircle $|s| = R$ in the right-half complex plane, where R is large enough to ensure that all right-half-plane zeros of $\rho_c(s)$ and $\rho_0(s)$ lie within D. If any zeros lie on the imaginary axis, D is indented into the left-half plane to include them in its interior. It will always be assumed that D is traversed in a clockwise manner.

Suppose that $\rho_c(s)$ has n_c zeros in the interior of D and $\rho_0(s)$ has n_0 zeros in the interior of D. If Γ is the closed-contour in the complex plane generated by $|T(s)|$ when s varies on D in a clockwise manner, it follows directly from the identity $\rho_c(s)/\rho_0(s) = |T(s)|$ and the 'principle of the argument'[57] that

$$n_c - n_0 = n_T \qquad (4.3.2)$$

where n_T is the number of clockwise encirclements of Γ about the origin of the complex plane. Noting that n_c and n_0 represent the number of unstable poles of the closed-loop and open-loop system, respectively, the following result is easily verified.

Theorem 4.3.1: The closed-loop system eqn. 4.2.1 is asymptotically stable if, and only if, $n_c = 0$ i.e.

$$n_0 + n_T = 0 \qquad (4.3.3)$$

This result is fundamental to the following development and is of great practical use as it enables graphical determination of stability by an examination of the behaviour of $|T(s)|$ on the Nyquist contour D. The evaluation of n_T (and hence n_c) could be undertaken directly or, by analysis of the characteristic transfer functions of $Q(s)$ using the identity,

$$|T(s)| = |I_m + Q(s)|$$

$$= |I_m + V(s)Q(s)W(s)| = \prod_{j=1}^{m} (1 + q_j(s)) \qquad (4.3.4)$$

Definition 4.3.2: Let Γ_j, $1 \leqslant j \leqslant m$, be the loci in the complex plane generated by the characteristic transfer functions $q_j(s)$, $1 \leqslant j \leqslant m$, as s varies on the contour D. The loci Γ_j, $1 \leqslant j \leqslant m$ are termed the *characteristic loci* of $Q(s)$ and Γ_j is said to be the *characteristic locus corresponding to* $q_j(s)$.

Eqn. 4.3.4 suggests a connection between the stability of the closed-loop system (i.e. n_T) and the properties of the characteristic loci Γ_i, $1 \leqslant i \leqslant m$. This connection has been discussed in some detail[22] using the properties of algebraic function defined on a Riemann surface. The majority of practical situations can however be described using the following development.

Throughout the following it is assumed that the characteristic loci Γ_i, $1 \leqslant i \leqslant m$, are *closed* contours in the complex plane. If this is so it is possible to define a sequence of integers n_i, $1 \leqslant i \leqslant m$, as the number of clockwise encirclements of the critical point $(-1, 0)$ by Γ_i, $1 \leqslant i \leqslant m$, as s varies in a clockwise manner over D. It then follows directly from eqn. 4.3.4 that

$$n_T = \sum_{i=1}^{m} n_i \qquad (4.3.5)$$

or, more precisely, using theorem 4.3.1.

Theorem 4.3.2: The closed-loop system (eqn. 4.2.1) is asymptotically stable if, and only if,

$$n_0 + \sum_{i=1}^{m} n_i = 0 \qquad (4.3.6)$$

A check of closed-loop stability hence reduces to the evaluation and graphical representation of the system characteristic loci, from which the encirclements n_i, $1 \leqslant i \leqslant m$, are obtained by inspection. The number of unstable poles of the open-loop system n_0 is usually known and hence eqn. 4.3.6 is easily checked. In particular, as $Q(s)$ is strictly proper, it follows that

$$\lim_{|s| \to \infty} q_i(s) = 0, \qquad 1 \leqslant i \leqslant m \qquad (4.3.7)$$

indicating that the encirclements n_i, $1 \leqslant i \leqslant m$, can be deduced from the behaviour of Γ_i as s varies on the imaginary axis alone i.e. the semicircular part of D can be neglected.

The technique is easily illustrated by a consideration of a multi-variable first-order lag $G^{-1}(s) = A_0 s + A_1$, $|A_0| \neq 0$ with forward-path controller $K = kA_0 - A_1$, when

$$Q(s) = G(s)K(s) = (sA_0 + A_1)^{-1}(kA_0 - A_1)$$

$$= (sI_m + A_0^{-1}A_1)^{-1}(kI_m - A_0^{-1}A_1) \qquad (4.3.8)$$

Suppose that $A_0^{-1}A_1$ has eigenvalues $-\lambda_j$, $1 \leqslant j \leqslant m$, then it is easily verified that the characteristic transfer functions are first-order lags of the form,

$$q_j(s) = \frac{k + \lambda_j}{s - \lambda_j}, \qquad 1 \leqslant j \leqslant m \qquad (4.3.9)$$

Assuming for simplicity that the eigenvalues λ_j are real and negative, then $n_0 = 0$ and

$$n_i = \begin{bmatrix} 0, & k > 0 \\ 1, & k < 0 \end{bmatrix} \qquad (4.3.10)$$

i.e. the closed-loop system is stable if, and only if, $n_i = 0, 1 \leqslant i \leqslant m$, or, equivalently, $k > 0$ (see Section 3.5).

Exercise 4.3.1

Verify this result if the eigenvalues λ_j are real with some strictly positive.

It is instructive to consider the case when the system has open-loop oscillatory behaviour reflected by the presence of complex eigenvalues λ_j. In such a case eqn. 4.3.9 indicates that $q_i(0)$ may be complex and $q_i(s)$ approaches zero at high frequency at a nonzero angle to both the real and imaginary axes. Also, from the computational viewpoint, it is normal to calculate the set of characteristic loci in the range $s = i\omega$, $0 \leqslant \omega \leqslant + \infty$, when the identity

$$Q(\bar{s}) = \overline{Q(s)} \qquad (4.3.11)$$

for a transfer-function matrix with real coefficients indicates that the set of characteristic loci in the range $-\infty < \omega < 0$ are obtained by taking the complex conjugate. Note however that, in general,

$$\overline{q_j(i\omega)} \neq q_j(-i\omega) \qquad (4.3.12)$$

(use eqn. 4.3.9 with λ_j complex) indicating that the complex-conjugation procedure for Γ_j, $s = i\omega$, $0 < \omega < + \infty$, can generate part of a characteristic locus Γ_l, $l \neq j$. This is easily resolved in practice by plotting the results on a single chart and obtaining Γ_j, $1 \leqslant j \leqslant m$, by separating out the closed contours.

Theorem 4.3.2 is only one of many possible stability criteria express-able in terms of the characteristic loci and their properties. For example, the relation

$$|T(s)| = \frac{\rho_c(s)}{\rho_0(s)} = |I_m + Q(s)| = |Q(s)||I_m + Q^{-1}(s)|$$

200 Eigenvalue-type methods in feedback design

$$= \frac{|I_m + Q^{-1}(s)|}{|Q^{-1}(s)|} \qquad (4.3.13)$$

and the observation that the characteristic transfer functions of $Q^{-1}(s)$, denoted $\hat{q}_j(s)$, $1 \leqslant j \leqslant m$, satisfy

$$\hat{q}_j(s) = \frac{1}{q_j(s)} \qquad (4.3.14)$$

suggest that stability can be expressed in terms of $\hat{q}_j(s)$, $1 \leqslant j \leqslant m$. More precisely, if $\hat{\Gamma}_j$ is the characteristic locus of $\hat{q}_j(s)$ encircling the $(-1, 0)$ point $\hat{n}_j$ times clockwise and the origin of the complex plane $\tilde{n}_j$ times in a clockwise manner, then the reader should verify from the identity,

$$\frac{|I_m + Q^{-1}(s)|}{|Q^{-1}(s)|} = \frac{\prod\limits_{j=1}^{m} (1 + \hat{q}_j(s))}{\prod\limits_{j=1}^{m} \hat{q}_j(s)} \qquad (4.3.15)$$

that,

Theorem 4.3.3: The closed-loop system (eqn. 4.2.1) is asymptotically stable if, and only if,

$$n_0 + \sum_{j=1}^{m} (\hat{n}_j - \tilde{n}_j) = 0 \qquad (4.3.16)$$

An alternative approach to the problem is to write eqn. 4.3.13 in the form

$$\rho_c(s) = z(s)|I_m + Q^{-1}(s)| \qquad (4.3.17)$$

where $z(s) = \rho_0(s)|Q(s)|$ is the zero polynomial of $Q(s)$. If n_z^+ is the number of zeros of $Q(s)$ within the interior of the contour D, application of the above techniques yields the result:

Theorem 4.3.4: The closed-loop system eqn. 4.2.1 is asymptotically stable if, and only if,

$$n_z^+ + \sum_{j=1}^{m} \hat{n}_j = 0 \qquad (4.3.18)$$

Exercise 4.3.2

Use the above analysis (with n_c not necessarily zero) to show that $Q(s)$ is minimum phase if, and only if,

$$n_z^+ = n_0 - \sum_{j=1}^{m} \tilde{n}_j = 0$$

which provides a convenient technique for checking the zero characteristics of the system $Q(s)$.

Finally, it should be noted that transformation techniques can be
used to simplify the analysis. For example, write

$$\rho_0(s) = \rho_G(s)\rho_K(s) \qquad (4.3.19)$$

where ρ_G, ρ_K are the characteristic polynomials of $G(s)$, $K(s)$, respectively. Define

$$G^{-1}(s) = G_1^{-1}(s) + L, \quad K(s) = K_1(s) - L \qquad (4.3.20)$$

$$Q_1(s) = G_1(s)K_1(s) \qquad (4.3.21)$$

where L is a constant $m \times m$ matrix. In effect, $G(s)$ is represented by
the system $G_1(s)$ with minor-loop constant-output feedback L. Noting
that the zero polynomial of $G(s)$ is invariant under constant state or
output feedback, gives

$$\rho_G(s)|G(s)| = \rho_{G_1}(s)|G_1(s)| \qquad (4.3.22)$$

and hence

$$\frac{\rho_c(s)}{\rho_0(s)} = |I_m + G(s)K(s)| = |G(s)||G^{-1}(s) + K(s)|$$

$$= |G(s)||G_1^{-1}(s) + K_1(s)|$$

$$= \frac{|G(s)|}{|G_1(s)|} |I_m + Q_1(s)| \qquad (4.3.23)$$

indicating that

$$\frac{\rho_c(s)}{\rho_1(s)} = |I_m + Q_1(s)| \qquad (4.3.24)$$

where

$$\rho_1(s) = \rho_{G_1}(s)\rho_K(s) \qquad (4.3.25)$$

Noting that $\rho_K(s) = \rho_{K_1}(s)$, it is seen that the transformation technique
used enables the investigation of the closed-loop stability in terms of
the characteristic loci of $Q_1(s)$. In fact, all the above results hold if $Q(s)$
and $\rho_0(s)$ are replaced by $Q_1(s)$, $\rho_1(s)$.

As a simple illustration of the technique, consider the second-order
lag

$$G^{-1}(s) = s^2 A_0 + sA_1 + A_2 = G_1^{-1}(s) + A_2 \qquad (4.3.26)$$

with forward-path controller

$$K(s) = K_1(s) - A_2 \qquad (4.3.27)$$

Assume that $A_0^{-1}A_1$ has eigenvalues $-\lambda_j$, $1 \leqslant j \leqslant m$, with eigenvector matrix T and that

$$K_1(s) = A_0 T \operatorname{diag}\{k_1(s), \ldots, k_m(s)\}T^{-1} \qquad (4.3.28)$$

It follows that

$$Q_1(s) = G_1(s)K_1(s) = T \operatorname{diag}\left\{\frac{k_j(s)}{s(s-\lambda_j)}\right\}_{1 \leqslant j \leqslant m} T^{-1} \quad (4.3.29)$$

with characteristic transfer functions

$$q_j(s) = \frac{k_j(s)}{s(s-\lambda_j)}, \qquad 1 \leqslant j \leqslant m \qquad (4.3.30)$$

4.4 Steady-state behaviour and interaction

The steady-state response of the closed-loop system can be examined using the decomposition eqn. 4.2.5. More precisely, the steady-state errors in response to unit-step demands in any loop are zero if, and only if, the closed-loop system is stable and

$$I_m = \lim_{s \to 0} H_c(s) = \lim_{s \to 0} W(s) \operatorname{diag}\left\{\frac{q_j(s)}{1+q_j(s)}\right\}_{1 \leqslant j \leqslant m} V(s)$$

$$= \lim_{s \to 0} W(s) \operatorname{diag}\left\{\frac{1}{1+\hat{q}_j(s)}\right\}_{1 \leqslant j \leqslant m} V(s) \qquad (4.4.1)$$

i.e. if, and only if,

$$\lim_{s \to 0} \hat{q}_j(s) = 0, \qquad 1 \leqslant j \leqslant m \qquad (4.4.2)$$

or, equivalently,

$$\lim_{|s| \to 0} |q_j(s)| = +\infty, \qquad 1 \leqslant j \leqslant m \qquad (4.4.3)$$

indicating the need for integral control action.

In more general circumstances, suppose that eqn. 4.4.3 is not satisfied, then

$$\lim_{s \to 0} H_c(s) = W(0) \operatorname{diag}\left\{\frac{q_j(0)}{1+q_j(0)}\right\}_{1 \leqslant j \leqslant m} V(0) \qquad (4.4.4)$$

suggesting that steady-state errors are small if $|q_j(0)| \gg 1, 1 \leqslant j \leqslant m$.

Exercise 4.4.1

Prove that, if $q_j(0) = 0$ for some j and $q_l(0)$ is finite for $l \neq j$, then $Q(s)$ has a zero at the point $s = 0$. (Hint: express $|Q(s)|$ in terms of its characteristic transfer functions).

For example, replacing $K(s)$ by $kK(s)$ where k is a real scalar gain parameter then $Q(s)$ is replaced by $kQ(s)$, giving

$$\lim_{s \to 0} H_c(s) = W(0) \, \text{diag}\left\{\frac{kq_j(0)}{1 + kq_j(0)}\right\}_{1 \leqslant j \leqslant m} V(0)$$

$$\to I_m \qquad (\text{as } k \to +\infty) \qquad (4.4.5)$$

if $q_j(0) \neq 0, 1 \leqslant j \leqslant m$. Interpreting the parameter k as an overall system gain, the result states that steady-state errors in response to unit-step demands can be reduced by increasing the control system gain. Note, however, that the result requires that the gain of *every* characteristic transfer function must be large at $s = 0$.

Turning now to the question of transient interaction, it is only possible to obtain intuitive guidelines to the required properties of $Q(s)$. Again we use the decomposition,

$$H_c(s) = \{I_m + Q(s)\}^{-1} Q(s)$$

$$= W(s) \, \text{diag}\left\{\frac{q_j(s)}{1 + q_j(s)}\right\}_{1 \leqslant j \leqslant m} V(s) \qquad (4.4.6)$$

The complex frequency-dependence of the terms precludes any exact characterisation of the closed-loop interaction behaviour in terms of the characteristic transfer functions $q_j(s), 1 \leqslant j \leqslant m$, and the eigenvector matrix $W(s)$. A useful but intuitive approach[23] is obtained by noting that $H_c(s)$ possesses small interaction implies that the frequency-response matrix $H_c(i\omega), 0 \leqslant \omega < +\infty$, is approximately diagonal at all frequencies. With this in mind, the following observations provide useful practical guidelines:

Use of high gains: Suppose that high controller gains are employed and hence that $|q_j(i\omega)| \gg 1$ in some low-frequency range $0 \leqslant \omega \leqslant \omega_l$, then it is easily verified from eqn. 4.4.6 that

$$H_c(i\omega) \simeq I_m, \qquad 0 \leqslant \omega \leqslant \omega_l \qquad (4.4.7)$$

indicating that high controller gains tend to reduce *low-frequency interaction* in the closed-loop system. Note, however, that high controller gains may introduce instability limiting the applicability of the approach.

Characteristic transfer functions and high-frequency interaction: As $Q(s)$ is strictly proper, suppose that $|q_j(i\omega)| \ll 1$, $\omega_h \leqslant \omega < +\infty$ when

$$H_c(i\omega) \simeq W(i\omega) \text{ diag } \{q_j(i\omega)\}_{1 \leqslant j \leqslant m} V(i\omega) = Q(i\omega),$$

$$\omega \geqslant \omega_h \qquad (4.4.8)$$

indicating the general conclusion that the *high-frequency interactive effects* of $H_c(i\omega)$ are essentially those of the forward-path element $Q(i\omega)$. In general terms, the only way to reduce high-frequency interaction is to ensure that $Q(i\omega)$ is approximately noninteracting at high frequency. This requirement is satisfied if, for example,

$$\lim_{\omega \to +\infty} \frac{q_j(i\omega)}{q_p(i\omega)} = 1, \qquad 1 \leqslant j \leqslant p \leqslant m \qquad (4.4.9)$$

when

$$Q(i\omega) \simeq q_1(i\omega)I_m, \qquad \omega \geqslant \omega_h \qquad (4.4.10)$$

Alternatively, the condition can be achieved by manipulation of the set of characteristic directions.

Characteristic directions and high-frequency interaction: Suppose that the characteristic directions $w_j(i\omega)$, $1 \leqslant j \leqslant m$, are *aligned* with the natural basis $e_1, e_2, \ldots, e_m$ at high frequencies in the sense that

$$\lim_{\omega \to +\infty} w_j(i\omega) = e_j, \qquad 1 \leqslant j \leqslant m \qquad (4.4.11)$$

then $W(i\omega) \simeq V(i\omega) \simeq I_m$ for $\omega \geqslant \omega_h$ giving

$$Q(i\omega) \simeq \text{diag } \{q_1(i\omega), \ldots, q_m(i\omega)\}, \qquad \omega \geqslant \omega_h \quad (4.4.12)$$

Noting that eqn. 4.4.9 cannot in many cases be satisfied (e.g. suppose that $q_1(s)$ is a first-order lag and $q_2(s)$ a second-order lag), the *alignment principle* described above represents a useful alternative approach. The question of whether or not alignment can be achieved is left for later discussions.

Exercise 4.4.2

If $w_j(i\omega) \simeq e_j$, $1 \leqslant j \leqslant m$, over the entire frequency range $0 \leqslant \omega < +\infty$, demonstrate that the closed-loop system will possess small interaction effects.

Finally, the observant reader will have noted the absence of any information concerning the requirements of $H_c(i\omega)$ in the range $\omega_l < \omega < \omega_h$ (when, say, $|q_j(i\omega)| \simeq 1$). It is fair comment to state that little is known on the effect of this frequency range on interaction behaviour.

4.5 Characteristic locus design method

The characteristic locus design method, as suggested by MacFarlane and Belletrutti[21] and revised by MacFarlane and Kouvaritakis[23] is based on the manipulation of the characteristic transfer functions and characteristic directions of the forward-path element $Q(s) = G(s)K(s)$ to produce a satisfactory closed-loop performance. The essential elements of the technique are as follows:

(*a*) the characteristic loci of $Q(s)$ must satisfy the stability criteria of Section 4.3 and the normal criteria of adequate gain and phase margins etc.

(*b*) the characteristic loci must all have a sufficiently high gain over a desired operating bandwidth $0 \leqslant \omega \leqslant \omega_l$ to ensure small steady-state errors and small low-frequency interaction

(*c*) high-frequency alignment of the characteristic directions of $Q(i\omega)$, $\omega \gg \omega_h$, should be sufficiently close to the natural basis set to keep high-frequency interaction within acceptable limits.

The design is approached as follows:

High-frequency alignment: Suppose that ω_h is a characteristically high frequency for the plant $G(s)$ obtained, say, by examination of the open loop poles λ_j, $1 \leqslant j \leqslant n$, and choosing $\omega_h|\lambda_j^{-1}| \gg 1$, $1 \leqslant j \leqslant n$. The requirement that the characteristic directions are aligned with the natural basis set at high frequency is now replaced by the single condition at the frequency ω_h,

$$Q(i\omega_h) = G(i\omega_h)K(i\omega_h) = \text{diag}\ \{f_j(i\omega_h)\}_{1 \leqslant j \leqslant m} \quad (4.5.1)$$

for some complex numbers $f_j(i\omega_h)$, $1 \leqslant j \leqslant m$. It is easily seen that

$$q_j(i\omega_h) = f_j(i\omega_h), \qquad 1 \leqslant j \leqslant m \qquad (4.5.2)$$

and it is necessary that

$$K(i\omega_h) = G^{-1}(i\omega_h)\ \text{diag}\ \{f_j(i\omega_h)\}_{1 \leqslant j \leqslant m} \qquad (4.5.3)$$

It is readily verified that, in general, it is possible to construct a proper dynamic element satisfying eqn. 4.5.3. Bearing in mind that the system characteristic loci may need phase compensation at a later stage in the design exercise, the overall complexity of the design will be reduced if $K(s)$ is a constant proportional controller $K(s) = K_h$. In this case eqn. 4.5.3 is not, in general, satisfied unless the right-hand-side is real. It may be possible however to obtain an *approximate real* solution to eqn. 4.5.3

$$K_h \simeq G^{-1}(i\omega_h) \text{ diag } \{f_j(i\omega_h)\}_{1 \leqslant j \leqslant m} \qquad (4.5.4)$$

when, roughly speaking,

$$Q(i\omega_h) = G(i\omega_h)K_h \simeq \text{diag } \{f_j(i\omega_h)\}_{1 \leqslant j \leqslant m} \qquad (4.5.5)$$

indicating that high-frequency interaction will be small at $\omega = \omega_h$ (but nonzero!).

Let

$$K_h = [k_1, k_2, \ldots, k_m] \qquad (4.5.6)$$

then eqn. 4.5.1 requires that

$$G(i\omega_h)k_j = f_j(i\omega_h)e_j, \qquad 1 \leqslant j \leqslant m \qquad (4.5.7)$$

This relation cannot be exactly satisfied for real vectors k_j, $1 \leqslant j \leqslant m$. Let

$$G(i\omega_h) = \begin{pmatrix} v_1^T \\ \vdots \\ v_m^T \end{pmatrix}, \quad v_j^T = e_j^T G(i\omega_h) \qquad (4.5.8)$$

then eqn. 4.5.7 is equivalent to the set of relations,

$$v_l^T k_j = f_j(i\omega_h)\delta_{j,l}, \qquad 1 \leqslant l \leqslant m, \quad 1 \leqslant j \leqslant m \qquad (4.5.9)$$

An approximate solution for real k_j, $1 \leqslant j \leqslant m$, is obtained by independent maximisation of the quotients (independent of $f_j(i\omega_h)$, $1 \leqslant j \leqslant m$!)

$$Q_j = \frac{|v_j^T k_j|^2}{\displaystyle\sum_{\substack{l=1 \\ l \neq j}}^{m} |v_l^T k_j|^2 + \epsilon k_j^T k_j} \qquad (4.5.10)$$

where ϵ is a small positive real number, introduced to guarantee that the maximum is finite. Write v_j in its real and imaginary parts,

$$v_j = \alpha_j + i\beta_j, \qquad 1 \leqslant j \leqslant m \qquad (4.5.11)$$

when

$$|v_j^T k_l|^2 = k_l^T \bar{v}_j v_j^T k_l = k_l^T \{\alpha_j \alpha_j^T + \beta_j \beta_j^T\} k_l \qquad (4.5.12)$$

or, defining, $1 \leqslant j \leqslant m$, the real matrices

$$C_j = \alpha_j \alpha_j^T + \beta_j \beta_j^T, \quad D_j = \sum_{\substack{l=1 \\ l \neq j}}^{m} \{\alpha_l \alpha_l^T + \beta_l \beta_l^T\} + \epsilon I_m \quad (4.5.13)$$

the quotient (eqn. 4.5.10) becomes,

$$Q_j = \frac{k_j^T C_j k_j}{k_j^T D_j k_j}, \quad 1 \leqslant j \leqslant m \quad (4.5.14)$$

For a maximum, differentiate eqn. 4.5.14 and set the derivative to zero, yielding,

$$C_j k_j = Q_j D_j k_j, \quad 1 \leqslant j \leqslant m \quad (4.5.15)$$

Noting that D_j is symmetric positive-definite for $\epsilon > 0$ (and, in general, for $\epsilon = 0$), then $|D_j| \neq 0$ and hence

$$(D_j^{-1} C_j) k_j = Q_j k_j, \quad 1 \leqslant j \leqslant m \quad (4.5.16)$$

suggesting that the maximum value of Q_j is simply the largest real eigenvalue of $D_j^{-1} C_j$ and k_j is the corresponding eigenvector of $D_j^{-1} C_j$. In fact, writing $D_j^{-1} = F_j^2$ where F_j is the unique symmetric positive-definite square root of D^{-1}, the relation

$$|\lambda I_m - D_j^{-1} C_j| = |\lambda I_m - F_j C_j F_j| \quad (4.5.17)$$

where $F_j C_j F_j$ is symmetric positive semidefinite indicates that all the eigenvalues of $D_j^{-1} C_j$ are real and zero or positive and hence that the solution vectors k_j are real and nonzero.

Let $k_1, k_2, \ldots, k_m$ be the vectors computed using the above algorithm. Noting that they are only defined to within multiplication by a scalar, generalise eqn. 4.5.6 to set

$$K_j = [k_1, k_2, \ldots, k_m] \text{ diag} \{\mu_1, \ldots, \mu_m\} \quad (4.5.18)$$

where μ_j, $1 \leqslant j \leqslant m$, are real nonzero scalars. Eqn. 4.5.1 now takes the form

$$Q(i\omega_h) = G(i\omega_h) K_h = \text{diag} \{v_j^T k_j \mu_j\}_{1 \leqslant j \leqslant m} + \Omega \quad (4.5.19)$$

where

$$\Omega_{jj} = 0, \quad 1 \leqslant j \leqslant m \quad (4.5.20)$$

but the off-diagonal elements of Ω may be nonzero owing to the approximations involved in the calculation of K_h. If Ω is small, then it can be anticipated that

$$q_j(i\omega_h) \simeq v_j^T k_j \mu_j, \quad 1 \leqslant j \leqslant m \quad (4.5.21)$$

indicating that the scaling parameters μ_j can be used to modify the gains of the characteristic loci of GK_h (but not the phases!) at $s = i\omega_h$. For example, an attempt could be made to satisfy expr. 4.4.9 by assuming that $k_1, k_2, \ldots, k_m$ remain constant for $\omega_h > \hat{\omega}_h$ and hence that

$$q_j(i\omega) \simeq e_j^T G(i\omega)k_j\mu_j, \qquad 1 \leqslant j \leqslant m, \qquad \omega > \hat{\omega}_h \qquad (4.5.22)$$

(Note: in general, the calculated k_j will vary with ω_h). The results of the approximation analysis can then be checked by direct numerical evaluation of the exact characteristic loci.

A convenient check on the success of the alignment procedure[23] is a plot of the *misalignment angles* $\theta_j(i\omega)$ (assumed to lie in the range $0 \leqslant \theta < \pi/2$) against frequency ω, where

$$\cos \theta_j(i\omega) = \max_{1 \leqslant k \leqslant m} \frac{|\overline{w_k^T(i\omega)e_j}|}{(w_j^T(i\omega)w_k(i\omega))^{1/2}} \leqslant 1 \qquad (4.5.23)$$

and $w_k(i\omega)$, $1 \leqslant k \leqslant m$, are the characteristic directions of GK_h. It is easily verified that alignment is achieved at a frequency ω if, and only if, $\cos \theta_j(i\omega) = 1$, $1 \leqslant j \leqslant m$, or, equivalent, if $\theta_j(i\omega) = 0$, $1 \leqslant j \leqslant m$.

In summary, in this initial stage of the design procedure, an attempt is made to align the system characteristic directions with the natural basis set using the alignment procedure and to use the gain parameters μ_j, $1 \leqslant j \leqslant m$, to provide the required absolute and relative gain characteristics for the characteristic loci at high frequency. The success of the approach is not guaranteed but is easily checked by calculation of the exact system characteristic loci and misalignment angles. If the system is found to be stable, possesses satisfactory gain and phase margins in each of the characteristic loci and the gains are sufficiently high to reduce steady-state errors to a satisfactory level then the design procedure can be terminated. In general, however, it is necessary to consider the problem of intermediate- and low-frequency compensation of the characteristic loci.

Exercise 4.5.1
Consider the $m \times m$ system with inverse transfer-function matrix

$$G^{-1}(s) = s^k A_0 + \ldots + sA_{k-1} + A_k + H(s)$$

where $|A_0| \neq 0$, $k \geqslant 1$, $H(s)$ is strictly proper and $A_0^{-1}A_1$ has nonzero, distinct eigenvalues and linearly-independent eigenvectors $z_1, z_2, \ldots, z_m$. Suggest an intuitive argument to justify the relation

$$K_h \simeq A_0 \operatorname{diag}\{\mu_1, \ldots, \mu_m\} \qquad (\omega_h \to +\infty)$$

If $\mu_1 = \mu_2 = \ldots = \mu_m$, show that

$$\lim_{\omega \to \infty} w_j(i\omega) = z_j, \qquad 1 \leqslant j \leqslant m$$

and hence that, the alignment procedure fails if $z_j \neq e_j$, $1 \leqslant j \leqslant m$ (as is generally the case). If however, $\mu_j \neq \mu_l$ for $j \neq l$, prove that the alignment procedure is successful (interpret this result in terms of sensitivity).

Intermediate frequency compensation: A facility for the approximate compensation and manipulation of characteristic loci in an intermediate frequency range is suggested by writing

$$K(s) = K_h K_m(s) \qquad (4.5.24)$$

where the dynamic term $K_m(s)$ is introduced to provide intermediate-frequency compensation. The results of the alignment procedure will remain approximately valid if

$$K_m(i\omega) \simeq I_m, \qquad \omega > \omega_h \qquad (4.5.25)$$

when

$$K(s) \simeq K_h, \qquad \omega > \omega_h \qquad (4.5.26)$$

Suppose that it is required to compensate the characteristic loci of $G(s)K_h$ in the vicinity of $s = i\omega_m$ using the element $K_m(s)$. Write (with a slight change of notation)

$$G(s)K_h = W(s) \operatorname{diag} \{g_j(s)\}_{1 \leqslant j \leqslant m} V(s) \qquad (4.5.27)$$

where $g_j(s)$, $1 \leqslant j \leqslant m$, are the characteristic transfer functions of $G(s)K_h$ with eigenvector matrix $W(s) = V^{-1}(s)$. A fundamental problem in the choice of $K_m(s)$ lies in the fact that very little is known of the way in which the eigenvalues and eigenvectors of the product of two matrices are related to the individual eigenvalues and eigenvectors of each individual matrix. A simple way out of this difficulty is to choose $K_m(s)$ to be a commutative controller for $G(s)K_h$ at the specified frequency ω_m i.e.

$$K_m(s) = W(i\omega_m) \operatorname{diag} \{k_j(s)\}_{1 \leqslant j \leqslant m} V(i\omega_m) \qquad (4.5.28)$$

where $k_j(s)$, $1 \leqslant j \leqslant m$, are scalar transfer functions i.e.

$$G(i\omega_m)K_h K_m(i\omega_m)$$
$$= W(i\omega_m) \operatorname{diag} \{g_j(i\omega_m)k_j(i\omega_m)\}_{1 \leqslant j \leqslant m} V(i\omega_m) \qquad (4.5.29)$$

Denoting the characteristic transfer functions of $GK_h K_m$ by $q_j(s)$, $1 \leqslant j \leqslant m$, then

$$q_j(i\omega_m) = g_j(i\omega_m)k_j(i\omega_m) \qquad (4.5.30)$$

Exercise 4.5.2
Show that eqn. 4.5.25 is satisfied if $\lim_{\omega \to \infty} k_j(i\omega) = 1, 1 \leqslant j \leqslant m$.

Eqn. 4.5.30 indicates that the characteristic loci can be manipulated exactly at the frequency $s = i\omega_m$ using eqn. 4.5.28. By continuity, eqn. 4.5.30 suggests that

$$q_j(i\omega) \simeq g_j(i\omega)k_j(i\omega), \qquad 1 \leqslant j \leqslant m \qquad (4.5.31)$$

in the vicinity of $\omega = \omega_m$ i.e. noting that $g_j(i\omega)$ is known from the previous alignment analysis, the compensation elements $k_j(s)$ can be designed individually using well known classical methods.

The major problem associated with this technique is the observation that $W(i\omega_m)$ is, in general complex (in particular, it is not real and, if complex, its columns do not occur in complex conjugate pairs). This leads naturally to the idea of approximation of eqn. 4.5.28 using the *'approximately commutative controller'*[23]

$$K_m(s) = A(i\omega_m) \operatorname{diag} \{k_j(s)\}_{1 \leqslant j \leqslant m} B(i\omega_m) \qquad (4.5.32)$$

where $A(i\omega_m)$ and $B(i\omega_m)$ are real $m \times m$ approximations to $W(i\omega_m)$ and $V(i\omega_m)$, respectively. If the approximation is good then expr. 4.5.31 can still be used to provide a technique for approximate compensation of the characteristic loci, the validity of the approximation being checked by direct calculation of the exact characteristic loci. This new approximation problem can be approached using the alignment procedure suggested previously i.e. by obtaining approximate real solutions of the relations (c.f. eqn. 4.5.1)

$$V(i\omega_m)A(i\omega_m) = I_m$$
$$W^T(i\omega_m)B^T(i\omega_m) = I_m \qquad (4.5.33)$$

the columns of the solutions $A(i\omega_m)$ and $B^T(i\omega_m)$ being scaled by real numbers to make the approximation as close as possible.

Low-frequency compensation: The success of the first two stages of the design is easily checked by direct evaluation of the characteristic loci of $G(s)K_hK_m(s)$ and application of the stability theorems. If integral control action is required, the controller can be updated to take the form,

$$K(s) = K_hK_m(s) \left\{ I_m + \frac{K_l}{s} \right\} \qquad (4.5.34)$$

when, provided the integral-gain matrix K_l is not too large,

$$G(s)K(s) \simeq G(s)K_h \qquad (\omega \to +\infty)$$

$$G(s)K(s) \simeq G(s)K_h K_m(s) \qquad \text{(at intermediate frequencies)}$$

$$G(s)K(s) \simeq G(s)K_h K_m(s) \frac{1}{s} K_l \qquad \text{(at low frequencies)} \qquad (4.5.35)$$

The term $\frac{1}{s} K_l$ can be constructed by application of the approximately commutative controller procedure to $G(s)K_h K_m(s)$ at a representative low frequency $s = i\omega_l$ i.e.

$$K_l = A(i\omega_l) \operatorname{diag} \{c_j\}_{1 \leqslant j \leqslant m} B(i\omega_l) \qquad (4.5.36)$$

where c_j, $1 \leqslant j \leqslant m$, are real constants and $A(i\omega_l)$, $B(i\omega_l)$ are real approximations to the eigenvector matrix and inverse eigenvector matrix, respectively, of $G(i\omega_l)K_h K_m(i\omega_l)$.

Stability check and overall gain: The final step in the design sets

$$K(s) = k K_h K_m(s) \left\{ I_m + \frac{K_l}{s} \right\} \qquad (4.5.37)$$

where k is a real scalar gain parameter. Noting that the introduction of k has the effect of scaling the characteristic loci, it can be used to generate final adjustments to the gain margins of the individual loci.

The technique described above has been applied successfully to the design of a feedback system for the control of a two-input/two-output open-loop unstable chemical reactor and it would appear to be a potentially powerful tool for multivariable feedback design. The method does suffer from several problems due to the basic philosophy underlying the design procedure

(a) It would appear that, in many cases of practical interest, alignment of the characteristic directions with the natural basis set is unnecessary. For example, considering the $m \times m$ plant $G^{-1}(s) = sA_0 + A_1, |A_0| \neq 0, K(s) = kA_0 - A_1$ gives

$$Q(s) = G(s)K(s) = \{sI_m + A_0^{-1}A_1\}^{-1}\{kI_m - A_0^{-1}A_1\} \quad (4.5.38)$$

indicating that the characteristic directions are simply the eigenvectors of $A_0^{-1}A_1$. In general, these vectors are not aligned with the natural basis yet the analysis of Section 3.5. indicates that the controller is capable of producing a high performance, low-interaction feedback system.

(b) The approximations in the calculation of K_h and the relevant matrices in the approximately commutative controllers give no guarantee that the working hypothesis expr. 4.5.31, say, is sensibly valid. In such cases the compensation procedures may only be partially successful.

The approach to design using characteristic loci is not unique. In the following Section, an alternative procedure is described based on the idea of dyadic decomposition. The technique places less emphasis on the concept of alignment but allows more exact approximations to be used in the compensation of the characteristic loci.

4.6 Dyadic expansions and characteristic loci

In this Section it should be understood that the basic approach to design remains, as in Section 4.5, as the systematic manipulation and compensation of characteristic loci. There are, however, distinct differences in emphasis and a much closer relation to the ideas of Chapter 3.

The basic mathematic ideas can be summarised as[38, 39]

(i) alignment of the characteristic directions at high frequency is, intuitively, only a sufficient condition for low interaction

(ii) a technique is needed for the *exact* compensation of characteristic loci at a specified frequency of interest, and the *approximate* compensation in the vicinity of this frequency with errors well-defined in terms of properties of the transfer-function matrix.

The intuitive basis of the method is best provided by analogy with the concepts of Section 3.16.

Modal behaviour at a specified frequency and manipulation of characteristic loci: The modal interpretation of the structure of a dyadic transfer-function matrix

$$G(s) = P_1 \operatorname{diag} \{g_j(s)\}_{1 \leqslant j \leqslant m} P_2 \qquad (4.6.1)$$

is an important step in the choice of controller structure

$$K(s) = P_2^{-1} \operatorname{diag} \{k_j(s)\}_{1 \leqslant j \leqslant m} P_1^{-1} \qquad (4.6.2)$$

when

$$Q(s) = G(s)K(s) = P_1 \operatorname{diag} \{g_j(s)k_j(s)\}_{1 \leqslant j \leqslant m} P_1^{-1} \qquad (4.6.3)$$

indicates that the system characteristic transfer functions take the form

$$q_j(s) = g_j(s)k_j(s), \qquad 1 \leqslant j \leqslant m \qquad (4.6.4)$$

and hence that the system characteristic loci are simply the Nyquist plots of the transfer functions $q_j(s)$, $1 \leqslant j \leqslant m$. This construction is an important feature of the technique, enabling the systematic compensation of characteristic loci by independent choice of proper scalar transfer functions $k_j(s)$, $1 \leqslant j \leqslant m$. Note that the eigenvector matrix $W(s) = P_1$ is frequency-independent, removing any interpretation problems inherent in the characteristic locus method and ensuring the absence of any increase in dynamic complexity of $K(s)$ owing to the transformation matrices in eqn. 4.6.2.

In the general case of a general form of $m \times m$ invertible $G(s)$ (not necessarily dyadic), it is natural to ask whether or not it is possible to associate a modal type of behaviour to $G(s)$ at a specified frequency $s = i\omega_1$? In mathematical terms, is it possible to construct a dyadic transfer-function matrix

$$G_A(s, \omega_1) = P_1(\omega_1) \text{ diag } \{g_j(s, \omega_1)\}_{1 \leqslant j \leqslant m} P_2(\omega_1)$$

$$|G_A(s, \omega_1)| \not\equiv 0 \qquad (4.6.5)$$

realisable in the sense that

$$\overline{G_A(s, \omega_1)} = G_A(\overline{s}, \omega_1) \qquad \text{(for all } s) \qquad (4.6.6)$$

such that G is indistinguishable from G_A at the frequency $s = i\omega_1$? That is,

$$G(i\omega_1) = G_A(i\omega_1, \omega_1) \qquad (4.6.7)$$

If so, then the modal structure of $G_A(s, \omega_1)$ can be interpreted as a reflection of modal types of behaviour in $G(s)$ at the fixed point $s = i\omega_1$. In particular, the matrix $P_1(\omega_1)$ can be regarded as the matrix of output modes at $s = i\omega_1$, the complex scalars $g_j(i\omega_1, \omega_1)$, $1 \leqslant j \leqslant m$, as the phaseshifts generated by the modes and $P_2(\omega_1)$ as the coupling matrix between the external input and the modal dynamics.

A characterisation of this type is, in general, possible under conditions specified by the following theorem:

Theorem 4.6.1: Suppose that $G(i\omega_1)$ is finite and nonsingular, then a necessary and sufficient condition for the existence of $G_A(s, \omega_1)$ satisfying eqns. 4.6.5–4.6.7 is that the matrix

$$M(\omega_1) = G(-i\omega_1)G^{-1}(i\omega_1) \qquad (4.6.8)$$

has a diagonal canonical form. In such cases $P_1(\omega_1)$ is an eigenvector matrix of $M(\omega_1)$.

Proof: Necessity is proven by noting from eqns. 4.6.5 and 4.6.7 that

$$M(\omega_1) = P_1(\omega_1) \text{ diag } \left\{\frac{g_j(-i\omega_1, \omega_1)}{g_j(i\omega_1, \omega_1)}\right\}_{1 \leqslant j \leqslant m} P_1^{-1}(\omega_1) \quad (4.6.9)$$

when $M(\omega_1)$ has a diagonal canonical form with eigenvector matrix

$P_1(\omega_1)$. To prove sufficiency, suppose that $M(\omega_1)$ has linearly indepen-
dent eigenvectors α_j, $1 \leqslant j \leqslant m$, and eigenvalues λ_j, $1 \leqslant j \leqslant m$,

$$M(\omega_1)\alpha_j = \lambda_j \alpha_j, \qquad 1 \leqslant j \leqslant m \qquad (4.6.9)$$

Noting that

$$\overline{M(\omega_1)}M(\omega_1) = I_m \qquad (4.6.10)$$

it is easily verified that

$$M(\omega_1)\bar{\alpha}_j = \frac{1}{\bar{\lambda}_j}\, \bar{\alpha}_j, \qquad 1 \leqslant j \leqslant m \qquad (4.6.11)$$

indicating that the eigenvectors of $M(\omega_1)$ occur in complex-conjugate
pairs

$$\alpha_{l(j)} = \bar{\alpha}_j, \qquad 1 \leqslant j \leqslant m \qquad (4.6.12)$$

when

$$\lambda_{l(j)}\bar{\lambda}_j = 1, \qquad 1 \leqslant j \leqslant m \qquad (4.6.13)$$

In particular it is possible to choose α_j to be real (when $l(j) = j$) if, and
only if $|\lambda_j| = 1$. Suppose that the eigenvectors are specified to satisfy
eqn. 4.6.12 and define

$$P_1(\omega_1) = [\alpha_1, \alpha_2, \ldots, \alpha_m] \qquad (4.6.14)$$

when

$$P_1^{-1}(\omega_1)M(\omega_1) = \text{diag}\,\{\lambda_j\}_{1 \leqslant j \leqslant m}P_1^{-1}(\omega_1) \qquad (4.6.15)$$

Using the notation

$$P_1^{-1}(\omega_1) = \begin{pmatrix} v_1^T \\ \cdot \\ \cdot \\ \cdot \\ v_m^T \end{pmatrix} \qquad (4.6.16)$$

it is easily verified that

$$v_j^T M(\omega_1) = \lambda_j v_j^T, \qquad 1 \leqslant j \leqslant m$$

$$v_{l(j)}^T = \bar{v}_j^T, \qquad 1 \leqslant j \leqslant m \qquad (4.6.17)$$

Choose complex numbers η_j, $1 \leqslant j \leqslant m$, such that

$$\frac{\bar{\eta}_{l(j)}}{\eta_j} = \lambda_j, \qquad 1 \leqslant j \leqslant m \qquad (4.6.18)$$

and define

$$v_j^T G(i\omega_1) = \eta_j \beta_j^T, \qquad 1 \leqslant j \leqslant m \qquad (4.6.19)$$

when

$$\eta_{l(j)}\beta_{l(j)}^T = v_{l(j)}^T G(i\omega_1) = \overline{v_j^T G(-i\omega_1)}$$

$$= \bar{\lambda}_j \overline{v_j^T G(i\omega_1)} = \bar{\lambda}_j \bar{\eta}_j \bar{\beta}_j^T \qquad (4.6.20)$$

indicates that

$$\beta_{l(j)}^T = \bar{\beta}_j^T, \qquad 1 \leqslant j \leqslant m \qquad (4.6.21)$$

Equivalently, the rows of the matrix

$$P_2(\omega_1) = \begin{pmatrix} \beta_1^T \\ \cdot \\ \cdot \\ \cdot \\ \beta_m^T \end{pmatrix} \qquad (4.6.22)$$

occur in complex-conjugate pairs corresponding to the equivalent pairing of the columns of $P_1(\omega_1)$, and

$$G(i\omega_1) = P_1(\omega_1)P_1^{-1}(\omega_1)G(i\omega_1)$$
$$= P_1(\omega_1) \operatorname{diag} \{\eta_j\}_{1 \leqslant j \leqslant m} P_2(\omega_1) \qquad (4.6.23)$$

The result now follows by choosing $g_j(s, \omega_1)$, $1 \leqslant j \leqslant m$, such that

$$g_j(i\omega_1, \omega_1) = \eta_j, \qquad 1 \leqslant j \leqslant m \qquad (4.6.24)$$

$$\overline{g_j(s, \omega_1)} = g_{l(j)}(\overline{s}, \omega_1) \quad \text{(for all } s\text{)}, \quad 1 \leqslant j \leqslant m \qquad (4.6.25)$$

when eqn. 4.6.6 is satisfied.

Exercise 4.6.1

Writing $G(i\omega_1) = A_1 + iA_2$ where A_1, A_2 are real $m \times m$ matrices, (a) prove that, if $|A_1| \neq 0$ and $A_2 A_1^{-1}$ has a nonsingular eigenvector matrix T and eigenvalues λ_j, $1 \leqslant j \leqslant m$, then

$$G(i\omega_1) = T \operatorname{diag} (1 + i\lambda_j)_{1 \leqslant j \leqslant m} T^{-1} A_1$$

so that we may choose $P_1(\omega_1) = T$, $P_2(\omega_1) = T^{-1}A_1$. Verify that T is an eigenvector matrix for $M(\omega_1)$.
(b) formulate and prove a similar result if A_2 is nonsingular.

Exercise 4.6.2

Verify that $P_2^{-1}(\omega_1)$ is an eigenvector matrix of $N(\omega_1) = G^{-1}(i\omega_1) G(-i\omega_1)$.

The above analysis has direct application to design by choosing a forward-path controller of dyadic form

$$K(s) = P_2^{-1}(\omega_1) \operatorname{diag} \{k_j(s, \omega_1)\}_{1 \leqslant j \leqslant m} P_1^{-1}(\omega_1) \qquad (4.6.26)$$

where $k_j(s, \omega_1)$ are proper scalar transfer functions satisfying

$$\overline{k_j(s, \omega_1)} = k_{l(j)}(\overline{s}, \omega_1), \qquad 1 \leqslant j \leqslant m \qquad (4.6.27)$$

when $K(s)$ is physically realisable in the sense that

$$\overline{K(s)} = K(\overline{s}) \qquad (4.6.28)$$

and the identity

$$G(i\omega_1)K(i\omega_1)$$
$$= P_1(\omega_1) \text{ diag } \{g_j(i\omega_1, \omega_1)k_j(i\omega_1, \omega_1)\}_{1 \leqslant j \leqslant m} P_1^{-1}(\omega_1)$$

$$(4.6.29)$$

indicates that

$$q_j(i\omega_1) = g_j(i\omega_1, \omega_1)k_j(i\omega_1, \omega_1), \qquad 1 \leqslant j \leqslant m \quad (4.6.30)$$

i.e. the characteristic loci of GK at the point $s = i\omega_1$ can be specified at will by suitable choice of compensation networks $k_j(s, \omega_1)$, $1 \leqslant j \leqslant m$. This is in contrast to the technique of approximately-commutative control where, in general, only approximate loci assignment is possible at any given frequency. Note, however, that this increased precision has been obtained at the expense of any control over the characteristic directions, the eigenvector matrix $W(i\omega_1) = P_1(\omega_1)$ being specified uniquely (to within scalar multiplication of columns) by the modal decomposition of $G(i\omega_1)$. The approach shares a common feature with the approximately commutative controller in that the constant transformations in eqn. 4.6.26 do not introduce any extra dynamic complexity into $K(s)$.

Exercise 4.6.3
Show that $P_1(\omega_1)P_2(\omega_1)K(s)$ is an *exact* commutative controller for $G(s)P_2^{-1}(\omega_1)P_1^{-1}(\omega_1)$ at the frequency point $s = i\omega_1$.

Exercise 4.6.4
If $G(s)$ has modal matrix $P_1(\omega_1)$ at $s = i\omega_1$, and K is a constant non-singular $m \times m$ matrix, prove that $G(s)K$ has modal matrix $P_1(\omega_1)$ at $s = i\omega_1$ i.e. the characteristic output modes are invariant under constant transformation of the input variables (as expected intuitively!)

Exercise 4.6.5
Using the state-vector model of Section 2.6, show directly that if $k_1 = k_2 = 1$,

$$G^{-1}(i\omega) \begin{pmatrix} 1 \\ 1 \end{pmatrix} = \begin{pmatrix} 1 - m_1 \omega^2 \\ 1 - m_2 \omega^2 \end{pmatrix}$$

$$G^{-1}(i\omega) \begin{pmatrix} 1 - m_2 \omega^2 \\ -(1 - m_1 \omega^2) \end{pmatrix} =$$

$$= \{(1 - m_1\omega^2)(1 - m_2\omega^2) + ci\omega(2 - (m_1 + m_2)\omega^2)\} \begin{pmatrix} 1 \\ -1 \end{pmatrix}$$

indicating that phase shift in the system response can be associated totally with input components of the form $(1, -1)^T e^{i\omega t}$ (i.e. when the inputs have equal amplitude but opposite phases). Hence show that $G(i\omega)$ has a modal decomposition of the form

$$G(i\omega) = P_1(\omega) \begin{pmatrix} g_1(\omega) & 0 \\ 0 & g_2(\omega) \end{pmatrix} P_2(\omega)$$

where

$$P_1(\omega) = \begin{pmatrix} 1 & 1 - m_2\omega^2 \\ 1 & -(1 - m_1\omega^2) \end{pmatrix},$$

$$P_2(\omega) = \begin{pmatrix} 1 & 1 \\ \dfrac{1 - m_2\omega^2}{2 - (m_1 + m_2)\omega^2} & \dfrac{1 - m_1\omega^2}{2 - (m_1 + m_2)\omega^2} \end{pmatrix}$$

$$g_1(\omega) = \frac{1}{2 - (m_1 + m_2)\omega^2},$$

$$g_2(\omega) = \frac{1}{(1 - m_1\omega^2)(1 - m_2\omega^2) + ic\omega(2 - (m_1 + m_2)\omega^2)}$$

Verify the result by direct application of Theorem 4.6.1 and the technique of exercise 4.6.1. Note that the decomposition indicates an oscillatory type of behaviour in $g_1(\omega)$ associated with the output mode $\alpha_1 = (1, 1)^T$ when the masses move in phase. Provide a physical interpretation of this observation.

Dyadic approximations over a range of frequencies: For design purposes, it is necessary to consider the possibility of compensation of characteristic loci over a range of frequencies in the vicinity of a specified point $s = i\omega_1$. For this purpose, define

$$G(s) = P_1(\omega_1)H(s, \omega_1)P_2(\omega_1) \qquad (4.6.31)$$

when, from the above analysis,

$$H_{jl}(i\omega_1, \omega_1) = 0, \qquad j \neq l \qquad (4.6.32)$$

A *dyadic approximation* to $G(s)$ at the point $s = i\omega_1$ is obtained by neglecting the interaction terms in $H(s, \omega_1)$ to obtain the dyadic transfer-function matrix,

$$G_A(s, \omega_1) = P_1(\omega_1) \operatorname{diag} \{g_j(s, \omega_1)\}_{1 \leqslant j \leqslant m} P_2(\omega_1)$$

$$g_j(s, \omega_1) = H_{jj}(s, \omega_1), \qquad 1 \leqslant j \leqslant m \qquad (4.6.33)$$

Exercise 4.6.6
Verify that $G_A(s, \omega_1)$ is physically realisable in the sense that $G_A(s, \omega_1) = G_A(\bar{s}, \omega_1)$ for all s.

Exercise 4.6.7
Prove that $G(s) = G_A(s, \omega_1)$ if, and only if, $G(s)$ is a dyadic transfer-function matrix.

The significance of the dyadic approximation can be seen by choosing $K(s)$ as in eqn. 4.6.26 when

$$Q(s) = G(s)K(s)$$

$$= P_1(\omega_1)H(s, \omega_1) \operatorname{diag} \{k_j(s, \omega_1)\}_{1 \leqslant j \leqslant m} P_1^{-1}(\omega_1) \qquad (4.6.34)$$

indicating that the characteristic transfer functions of $Q(s)$ are identical to the characteristic transfer functions of $H(s, \omega_1)$ diag $\{k_j(s, \omega_1)\}_{1 \leqslant j \leqslant m}$. Moreover, in the vicinity of $s = i\omega_1$,

$$Q(s) = G(s)K(s) \simeq G_A(s, \omega_1)K(s)$$

$$= P_1(\omega_1) \operatorname{diag} \{g_j(s, \omega_1)k_j(s, \omega_1)\}_{1 \leqslant j \leqslant m} P_1^{-1}(\omega_1) \qquad (4.6.35)$$

suggesting that

$$q_j(i\omega) \simeq g_j(i\omega, \omega_1)k_j(i\omega, \omega_1), \qquad 1 \leqslant j \leqslant m \quad (4.6.36)$$

in the vicinity of $s = i\omega_1$, equality holding when $\omega = \omega_1$. In particular, (a) the characteristic loci can be manipulated at will at the point $s = i\omega_1$

(b) in the vicinity of the point $s = i\omega_1$, expr. 4.6.36 provides a technique for approximate compensation of individual characteristic loci by classical analysis of the transfer functions $g_j(s, \omega_1)$, $1 \leqslant j \leqslant m$, and subsequent choice of compensation networks $k_j(s, \omega_1)$, $1 \leqslant j \leqslant m$.

The approximation inherent in expr. 4.6.36 can be quantified by application of Gershgorin's theorem, by noting that the characteristic loci $q_j(i\omega)$, $1 \leqslant j \leqslant m$, lie in the union of the Gershgorin circles in the complex plane of centre $g_j(i\omega, \omega_1)k_j(i\omega, \omega_1)$ and radius,

$$d_j(i\omega, \omega_1) = |k_j(i\omega, \omega_1)| \sum_{\substack{l=1 \\ l \ne j}}^{m} |H_{lj}(i\omega, \omega_1)|,$$

$$1 \le j \le m \qquad (4.6.37)$$

and, from eqn. 4.6.32,

$$d_j(i\omega_1, \omega_1) = 0, \qquad 1 \le j \le m \qquad (4.6.38)$$

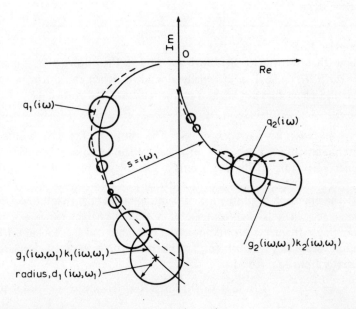

Fig. 4.6.1 Estimation of characteristic loci (m = 2)

This observation has a graphical interpretation as illustrated in Fig. 4.6.1, consisting of a plot of the elements $g_j(s, \omega_1)k_j(s, \omega_1)$, $1 \le j \le m$, with Gershgorin circles superimposed at a finite selection of frequency points, the exact characteristic loci being constrained to lie in the bands swept out by the circles. Assuming, for simplicity, that the points $g_j(i\omega_1, \omega_1)k_j(i\omega_1, \omega_1)$, $1 \le j \le m$, are distinct, then, by continuity and eqn. 4.6.38, it is seen that $q_j(i\omega)$ must lie in the Gershgorin circle of centre $g_j(i\omega, \omega_1)k_j(i\omega, \omega_1)$ and radius $d_j(i\omega, \omega_1)$ in some vicinity of $s = i\omega_1$. In such cases, eqn. 4.6.37 indicates that the fractional error in expr. 4.6.36

$$\frac{|q_j(i\omega) - g_j(i\omega, \omega_1)k_j(i\omega, \omega_1)|}{|g_j(i\omega, \omega_1)k_j(i\omega, \omega_1)|} \le \frac{d_j(i\omega, \omega_1)}{|g_j(i\omega, \omega_1)k_j(i\omega, \omega_1)|} \qquad (4.6.39)$$

is independent of the choice of compensation elements. Equivalently, the validity of expr. 4.6.36 is independent of the choice of compensation elements and can be estimated by graphical analysis of $H(s, \omega_1)$ alone.

Exercise 4.6.8
If $G(s)$ is strictly proper and $K(s)$ is proper, prove that $\lim\limits_{\omega \to +\infty} d_j(i\omega, \omega_1) = 0, 1 \leqslant j \leqslant m$.

Exercise 4.6.9
Show that the fractional errors are all less than unity at the point $s = i\omega$ if $H(i\omega, \omega_1)$ is diagonally dominant, when the origin of the complex plane does not lie in or on the relevant Gershgorin circle.

Application to feedback design: The above results have a direct interpretation in terms of a practical design technique[39] similar in general structure to the characteristic locus design method of Section 4.5.

(a) The approach begins by a consideration of the high to intermediate-frequency analysis and compensation of the characteristic loci, by choosing a frequency ω_h of interest in this range and subsequent calculation of $P_1(\omega_h)$ and $P_2(\omega_h)$. The matrix $H(s, \omega_h)$ is calculated directly from eqn. 4.6.31

$$H(s, \omega_h) = P_1^{-1}(\omega_h)G(s)P_2^{-1}(\omega_h) \qquad (4.6.40)$$

from which the subsystem transfer functions $g_j(s, \omega_h)$ are obtained by inspection of the diagonal terms. At this stage a preliminary investigation of the validity of the approximations to be invoked is best undertaken by obtaining Nyquist plots of $g_j(i\omega, \omega_h)$, $1 \leqslant j \leqslant m$, and superimposing the Gershgorin circles of radius specified by eqn. 4.6.37 with $k_j(s, \omega_h) \equiv 1, 1 \leqslant j \leqslant m$. In particular, the plots will indicate the range of frequencies over which the approximation is sensibly valid (for example, by searching for the range of frequencies over which the fractional error is less than 0·5). In some cases it is anticipated that the range may appear to be small, but the situation can very often be improved by scaling the rows of $H(s, \omega_h)$ i.e. write

$$G(s) = P_1(\omega_h) \operatorname{diag} \{\mu_j\}_{1 \leqslant j \leqslant m} \operatorname{diag} \{\mu_j^{-1}\}_{1 \leqslant j \leqslant m} H(s, \omega_h)P_2(\omega_h)$$

$$(4.6.41)$$

and replace $P_1(\omega_h)$ by $P_1(\omega_h) \operatorname{diag} \{\mu_j\}_{1 \leqslant j \leqslant m}$ and $H(s, \omega_h)$ by $\operatorname{diag} \{\mu_j^{-1}\}_{1 \leqslant j \leqslant m} H(s, \omega_h)$ where the scalars μ_j, $1 \leqslant j \leqslant m$, are chosen to reduce the radii of the Gershgorin circles over the frequency range of interest. Alternatively the situation may be improved by changing the value of ω_h.

(b) Set the forward-path controller to be of the form,

$$K(s) = K(s, \omega_h) = P_2^{-1}(\omega_h) \, \text{diag} \, \{k_j(s, \omega_h)\}_{1 \leqslant j \leqslant m} P_1^{-1}(\omega_h) \quad (4.6.42)$$

where $k_j(s, \omega_h)$, $1 \leqslant j \leqslant m$, are proper scalar minimum-phase compensation elements chosen such that the approximations $g_j(i\omega, \omega_h)$ $k_j(i\omega, \omega_h)$ to the characteristic loci $q_j(i\omega)$ have the desired gain and phase characteristics over the frequency range of interest (remember that the approximation is exact at $\omega = \omega_h$, and that the fractional errors involved are independent of the control elements). Check the success of the procedure by direct evaluation of the characteristic loci and check closed-loop stability by application of the encirclement theorems of Section 4.3. Suitably modify the compensation elements to remove any undesirable features.

At this stage of the design, some insight can be obtained into interaction behaviour by approximating the closed-loop system by a dyadic system as follows

$$H_c(s) = \{I_m + G(s)K(s)\}^{-1} G(s)K(s)$$

$$\simeq \{I_m + G_A(s, \omega_h)K(s)\}^{-1} G_A(s, \omega_h)K(s)$$

$$= P_1(\omega_h) \, \text{diag} \left\{ \frac{g_j(s, \omega_h)k_j(s, \omega_h)}{1 + g_j(s, \omega_h)k_j(s, \omega_h)} \right\}_{1 \leqslant j \leqslant m} P_1^{-1}(\omega_h) \quad (4.6.43)$$

in the vicinity of $s = i\omega_h$. For example, by analogy with exprs. 4.4.9–4.4.10, if, at high frequencies,

$$g_j(i\omega, \omega_h)k_j(i\omega, \omega_h) \simeq g_l(i\omega, \omega_h)k_l(i\omega, \omega_h), \qquad l \neq j \quad (4.6.44)$$

then

$$H_c(i\omega) \simeq \frac{g_1(i\omega, \omega_h)k_1(i\omega, \omega_h)}{1 + g_1(i\omega, \omega_h)k_1(i\omega, \omega_h)} I_m, \qquad \omega \geqslant \omega_h \quad (4.6.45)$$

suggesting that interaction effects are small. In time-domain terms, the rise-times, overshoots and oscillatory characteristic of the scalar feedback systems in eqn. 4.6.43 must be similar to ensure overall small interaction effects. The modal matrix $P_1(\omega_h)$ will also have an effect on interaction (see problem 12 of Section 3.19). In general terms if $P_1(\omega_h)$ is nearly diagonal or if the columns of $P_1(\omega_h)$ are nearly orthogonal and expr. 4.6.44 is satisfied, then interaction is likely to be small. If, however, the columns of $P_1(\omega_h)$ are skew then interaction may be significant.

(c) In many cases the design procedure can be terminated at step (b). If, however, the simulated unit-step responses of the closed-loop system indicate undesirably large steady-state errors, integral action can be included in the control system by replacing eqn. 4.6.42 by

$$K(s) = K(s, \omega_h) \left\{ I_m + \frac{K(\omega_l)}{s} \right\} \qquad (4.6.46)$$

where ω_l is a characteristically low frequency of the system and

$$K(\omega_l) = P_2^{-1}(\omega_l) \, \text{diag} \, \{k_j(\omega_l)\}_{1 \leqslant j \leqslant m} P_1^{-1}(\omega_l) \qquad (4.6.47)$$

Here $P_1(\omega_l)$, $P_2(\omega_l)$ are the modal matrices in the decomposition of $G(s)K(s, \omega_h)$ at $s = i\omega_l$ and $k_j(\omega_l)$, $1 \leqslant j \leqslant m$, are integral gain constants. At high frequencies,

$$G(s)K(s) \simeq G(s)K(s, \omega_h), \qquad \omega \geqslant \omega_h \qquad (4.6.48)$$

indicating that the inclusion of the integral term has negligible effect on the high-frequency design provided that the gains $k_j(\omega_l)$, $1 \leqslant j \leqslant m$, are not too large. In a similar manner, at low frequencies

$$G(s)K(s) \simeq G(s)K(s, \omega_h) \frac{1}{s} K(\omega_l)$$

$$= P_1(\omega_l) \, \text{diag} \left\{ g_j(s, \omega_l) \frac{k_j(\omega_l)}{s} \right\} P_1^{-1}(\omega_l) \quad (4.6.49)$$

and hence, in the vicinity of $s = i\omega_l$,

$$q_j(s) \simeq g_j(s, \omega_l) \frac{1}{s} k_j(\omega_l), \qquad 1 \leqslant j \leqslant m \qquad (4.6.50)$$

This approximation provides a technique for the compensation of characteristic loci similar to the methods of (b). The success of the approach is easily checked by direct evaluation of the exact characteristic loci, and application of the stability theorem of Section 4.3.

(d) Replace $K(s)$ by the form

$$K(s) = kK(s, \omega_h) \left\{ I_m + \frac{K(\omega_l)}{s} \right\} \qquad (4.6.51)$$

where $k > 0$ is a real overall gain parameter. Noting that this has the effect of scaling the characteristic loci obtained in the previous steps, k can be used to provide a final adjustment to gain margins.

Use of the inverse system: The feedback design can proceed in an analogous manner to the above by use of the inverse system $Q^{-1}(s) = K^{-1}(s)G^{-1}(s)$ and application of theorems 4.3.3 or 4.3.4 to the inverse characteristic transfer functions $\hat{q}_j(s)$, $1 \leqslant j \leqslant m$. The basic principle of the technique can be illustrated by considering the decomposition of $G^{-1}(s)$ in the vicinity of a specified point $s = i\omega_1$,

$$G^{-1}(s) = P_2^{-1}(\omega_1)\hat{H}(s, \omega_1)P_1^{-1}(\omega_1) \qquad (4.6.52)$$

where, comparing with eqn. 4.6.31,

$$\hat{H}(s, \omega_1) = H^{-1}(s, \omega_1) \qquad (4.6.53)$$

and

$$\hat{H}_{jl}(i\omega_1, \omega_1) = 0, \qquad j \neq l \qquad (4.6.54)$$

The *inverse dyadic approximation* to $G^{-1}(s)$ at the point $s = i\omega_1$ is then defined by the form

$$G_A^{-1}(s, \omega_1) = P_2^{-1}(\omega_1) \, \text{diag} \, \{g_j^{-1}(s, \omega_1)\}_{1 \leqslant j \leqslant m} P_1^{-1}(\omega_1)$$

$$g_j^{-1}(s,\omega_1) = \hat{H}_{jj}(s, \omega_1), \qquad 1 \leqslant j \leqslant m \qquad (4.6.55)$$

Choosing the forward-path controller of eqn. 4.6.26 then, in the vicinity of $s = i\omega_1$,

$$Q^{-1}(s) = K^{-1}(s)G^{-1}(s) \simeq K^{-1}(s)G_A^{-1}(s, \omega_1)$$

$$= P_1(\omega_1) \, \text{diag} \, \{k_j^{-1}(s, \omega_1)g_j^{-1}(s, \omega_1)\}_{1 \leqslant j \leqslant m} P_1^{-1}(\omega_1) \qquad (4.6.56)$$

suggesting that

$$\hat{q}_j(s, \omega_1) \simeq k_j^{-1}(s, \omega_1)g_j^{-1}(s, \omega_1) \qquad (4.6.57)$$

in the vicinity of $s = i\omega_1$, equality holding when $s = i\omega_1$. The validity of the approximation is assessed by plotting the inverse Nyquist loci of $g_j(s, \omega_1)k_j(s, \omega_1)$, $1 \leqslant j \leqslant m$, on the D contour and superimposing Gershgorin circles of radius

$$d_j(s, \omega_1) = |k_j^{-1}(s, \omega_1)| \sum_{\substack{l=1 \\ l \neq j}}^{m} |\hat{H}_{jl}(s, \omega_1)| \qquad (4.6.58)$$

when Gershgorins theorem tells us that the inverse characteristic loci must lie in the union of such circles at each frequency point. In a similar manner to expr. 4.6.39, the estimated fractional error is

$$\frac{|\hat{q}_j(s) - k_j^{-1}(s, \omega_1)g_j^{-1}(s, \omega_1)|}{|k_j^{-1}(s, \omega_1)g_j^{-1}(s, \omega_1)|} \leqslant \frac{d_j(s, \omega_1)}{|k_j^{-1}(s, \omega_1)g_j^{-1}(s, \omega_1)|} \qquad (4.6.59)$$

which is independent of the choice of compensation elements.

A feedback design can now be attempted as follows:

(i) Choose a frequency $s = i\omega_h$ in the intermediate to high frequency range, compute $\hat{H}(s, \omega_h)$ from eqn. 4.6.52. Check the validity of the approximation expr. 4.6.57 by plots of the inverse Nyquist loci of $g_j(s, \omega_1)$, $1 \leqslant j \leqslant m$, with superimposed Gershgorin circles. Note that it is necessary to include the component from the semicircular part of D.

(ii) Using the approximations $\hat{q}_j(s, \omega_1) \simeq k_j^{-1}(s, \omega_1)g_j^{-1}(s, \omega_1)$, design a forward-path controller of the form of eqn. 4.6.42 generating the required form of gain and phase characteristics in the vicinity of $s = i\omega_1$. Check the success of the procedure by direct evaluation of $\hat{q}_j(s)$ on the contour D, application of the stability theorems, and examination of the closed-loop response using the dyadic approximation,

$$
\begin{aligned}
H_c(s) &= \{I_m + Q(s)\}^{-1}Q(s) = \{I_m + Q^{-1}(s)\}^{-1} \\
&= \{K^{-1}(s)G^{-1}(s) + I_m\}^{-1} \simeq \{K^{-1}(s)G_A^{-1}(s, \omega_1) + I_m\}^{-1} \\
&= \{I_m + G_A(s, \omega_1)K(s)\}^{-1}G_A(s, \omega_1)K(s) \\
&= P_1(\omega_1) \operatorname{diag} \left\{ \frac{g_j(s, \omega_1)k_j(s, \omega_1)}{1 + g_j(s, \omega_1)k_j(s, \omega_1)} \right\}_{1 \leqslant j \leqslant m} P_1^{-1}(\omega_1) \quad (4.6.60)
\end{aligned}
$$

(iii) Replace $K(s)$ by eqns. 4.6.46 and 4.6.47 where ω_l is a characteristically low frequency for the system and note that, at high frequencies $Q^{-1}(s) \simeq K^{-1}(s, \omega_h)G^{-1}(s)$ as in expr. 4.6.48. At low frequencies

$$
\begin{aligned}
Q^{-1}(s) &\simeq sK^{-1}(\omega_l)\{G(s)K(s, \omega_h)\}^{-1} \\
&= P_1(\omega_l) \operatorname{diag} \{sk_j^{-1}(\omega_l)g_j^{-1}(s, \omega_l)\}_{1 \leqslant j \leqslant m} P_1^{-1}(\omega_l)
\end{aligned}
$$

and hence, at frequencies in the vicinity of $s = i\omega_l$, $\hat{q}(s) \simeq sk_j^{-1}(\omega_l) g_j^{-1}(s, \omega_l)$. After choice of suitable integral gains, check the stability of the closed-loop system by application of the encirclement theorems.

(iv) Replace $K(s)$ by eqn. 4.6.51 and proceed as before to implement final adjustments to the system gain margins.

Exercise 4.6.10

Writing $G^{-1}(i\omega_1) = A_1 + iA_2$ where A_1, A_2 are real $m \times m$ matrices, prove that, if $|A_1| \neq 0$ and $A_1^{-1}A_2$ has a nonsingular eigenvector matrix T and eigenvalues λ_j, $1 \leqslant j \leqslant m$, then

$$
G^{-1}(i\omega_1) = A_1 T \operatorname{diag} \{1 + i\lambda_j\}T^{-1}
$$

indicating that $P_2^{-1}(\omega_1) = A_1 T$ and $P_1^{-1}(\omega_1) = T^{-1}$. Formulate and prove a similar result if A_2 is nonsingular. Compare with Exercise 4.6.1.

Special case of practical interest: If $G(s)$ is a dyadic transfer function matrix, it is easily verified that $H(s, \omega_1)$ (and hence $\hat{H}(s, \omega_1)$) is diagonal at all frequencies s on D, that $G(s) \equiv G_A(s, \omega_1)$ and that the above techniques reduce to the exact analysis of Section 3.16. If $H(s, \omega_1)$ (and hence $\hat{H}(s, \omega_1)$) is approximately diagonal for all s on D, it is intuitively reasonable to replace $G(s)$ by its dyadic approximation $G_A(s, \omega_1)$ at all frequencies and design a forward-path controller $K(s)$ using the methods of Section 3.16. The dynamics of the closed-loop systems $\{I_m + G(s)K(s)\}^{-1}G(s)K(s)$ and $\{I_m + G_A(s, \omega_1)K(s)\}^{-1}G_A(s, \omega_1)K(s)$ will be essentially identical if the approximation is sufficiently good. An exact formulation of this intuitive concept is possible using techniques introduced by Rosenbrock[59] in the context of the inverse Nyquist array.

Suppose that $L(s)$ is an $m \times m$ transfer-function matrix, then we state without proof the following result due to Rosenbrock.[57,58]

Theorem 4.6.2: Let $L(s)$ be diagonally- (row or column) dominant and analytic at every point of the contour D. Let $L_{jj}(s)$ map D into a closed contour C_j, $1 \leqslant j \leqslant m$ and $|L(s)|$ map D into C_0. Let C_j encircle the origin of the complex plane N_j times, $0 \leqslant j \leqslant m$ (all encirclements being clockwise). Then

$$N_0 = \sum_{j=1}^{m} N_j \qquad (4.6.61)$$

In essence, if $L(s)$ is diagonally-dominant on D, then the problem of deducing the clockwise encirclements of $|L(s)|$ on D reduces to the elementary problem of counting the encirclements generated by the diagonal terms of $L(s)$. The result has many applications,[58] and in particular, to the analysis of *approximately dyadic systems*.

Theorem 4.6.3: Suppose that the $m \times m$ invertible, strictly proper system $G(s)$ has decomposition,

$$G(s) = P_1(\omega_1)H(s, \omega_1)P_2(\omega_1) \qquad (4.6.62)$$

at the point $s = i\omega_1$, and is subject to unity-negative feedback control with forward-path controller

$$K(s) = P_2^{-1}(\omega_1) \, \text{diag} \, \{k_j(s)\}_{1 \leqslant j \leqslant m} P_1^{-1}(\omega_1) \qquad (4.6.63)$$

Suppose that $I_m + H(s, \omega_1) \, \text{diag} \, \{k_j(s)\}_{1 \leqslant j \leqslant m}$ is diagonally (row or column) dominant at every point s on D. Let the transfer functions $g_j(s, \omega_1)k_j(s, \omega_1)$ map D onto the closed-contours C_j encircling the $(-1, 0)$ point of the complex plane n_j times, $1 \leqslant j \leqslant m$, in a clockwise manner. Then, using the notation of theorem 4.3.1,

$$n_T = \sum_{j=1}^{m} n_j \qquad (4.6.64)$$

and the closed-loop system is asymptotically stable if, and only if,

$$n_0 + \sum_{j=1}^{m} n_j = 0 \qquad (4.6.65)$$

Proof: From theorem 4.6.2, noting that D always excludes the system poles, the identity

$$|T(s)| = |I_m + G(s)K(s)| = |I_m + H(s, \omega_1) \operatorname{diag} \{k_j(s)\}_{1 \leqslant j \leqslant m}|$$

indicates that n_T is just the sum of the clockwise encirclements of the Nyquist plots of $1 + H_{jj}(s, \omega_1)k_j(s) = 1 + g_j(s, \omega_1)k_j(s)$ about the origin of the complex plane. But this is simply the sum of the clockwise encirclements of the Nyquist plots of $g_j(s, \omega_1)k_j(s)$ about the $(-1, 0)$ point, proving eqn. 4.6.64. Eqn. 4.6.65 follows from theorem 4.3.1. Note that, under the stated conditions, stability depends only upon the properties of the diagonal terms of $H(s, \omega_1)$ and the controller functions $k_j(s)$, $1 \leqslant j \leqslant m$, and hence upon the properties of the approximate closed-loop system $\{I_m + G_A(s, \omega_1)K(s)\}^{-1}G_A(s, \omega_1)K(s)$. A graphical check of the validity of the assumptions of the result is obtained by sketching the Nyquist diagrams of the transfer functions $g_j(s, \omega_1)k_j(s)$ and superimposing Gershgorin circles of radius given by eqn. 4.6.37. It is easily verified that the conditions of the theorem are satisfied if, and only if, the $(-1, 0)$ point does not lie in or on any Gershgorin circle at any frequency. For example, consider the system illustrated schematically in Fig. 4.6.2 with $n_0 = 0$, $m = 2$. The conditions of theorem 4.6.3 are satisfied and $n_1 = 1, n_2 = 0$ indicating that $n_T = 1$ and that the closed-loop system will be unstable.

An alternative formulation is possible in terms of the inverse system and application of theorem 4.6.2.

Theorem 4.6.4: Suppose that the $m \times m$ invertible, strictly proper system has the decomposition (see eqns. 4.6.52–4.6.55)

$$G^{-1}(s) = P_2^{-1}(\omega_1)\hat{H}(s, \omega_1)P_1^{-1}(\omega_1) \qquad (4.6.66)$$

in the vicinity of $s = i\omega_1$, and is subject to unity-negative feedback with forward-path controller eqn. 4.6.63. Suppose that $I_m + \operatorname{diag} \{k_j^{-1}(s)\}_{1 \leqslant j \leqslant m}\hat{H}(s, \omega_1)$ and $\operatorname{diag} \{k_j^{-1}(s)\}\hat{H}(s, \omega_1)$ are diagonally (row or column) dominant on D. Let the inverse transfer functions $k_j^{-1}(s)$ $g_j^{-1}(s, \omega_1)$ map D onto closed contours C_j encircling the origin and $(-1, 0)$ points $\tilde{n}_j$ and $\hat{n}_j$ times respectively, $1 \leqslant j \leqslant m$, in a clockwise manner. Then,

$$n_T = \sum_{j=1}^{m} (\hat{n}_j - \tilde{n}_j) \tag{4.6.67}$$

and the closed-loop system is asymptotically stable if, and only if,

$$n_0 + \sum_{j=1}^{m} (\hat{n}_j - \tilde{n}_j) = 0 \tag{4.6.68}$$

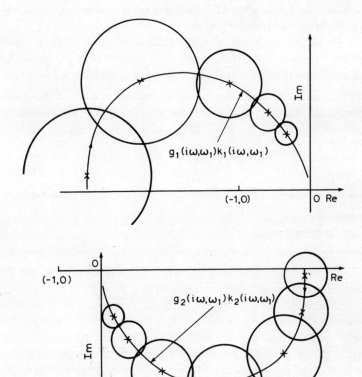

Fig. 4.6.2 Nyquist plots of $g_j(s, \omega_1)\, k_j(s, \omega_1)$ for $s = i\omega$
$0 \leqslant \omega$, ω_1 large

Proof: The result is easily verified from the identity,

$$|I_m + G(s)K(s)| = \frac{|I_m + K^{-1}(s)G^{-1}(s)|}{|K^{-1}(s)G^{-1}(s)|}$$

$$= \frac{|I_m + \text{diag}\,\{k_j^{-1}(s)\}\hat{H}(s,\omega_1)|}{|\text{diag}\,\{k_j^{-1}(s)\}\hat{H}(s,\omega_1)|}$$

and application of theorems 4.3.1 and 4.6.2.

All the observations following theorem 4.6.3 still hold except that (a) both the $(-1,0)$ and $(0,0)$ points of the complex plane must not lie in or on any Gershgorin circle of centre $k_j^{-1}(s)g_j^{-1}(s,\omega_1)$, and radius given by eqn. 4.6.58 when s lies on D and (b) it is, in general, necessary to consider the semicircular part of D.

A simplified result can also be obtained, if the number of right-halfplane zeros, n_z^+, of $Q(s)$ is known. by a consideration of eqn. 4.3.17 and the formulation of the following analogue to theorem 4.3.4.

Theorem 4.6.5: With notation as in theorem 4.6.4 and the single assumption that $I_m + \text{diag}\,\{k_j^{-1}(s)\}_{1\leqslant j\leqslant m}\hat{H}(s,\omega_1)$ is diagonally-dominant on D, then the closed-loop system is asymptotically stable if, and only if,

$$n_z^+ + \sum_{j=1}^{m} \hat{n}_j = 0 \qquad (4.6.69)$$

Exercise 4.6.11
Prove theorem 4.6.5.

Note in this case that $\text{diag}\,\{k_j^{-1}(s)\}_{1\leqslant j\leqslant m}\hat{H}(s,\omega_1)$ need not be diagonally- (row or column) dominant on D.

In summary, the concept of diagonal dominance is of extreme importance in feedback design and stability analysis by reducing the multi-input/multi-output problem to m independent single-input/single-output design problems and application of one of the above stability theorems. The dominance conditions are not always satisfied in which case it may be necessary to revert to the approximation methods discussed earlier. Alternatively, dominance may be achieved by the use of precompensation networks as discussed in later Sections on the inverse Nyquist array and its generalisations. An interesting aspect of the method of dyadic expansion is that diagonal dominance is guaranteed over a frequency range in the vicinity of the point $s = i\omega_1$.

4.7 Illustrative design examples

The above accounts of the characteristic locus and dyadic expansion methods indicates a great similarity in overall structure and operational sequence, the basic differences being the degree of approximation involved, the interpretation of the significance of characteristic directions and the computational difference in system-decomposition methods. The essential operational steps can be illustrated by considering the method of dyadic expansion. Interested readers are referred to MacFarlane and Kouvaritakis[23] for details of the application of the characteristic locus method.

The method of dyadic expansion[39] has been successfully applied to the design of nuclear-reactor control systems[37] and power station boiler control systems.[32] In this Section we consider the liquid level system of Section 3.14 to illustrate the relation of the approach to the analytical techniques of Chapter 3. The inverse frequency-response matrix takes the form

$$G^{-1}(i\omega_1) = \beta^{-1}\begin{pmatrix} 2\beta + 1 & -(2\beta + 1) \\ -(2\beta + 1) & 2\beta + 1 - \omega_1^2 \end{pmatrix}$$

$$+ i\omega_1\beta^{-1}\begin{pmatrix} \beta & -1 \\ -1 & 2(1 + \beta) \end{pmatrix} \qquad (4.7.1)$$

by inspection of eqn. 3.14.4. This expression can be written in the form

$$G^{-1}(i\omega_1) = \beta^{-1}A_1(\omega_1) + i\omega_1\beta^{-1}A_2(\omega_1) \qquad (4.7.2)$$

where $A_i(\omega_1)$, $i = 1, 2$, are real matrices. Applying an obvious analogue of Exercise 4.6.10, the matrix $P_1(\omega_1)$ is taken to be an eigenvector matrix of

$$A_1^{-1}(\omega_1)A_2(\omega_1) = \frac{(-1)}{(2\beta + 1)\omega_1^2}\begin{pmatrix} 2\beta + 1 - \omega_1^2 & 2\beta + 1 \\ 2\beta + 1 & (2\beta + 1) \end{pmatrix}$$

$$\begin{pmatrix} \beta & -1 \\ -1 & 2(1 + \beta) \end{pmatrix} \qquad (4.7.3)$$

Rather than getting bogged down with complex computational detail, the essential ingredients of the design approach can be illustrated by letting $\omega_1 = \omega_h \to +\infty$, when

$$\lim_{\omega_1 \to \infty} A_1^{-1}(\omega_1)A_2(\omega_1) = \frac{1}{(2\beta + 1)}\begin{pmatrix} \beta & -1 \\ 0 & 0 \end{pmatrix} \qquad (4.7.4)$$

so that we can take

$$P_1(\infty) = \lim_{\omega_1 \to \infty} P_1(\omega_1) = \begin{pmatrix} 1 & 1 \\ 0 & \beta \end{pmatrix} \qquad (4.7.5)$$

By Exercise 4.6.2, $P_2^{-1}(\omega_1)$ is an eigenvector matrix of $G^{-1}(i\omega_1)$ $G(-i\omega_1)$ or, more simply, an eigenvector matrix of

$$A_2(\omega_1)A_1^{-1}(\omega_1) = \frac{(-1)}{(2\beta + 1)\omega_1^2} \begin{pmatrix} \beta & -1 \\ -1 & 2(1 + \beta) \end{pmatrix}$$

$$\begin{pmatrix} 2\beta + 1 - \omega_1^2 & 2\beta + 1 \\ 2\beta + 1 & 2\beta + 1 \end{pmatrix}$$

$$\to \frac{1}{(2\beta + 1)} \begin{pmatrix} \beta & 0 \\ -1 & 0 \end{pmatrix} \qquad (\omega_1 \to +\infty) \qquad (4.7.6)$$

giving

$$P_2^{-1}(\infty) = \lim_{\omega_1 \to \infty} P_2^{-1}(\omega_1) = \beta^{-1} \begin{pmatrix} \beta & 0 \\ -1 & 1 \end{pmatrix} \qquad (4.7.7)$$

or

$$P_2(\infty) = \begin{pmatrix} 1 & 0 \\ 1 & \beta \end{pmatrix} \qquad (4.7.8)$$

It is of interest to compare exprs. 4.7.5 and 4.7.8 with eqn. 3.14.9 when it is noted that the method of dyadic expansion generates the modal matrices derived using the techniques of Section 3.13. This provides some justification for the contention that the dyadic decomposition is a real reflection of system structure.

The matrix $\hat{H}(s, \infty)$ can now be calculated using eqn. 4.6.52 to be the matrix of eqn. 3.14.10 i.e.

$$\hat{H}(s, \infty) = s^2 \begin{pmatrix} 0 & 0 \\ 0 & \beta \end{pmatrix} + s \begin{pmatrix} 1 & 0 \\ 0 & 2\beta^2 + 2\beta - 1 \end{pmatrix}$$

$$+ \frac{(2\beta + 1)}{\beta} \begin{pmatrix} 1 & 1 - \beta \\ 1 - \beta & (1 - \beta)^2 \end{pmatrix} \qquad (4.7.9)$$

The inverse dyadic approximation $G_A^{-1}(s, \infty)$ is obtained by comparison of eqns. 4.6.55 and 4.7.9 and is characterised by transfer functions

$$g_1^{-1}(s, \infty) = s + \frac{2\beta + 1}{\beta},$$

$$g_2^{-1}(s, \infty) = \beta s^2 + (2\beta^2 + 2\beta - 1)s + \frac{(2\beta + 1)(1 - \beta)^2}{\beta} \quad (4.7.10)$$

and the relation

$$G_A(s, \infty) = P_1(\infty) \begin{pmatrix} g_1(s, \infty) & 0 \\ 0 & g_2(s, \infty) \end{pmatrix} P_2(\infty) \quad (4.7.11)$$

(compare eqns. 4.7.10 with 3.14.11). If $\beta = 1$, $\hat{H}(s, \infty)$ is diagonal at all frequencies and $G(s) \equiv G_A(s, \infty)$ indicating that $G(s)$ is a dyadic transfer-function matrix and the feedback design can be approached using the techniques of Section 3.16. Suppose, therefore, that $\beta \neq 1$. The effectiveness of the approximation can be estimated by an examination of the diagonal dominance of $\hat{H}(s, \infty)$ on D. Noting that the diagonal terms are unbounded as $|s| \to +\infty$, and that the off-diagonal terms are constant, it is easily verified that $\hat{H}(s, \infty)$ is diagonally- (row) dominant at all high frequencies $s = i\omega$ and on the semicircular part of D. At low frequencies, however, the situation is very different. Consider the point $s = i\omega = 0$, when diagonal- (row) dominance requires that

$$\left| \frac{(2\beta + 1)}{\beta} \right| > \left| \frac{(2\beta + 1)(1 - \beta)}{\beta} \right|,$$

$$\left| \frac{(2\beta + 1)(1 - \beta)^2}{\beta} \right| > \left| \frac{(2\beta + 1)(1 - \beta)}{\beta} \right| \quad (4.7.12)$$

From physical considerations, $\beta > 0$, so that expr. 4.7.12 reduces to

$$1 > |1 - \beta|, \quad |1 - \beta| > 1 \quad (4.7.13)$$

which is absurd i.e. $\hat{H}(s, \infty)$ is not diagonally- (row) dominant at $s = 0$ independent of the plant data $\beta \neq 1$.

Using the data $\beta = 2$ (as in Section 3.14), the inverse Nyquist plots of $g_j^{-1}(s, \infty)$, $j = 1, 2$, are shown in Fig. 4.7.1 with superimposed Gershgorin circles computed from eqn. 4.6.58 with $k_j(s, \infty) \equiv 1$, $j = 1, 2$. In particular, it is seen that $g_j^{-1}(s, \infty)$ will provide an excellent approximation to the characteristic loci at high frequency (when the fractional errors are small) but, at low frequency, the errors in the approximation may be large (the fractional error could be unity).

The high frequency compensation element takes the form of eqn. 4.6.42

$$K(s) = K(s, \infty) = P_2^{-1}(\infty) \text{ diag } \{k_j(s, \infty)\}_{j=1,2} P_1^{-1}(\infty) \qquad (4.7.14)$$

and the compensation procedure is approached by using the approximation

$$\hat{q}_j(i\omega) \simeq k_j^{-1}(i\omega, \infty) g_j^{-1}(i\omega, \infty) \qquad (4.7.15)$$

to the inverse characteristic loci at high frequency.

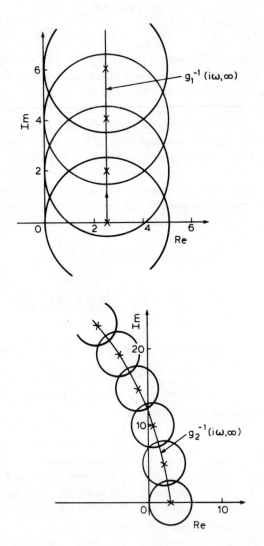

Fig. 4.7.1 Inverse Nyquist plots of $g_j(s, \infty)$, $j = 1, 2$ with Gershgorin circles

Exercise 4.7.1

Show that the fractional error in the estimation of $\hat{q}_2(i\omega)$ is less than 0·5 for $\omega \geqslant 0·5$ and less than 0·5 for $\hat{q}_1(i\omega)$ for $\omega \geqslant 2·5$.

The closed-loop system is approximated as follows,

$$
\begin{aligned}
H_c(s) &= \{I_m + G(s)K(s)\}^{-1}G(s)K(s) = \{G^{-1}(s) + K(s)\}^{-1}K(s) \\
&\simeq \{G_A^{-1}(s, \infty) + K(s)\}^{-1}K(s) \\
&= \{I_m + G_A(s, \infty)K(s)\}^{-1}G_A(s, \infty)K(s) \\
&= P_1(\infty) \operatorname{diag} \left\{ \frac{g_j(s, \infty)k_j(s, \infty)}{1 + g_j(s, \infty)k_j(s, \infty)} \right\}_{j=1, 2} P_1^{-1}(\infty)
\end{aligned} \tag{4.7.16}
$$

and closed-loop interaction is suppressed by ensuring that the closed-loop scalar systems in expr. 4.7.16 have similar high-frequency transient characteristics. This is precisely the problem considered in Section 3.14 leading to the choice of

$$
k_1(s, \infty) = 7·5, \quad k_2(s, \infty) = 390·0 \frac{(s + 5·0)}{(s + 19·5)} \tag{4.7.17}
$$

so that

$$
K(s) = \begin{pmatrix} 1 & 0 \\ -0·5 & 0·5 \end{pmatrix} \begin{pmatrix} 7·5 & 0 \\ 0 & 390·0 \dfrac{(s + 5·0)}{(s + 19·5)} \end{pmatrix} \begin{pmatrix} 1 & -0·5 \\ 0 & 0·5 \end{pmatrix} \tag{4.7.18}
$$

The plots of $k_j^{-1}(s, \infty)g_j^{-1}(s, \infty)$, $j = 1, 2$, on D are shown in Fig. 4.7.2 together with Gershgorin circles (only the plots for a finite range of positive frequencies is shown, negative frequencies are obtained by taking complex conjugates and the behaviour on the semicircular part of D is well defined by the approximation as the system diag $\{k_j^{-1}(s, \infty)\}$ $\hat{H}(s, \infty)$ is diagonally (row) dominant for $|s|$ large). The stability of the design could now be checked by direct evaluation of the inverse characteristic loci, but, more conveniently, note that $I_m + \operatorname{diag}$ $\{k_j^{-1}(s, \infty)\}\hat{H}(s, \infty)$ is diagonally (row) dominant on D and apply theorem 4.6.5. The analysis of Section 3.13 indicates that $G(s)$ has no zeros and $K(s)$ has a zero at $s = -5·0$ i.e. $n_z^+ = 0$. Noting that $\hat{n}_1 = \hat{n}_2 = 0$, eqn. 4.6.69 is satisfied and the closed-loop system is asymptotically stable. The control structure (eqn. 4.7.18) is essentially identical to the design (eqn. 3.14.16) produced in Section 3.14 so that the closed-loop transient responses will be similar in magnitude and form to Fig. 3.14.2.

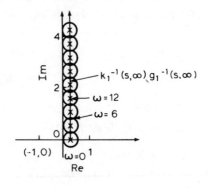

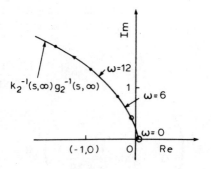

Fig. 4.7.2 Loci for $k_j^{-1}(s, \infty)g_j^{-1}(s, \infty), j = 1, 2$ with Gershgorin circles

The design could now proceed using a decomposition of $K^{-1}(s, \infty)$ $G^{-1}(s, \infty)$ at a characteristic low frequency point ω_l to introduce integral-control action as in eqn. 4.6.46 to offset steady-state errors. Alternatively, the controller (eqn. 4.7.14) could be augmented by writing,

$$k_1(s, \infty) = 7 \cdot 5 \left(1 + \frac{c_1}{s}\right),$$

$$k_2(s, \infty) = 390 \cdot 0 \frac{(s + 5 \cdot 0)}{(s + 19 \cdot 5)} \left(1 + \frac{c_2}{s}\right),$$

analysis of the plots of $k_j^{-1}(s, \infty)g_j^{-1}(s, \infty)$ on D, and application of theorem 4.6.5. This is left as an exercise for the reader.

4.8 Summary

The material of this Chapter follows naturally (but not chronologically) from the introductory material of chapter three and the reader is encouraged to return there to reinterpret the ideas in terms of characteristic loci and dyadic approximations. The common theme throughout the discussion in this chapter has been the relevance and interpretation of eigenvector-type transformations in the assessment of system dynamic characteristics. These concepts were introduced initially by MacFarlane[18] in the form of the commutative-controller design technique which, despite its inherent difficulties, is the fundamental conceptual base of all the techniques discussed. The author feels that the ideas have matured considerably in the form of the characteristic locus method and the related method of dyadic expansion, although the techniques have not yet been applied to sufficient practical examples to enable a general assessment of their usefulness to be made. This is left as an exercise for the reader. The reader should not be led astray by the notion that there exists a universally 'best' design method, to be used in all circumstances. In the author's opinion a particular technique may well suit a particular application owing to the physical characteristics of the system under consideration. In this sense any general comparison is impossible.

An important aspect of the techniques is the introduction of the idea of eigenvalue and eigenvector approximation. This would seem to be a necessary aspect of any technique based on the system transfer function matrix where, in essence, one has the difficult task of obtaining information on state dynamics from output information. These approximation methods will play an important role in the following chapters.

The field is, by no means, tied up. There remains open questions as to the identification of the dominant dynamic characteristics of $G(s)$ and the construction of alternative procedures to cover cases when the approximations involved in the above techniques are too gross. In recent contributions[22, 55] attention has been focussed on the rigorous formulation of eigenvalue-type methods. Such techniques have yet to demonstrate their usefulness to design, but it seems that they will play an important role in the generalisation to multivariable systems of the well known root-locus method[14, 49, 61] (see Chapter 6).

4.9 Problems and exercises

1 Show that the system

$$G(s) = \frac{1}{(s+1)(s+3)}\begin{pmatrix} s+3 & -2 \\ 1 & s \end{pmatrix}$$

has frequency-independent eigenvectors. Hence, use the cummutative-controller design approach to construct a unity-negative feedback system with fast-response speed, small (or zero) steady-state errors and small interaction effects in response to unit-step demands. Comment on the skewness of the eigenvectors and its impact on system performance.

2 Apply the alignment algorithm to the system of problem 1. Show that K_h takes the form

$$K_h = \begin{pmatrix} K_{11}(\omega_h) & K_{12}(\omega_h) \\ K_{21}(\omega_h) & K_{22}(\omega_h) \end{pmatrix} \begin{pmatrix} \mu_1 & 0 \\ 0 & \mu_2 \end{pmatrix}$$

where

$$\lim_{\omega_h \to \infty} K_{jl}(\omega_h) = \delta_{jl}$$

Letting $\omega_h \to \infty$, comment on the alignment obtained if $\mu_1 = \mu_2$ and $\mu_1 \neq \mu_2$. Compare your results with those of Exercise 4.5.1. Choosing $\mu_1 = \mu_2$, complete the design using the characteristic locus method and show that the approximately commutative controller commutes exactly with the plant. What happens if $\mu_1 \neq \mu_2$?

3 Consider the dyadic decomposition of the $m \times m$ second-order lag

$$G^{-1}(s) = s^2 A_0 + s A_1 + A_2, \qquad |A_0| \neq 0.$$

Prove that, in general, the matrix $P_1(\omega_1)$ can be computed as an eigenvector matrix of

$$\omega_1^2 \{\omega_1^2 I_m - A_0^{-1} A_2\}^{-1} A_0^{-1} A_1 \to A_0^{-1} A_1 \qquad (\omega_1 \to +\infty)$$

and that, if $A_0^{-1} A_1$ has distinct eigenvalues λ_j, $1 \leqslant j \leqslant m$,

$$\lim_{\omega_1 \to \infty} P_1(\omega_1) = T$$

where T is an eigenvector matrix of $A_0^{-1} A_1$. (Note: the existence of the limit is guaranteed if the maximum modulus of the entries in each column of $P_1(\omega_1)$ is taken to be equal to unity). In a similar manner show that

$$\lim_{\omega_1 \to \infty} P_2(\omega_1) = T^{-1} A_0^{-1}$$

and hence that

$$\hat{H}(s, \infty) = s^2 I_m + s \, \text{diag} \, (\lambda_j)_{1 \leqslant j \leqslant m} + \Omega$$

$$\Omega = T^{-1} A_0^{-1} A_2 T$$

The inverse-dyadic approximation $G_A(s, \infty)$ is defined by the subsystem transfer functions

$$g_j^{-1}(s, \infty) = s^2 + \lambda_j s + \Omega_{jj}, \qquad 1 \leqslant j \leqslant m.$$

If λ_j and Ω_{jj}, $1 \leqslant j \leqslant m$, are real and strictly positive, investigate the conditions for $H(s, \infty)$ to be diagonally (row) dominant for all s on D. (Hint: note that the radii of the Gershgorin circles are independent of frequency). Prove also that the forward-path controller

$$K(s) = A_0 T \, \text{diag} \, \{k_j\}_{1 \leqslant j \leqslant m} T^{-1}$$

will produce a stable closed-loop system for all high-enough gains k_j, $1 \leqslant j \leqslant m$, and if $\hat{H}(s, \infty)$ is diagonally (row) dominant on D, the system is stable for all $k_j > 0$, $1 \leqslant j \leqslant m$. (Hint: construct the loci $k_j^{-1} g_j^{-1}(s, \infty)$, investigate the behaviour of the Gershgorin circles as k_j increases, $1 \leqslant j \leqslant m$, and show that it is always possible to make $I_m + \text{diag} \, \{k_j^{-1}\}\hat{H}(s, \infty)$ diagonally (row) dominant on D).

4 Show that the essential principles of the design accomplished in Section 4.7 are retained if ω_h is large but finite.

5 In the example of Section 4.7, show that an increase in β reduces the maximum fractional error in the estimation of $\hat{q}_2(i\omega)$ but increases the fractional error in the estimation of $\hat{q}_1(i\omega)$. Noting that the error is pushed into the easily controlled first order type mode, comment on the effect on the final design and system performance.

Chapter 5

Noneigenvalue methods in feedback design

This chapter represents a fundamental change in emphasis when compared with the discussions of Chapters 3 and 4 where attention was focused on the interpretation of the system dynamics in terms of eigen/modal entities. Here, we stay firmly in the space of inputs and outputs and attempt the systematic compensation of the transfer-function elements of $H_c(s)$. This avoids the interaction interpretation problems inherent in the use of transformation techniques and may enable the design of structurally constrained $K(s)$ (note that eigenvalue-based methods require the independent specification of all elements of $K(s)$). It does, however, introduce some new and interesting problems.

5.1 Diagonal dominance and the return-difference

Consider a unity-negative feedback system for the control of the $m \times m$ strictly proper plant $G(s)$ with proper forward-path controller $K(s)$. Denoting $Q(s) = G(s)K(s)$, then closed-loop stability is described by the return-difference determinant

$$|T(s)| = \frac{\rho_c(s)}{\rho_0(s)} = |I_m + Q(s)| \qquad (5.1.1)$$

Throughout this chapter we will constantly need theorem 4.3.1 relating the stability of the closed-loop system to the clockwise encirclements n_T of $|T(s)|$ on the D contour. The stability theorems invoked enable the graphical evaluation of n_T by frequency-response plots of elements of $Q(s)$. This requires some structural constraint on $Q(s)$ in the form of diagonal-dominance conditions (Section 4.6 and Reference 19).

The following result parallels theorem 4.6.3,

Theorem 5.1.1: Let $I_m + Q(s)$ be diagonally- (row or column) dominant at every point s on the D contour. Let the diagonal transfer functions $Q_{jj}(s)$ map D onto closed-contours C_j encircling the $(-1,0)$ point of the complex plane n_j times, $1 \leqslant j \leqslant m$, in a clockwise manner. Then,

$$n_T = \sum_{j=1}^{m} n_j \qquad (5.1.2)$$

and the closed-loop system is asymptotically stable if, and only if,

$$n_0 + \sum_{j=1}^{m} n_j = 0 \qquad (5.1.3)$$

Proof: Apply theorem 4.6.2 to eqn. 5.1.1 and set $n_c = 0$.

The diagonal-dominance condition is easily checked graphically by plotting the frequency responses of the diagonal entries $Q_{jj}(s)$, $1 \leqslant j \leqslant m$, and superimposing Gershgorin circles of radius,

$$d_j(s) = \sum_{\substack{l=1 \\ l \neq j}}^{m} |Q_{jl}(s)|, \qquad 1 \leqslant j \leqslant m, \quad \text{(row estimates)} \qquad (5.1.4)$$

or,

$$d_j(s) = \sum_{\substack{l=1 \\ l \neq j}}^{m} |Q_{lj}(s)|, \qquad 1 \leqslant j \leqslant m, \quad \text{(column estimates)} \qquad (5.1.5)$$

at selected frequency points. It is easily verified that $I_m + Q(s)$ is diagonally- (row or column) dominant at each point of D if, and only if, the $(-1,0)$ point does not lie in or on any Gershgorin circle at any frequency. Note also that the assumption that $Q(s)$ is strictly proper implies that $Q_{jj}(s)$ need only be plotted on the imaginary axis $s = i\omega$, $\omega \geqslant 0$ as $I_m + Q(s)$ is automatically diagonally-dominant as $|s| \to +\infty$.

In essence the result states that, under diagonal-dominance conditions, the stability of the m-input/m-output system can be investigated by the analysis of m single-input/single-output system with forward-path transfer functions $Q_{jj}(s)$, $1 \leqslant j \leqslant m$. In this sense, the approach shares much in common with the techniques of previous chapters, but has the intuitive advantage that $Q_{jj}(s)$, $1 \leqslant j \leqslant m$, has a more direct relation to the input-output behaviour of the closed-loop system. The application of the result depends upon the construction of $K(s)$ such that $Q(s)$ is diagonally dominant on D. This is where the problem lies! The existence of such a $K(s)$ is guaranteed (mathematically) if $G(s)$ is invertible by choosing

$$K(s) = G^{-1}(s) \, \text{diag} \, \{q_j(s)\}_{1 \leqslant j \leqslant m} \qquad (5.1.6)$$

when
$$I_m + Q(s) = \text{diag}\,\{1 + q_j(s)\}_{1 \leqslant j \leqslant m} \qquad (5.1.7)$$

which is diagonal and hence diagonally- (row and column) dominant on D. Eqn. 5.1.6 is a noninteracting controller and suffers from stability and nonminimum-phase problems together with a complex dynamic structure (see Section 3.2). For practical applications it would be necessary to construct a control system $K(s)$ of simple form e.g. a simple proportional controller or a controller with elements represented by phase compensation, proportional and integral terms. In such cases, the existence of a suitable $K(s)$ is nonobvious, except in certain special cases.

Exercise 5.1.1
Compare the above with the method of dyadic expansion where diagonal-dominance of $H(s, \omega_1)$ is guaranteed over a finite range of frequencies.

Exercise 5.1.2
If $G(s)$ is asymptotically stable and minimum-phase, show that the closed-loop system with $K(s) = kI_m$ ($k > 0$ scalar) is asymptotically stable in some range $0 \leqslant k < k^*$. (Hint: note that $|G_{jj}(s)| + d_j(s) < M$ for all s on D for some real number $M > 0$ and set $k^* = M^{-1}$. Show that $n_j = 0$, $1 \leqslant j \leqslant m$ and that $I_m + Q(s)$ is diagonally-dominant on D). Provide a physical interpretation of the result, and comment on the closed-loop behaviour if k^* is small.

A practical approach to the use of the result can be formulated by the use of controller-factorisation methods. Write,
$$K(s) = kK_c(s)\,\text{diag}\,\{k_j(s)\}_{1 \leqslant j \leqslant m} \qquad (5.1.8)$$

where k is a scalar gain factor, $K_c(s)$ is a precompensation matrix, designed such that the composite plant $G(s)K_c(s)$ has required properties and $\text{diag}\,\{k_j(s)\}$ represents the matrix of loop compensation networks. The stability analysis can be undertaken using the following simple step by step method:

Step 1: choose a precompensator $K_c(s)$ of simple dynamic elements (preferably a constant matrix) such that $Q_1(s) = G(s)K_c(s)$ has a substantial degree of diagonal dominance in a frequency range containing, say, the crossover frequencies of its diagonal elements. This reduces the magnitude of the Gershgorin circles in the vicinity of the $(-1,0)$ point and increases the gain range over which $I_m + Q(s)$ will be diagonally-dominant.

Step 2: choose compensation elements $k_j(s)$, $1 \leqslant j \leqslant m$, such that the frequency response plots of $(Q_1(s))_{jj}k_j(s)$, $1 \leqslant j \leqslant m$, have the required gain and phase margins.

Step 3: use the gain factor k to implement final adjustments to the gain margins to ensure that $I_m + Q(s) = I_m + kG(s)K_c(s)$ diag $\{k_j(s)\}_{1 \leqslant j \leqslant m}$ is diagonally- (row or column) dominant on D. Alternatively, choose k by trial and error simulation methods to obtain the best closed-loop responses.

Exercise 5.1.3

Using the controller of eqn. 5.1.8, show that theorem 5.1.1 is still valid if, at each point s on D, either $I_m + k$ diag $\{k_j(s)\}_{1 \leqslant j \leqslant m}G(s)K_c(s)$ or $I_m + kG(s)K_c(s)$ diag $\{k_j(s)\}_{1 \leqslant j \leqslant m}$ is diagonally- (row or column) dominant.

Techniques for achieving dominance are discussed in the next Section. The essential principle of the approach can be illustrated by considering the asymptotically-stable system,

$$G(s) = \frac{1}{(s + 1)(s + 2)} \begin{pmatrix} 10(s + 1) & 60s + 62 \\ 4 & 34 \end{pmatrix} \quad (5.1.9)$$

The reader should verify that $G(s)$ is neither row- nor column-dominant on D (this is obvious by setting $s = 0$, but the reader is encouraged to sketch the frequency responses of the diagonal terms and superimpose a few Gershgorin circles based on column estimates). The first- and second-order characters of the diagonal terms of $G(s)$ suggest that the stability properties of the system will be dictated by the high-frequency system properties. Choosing the constant precompensator

$$K_c(s) = \begin{pmatrix} 1 & -6 \\ 0 & 1 \end{pmatrix} \quad (5.1.10)$$

then

$$Q_1(s) = G(s)K_c(s) = \frac{1}{(s + 1)(s + 2)} \begin{pmatrix} 10(s + 1) & 2 \\ 4 & 10 \end{pmatrix}$$

which is diagonally- (row and column) dominant at every point s on D. This is represented graphically in Fig. 5.1.1 consisting of frequency-response plots of the diagonal elements of $Q_1(s)$ in the range

$0 < \omega < + \infty$, with a few superimposed Gershgorin circles based on column estimates. Neglecting the overall gain factor k, the controller takes the form

$$K(s) = \begin{pmatrix} 1 & -6 \\ 0 & 1 \end{pmatrix} \begin{pmatrix} k_1(s) & 0 \\ 0 & k_2(s) \end{pmatrix} \qquad (5.1.12)$$

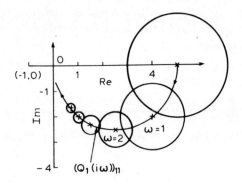

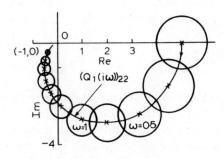

Fig. 5.1.1 Diagonal terms of $Q_1(i\omega)$ with Gershgorin circles

and it is easily verified that $Q(s) = G(s)K(s)$ is, in fact, diagonally-(column) dominant on D, independent of the choice of (nonzero) $k_1(s)$, $k_2(s)$. Choosing, for simplicity, proportional elements, the reader should verify that the first column of $I_m + Q(s)$ is dominant on D for all $k_1 > 0$, but that the second column of $I_m + Q(s)$ is not dominant for all $k_2 > 0$ (Hint: show that the Gershgorin circles intersect the negative real axis at high frequency). This does not introduce any problems in the practical range of gains however e.g. choosing $k_2 = 0.25$ to produce a damping ratio of approximately 0·7 in the second loop $(Q_1(s))_{22}$ it can be verified that $I + Q(s)$ is diagonally-(column) dominant for all $k_1 > 0$ with $n_1 = n_2 = 0$ indicating that the closed-loop system is asymptotically stable (apply theorem 5.1.1).

Exercise 5.1.4

Use Gershgorin's theorem to prove that the characteristic loci of $Q(s)$ lie in the Gershgorin bands generated by the frequency plots of $Q_{jj}(s)$, $1 \leqslant j \leqslant m$, with superimposed Gershgorin circles. In this sense, $Q_{jj}(s)$ can be regarded as approximations to the characteristic transfer functions of $Q(s)$. Compare theorem 5.1.1 with theorem 4.6.3 and see MacFarlane.[19]

5.2 Inverse Nyquist array

Although the above discussion illustrates the basic idea pursued in this Section, it suffers from the difficulty that little insight is provided into closed-loop transient behaviour other than that derived from the characteristic locus method requiring high low-frequency gains and $Q(s)$ approximately diagonal at high frequency. In this Section we discuss a route out of this difficulty in the form of the inverse-Nyquist-array technique suggested by Rosenbrock.[58, 59]

Denoting the inverse of any invertible transfer-function matrix $L(s)$ by the notation

$$\hat{L}(s) = L^{-1}(s) \tag{5.2.1}$$

the inverse of the closed-loop transfer-function matrix takes the form

$$\hat{H}_c(s) = I_m + \hat{Q}(s) \tag{5.2.2}$$

providing an intuitive link between the closed-loop dynamics and the inverse forward-path system $\hat{Q}(s)$. This can be related to closed-loop stability by the identity, (see eqn. 4.3.13)

$$|T(s)| = |I_m + Q(s)| = \frac{|I_m + \hat{Q}(s)|}{|\hat{Q}(s)|} \tag{5.2.3}$$

or, equivalently,

$$|T(s)| = \frac{|\hat{H}_c(s)|}{|\hat{Q}(s)|} \tag{5.2.4}$$

The following result is proved in a similar manner to theorem 4.6.4 (Reference 58).

Theorem 5.2.1: Let $Q(s)$ be the $m \times m$ strictly proper invertible forward path system. Let $I_m + \hat{Q}(s)$ and $\hat{Q}(s)$ be diagonally- (row or column) dominant on D. Let the diagonal elements $\hat{Q}_{jj}(s), 1 \leqslant j \leqslant m$, of $\hat{Q}(s)$ map D onto closed-contours in the complex plane encircling the origin and $(-1,0)$ points $\tilde{n}_j$ and $\hat{n}_j$ times respectively, $1 \leqslant j \leqslant m$, in a clockwise manner. Then the closed-loop system is asymptotically stable if, and only if,

$$n_0 + \sum_{j=1}^{m} (\hat{n}_j - \tilde{n}_j) = 0 \qquad (5.2.5)$$

Again, stability can be assessed from Nyquist analysis of the diagonal terms of $\hat{Q}(s)$ on D provided that the Gershgorin circles generated from the diagonal terms of $\hat{Q}(s)$ do not include the origin or the critical $(-1,0)$ point of the complex plane. Note also that it is, in general, necessary to check diagonal-dominance on the semicircular part of D.

Exercise 5.2.1
Suppose that the first row of $\hat{Q}(s)$ takes the form $(s-1, s)$. Show that $\hat{Q}(s)$ is diagonally(row)-dominant at every point $s = i\omega$ but is not dominant on the semicircular part of D (Hint: choose s real and positive and greater than unity).

The application to stability analysis follows essentially the same form as previously discussed. In general, it appears to be easier to make $I + \hat{Q}$ dominant than to make $\hat{Q}$ dominant. In such cases, the following result provides a useful alternative stability criterion (theorems 4.3.4 and 4.6.5).

Theorem 5.2.2: Let $Q(s)$ be the $m \times m$ invertible strictly proper forward-path system. Let $I_m + \hat{Q}(s)$ be diagonally (row or column)-dominant at every point s on D. Let the diagonal elements $\hat{Q}_{jj}(s)$, $1 \leqslant j \leqslant m$, of $\hat{Q}(s)$ map D onto closed-contours in the complex plane encircling the critical $(-1,0)$ point $\hat{n}_j$ times, $1 \leqslant j \leqslant m$, in a clockwise manner. Then the closed-loop system is asymptotically stable if, and only if,

$$n_z^+ + \sum_{j=1}^{m} \hat{n}_j = 0 \qquad (5.2.6)$$

Proof: Apply theorem 4.6.2 to the identity eqn. 4.3.17 and set $n_c = 0$.

The application of these results to design is illustrated later in the Section and has been illustrated in great detail by Rosenbrock.[58] For our purposes, it is sufficient to discuss the possibility of achieving the dominance conditions using simple control schemes. Consider, for example, an asymptotically stable (i.e. $n_0 = 0$) and minimum phase (i.e. $n_z^+ = 0$) system of the form

$$G^{-1}(s) = sA_0 + A_1 + H(s), \quad |A_0| \neq 0, \quad H(s) \text{ strictly proper} \quad (5.2.7)$$

with forward-path control system $K(s) = kA_0$ (k being a positive real scalar). It follows that

$$\hat{Q}(s) = k^{-1}\{sI_m + A_0^{-1}A_1 + A_0^{-1}H(s)\} \quad (5.2.8)$$

The assumptions guarantee the existence of a positive real number M such that the radii of the Gershgorin circles (row or column estimates) satisfy

$$d_j(s) \leqslant k^{-1}M \quad (5.2.9)$$

for all points s on D (Hint: note that the off-diagonal elements of $\hat{Q}(s)$ are proper). In particular, the absolute magnitude of the radii of the Gershgorin circles decreases as k^{-1} at each point on D. It follows directly that there exists $k^* > 0$ such that $k > k^*$ implies that $I + \hat{Q}$ is dominant on D with $\hat{n}_j = 0$, $1 \leqslant j \leqslant m$ (Hint: consider the effect of increasing k graphically and note the behaviour of the contribution from the semicircular part of D). It follows directly from theorem 5.2.2 that the closed-loop system is asymptotically stable for $k \geqslant k^*$ (it may be stable for some $k < k^*$ but the diagonal-dominance theorems cannot be used in such cases). Alternatively, if $\hat{Q}(s)$ is diagonally-dominant on D for $k = k^*$, then it is easily verified that it is dominant for all $k \geqslant k^*$ with $\sum_{j=1}^{m} \tilde{n}_j$. Application of theorem 5.2.1 again indicates closed-loop stability.

Exercise 5.2.2
Verify the above analysis if $K(s) = A_0 \text{ diag } \{k_j\}_{1 \leqslant j \leqslant m}(k_j, 1 \leqslant j \leqslant m,$ positive real scalars) and $k = \min_j k_j$.

Exercise 5.2.3
A stable first-order lag $G^{-1}(s) = sA_0 + A_1$, $|A_0| \neq 0$ is to be controlled by $K(s) = kA_0$. Show that $\hat{Q}(s)$ is diagonally-dominant on D if, and only if, $A_0^{-1}A_1$ is diagonally-dominant, but that $I_m + \hat{Q}(s)$ is diagonally-dominant on D for all large enough positive gains k.

The diagonal-dominance conditions provide some intuitive measure of closed-loop interaction behaviour. In particular, if $\hat{Q}(s)$ is diagonally-dominant as $|s| \to +\infty$ then it may be anticipated that $Q(s)$ is approximately diagonal at high frequencies from which the closed-loop system will possess small interaction behaviour if the control system gains are high (see Section 4.4). Given the possibility of attaining dominance, the techniques can be extended to provide information on integrity and more accurate estimates of closed-loop behaviour.[58]

Ostrowski circles and closed-loop response: Suppose that the conditions of either theorem 5.2.1 or theorem 5.2.2 are satisfied. The behaviour of the closed-loop system could be evaluated by calculation of $H_c(s)$ directly from eqn. 5.2.2, or, if a state-vector model of $Q(s)$ is available, by simulation studies. There is, however, a useful initial estimate of the closed-loop response characteristics available by application of Ostrowski's theorem[34, 57, 58] as follows.

Theorem 5.2.3: Let A be a complex $m \times m$ matrix. Let A be diagonally-row (respt. column) dominant with inverse $\hat{A}$. Then

$$|(\hat{A}_{jj})^{-1} - A_{jj}| < \phi_j d_j < d_j, \qquad 1 \leqslant j \leqslant m \qquad (5.2.10)$$

where

$$\phi_j = \max_{\substack{1 \leqslant l \leqslant m \\ l \neq j}} \frac{d_l}{|A_{ll}|}, \qquad 1 \leqslant j \leqslant m \qquad (5.2.11)$$

and d_j are the radii of the Gershgorin circles of A based on row (respt. column) estimates.

Let the diagonal terms of $H_c(s)$ be $h_{jj}(s)$, $1 \leqslant j \leqslant m$, representing the direct effect of demand $r_j(t)$ on output $y_j(t)$, $1 \leqslant j \leqslant m$. Then,

Theorem 5.2.4: Suppose that the conditions of either theorem 5.2.1 or theorem 5.2.2 are satisfied. Then, for each s on D

$$|h_{jj}^{-1}(s) - (1 + \hat{Q}_{jj}(s))| < \phi_j(s)d_j(s) < d_j(s) \qquad (5.2.12)$$

where d_j is the radius of the Gershgorin circle of centre $\hat{Q}_{jj}(s)$ based on row (respt. column) estimates if $I_m + \hat{Q}(s)$ is row (respt. column) dominant.

Proof: Both theorem 5.2.1 and 5.2.2 require that $I_m + \hat{Q}(s)$ be diagonally- (row or column) dominant at each point s on D. Apply theorem 5.2.3 to $A = \hat{H}_c(s) = I_m + \hat{Q}(s)$, noting that $\hat{A} = H_c(s)$.

The result has the following graphical interpretation. Suppose that the plots of $\hat{Q}_{jj}(s)$, $1 \leqslant j \leqslant m$, on D are available with superimposed Gershgorin circles of radius $d_j(s)$, $1 \leqslant j \leqslant m$, based on row or column estimates. If the critical $(-1,0)$ point does not lie in or on any such circle, then $I_m + \hat{Q}(s)$ is dominant on D. At each point on D (in practice, at a selection of points on D) calculate the radii

$$r_j(s) = \max_{\substack{1 \leqslant l \leqslant m \\ l \neq j}} \frac{d_l(s) d_j(s)}{1 + \hat{Q}_{ll}(s)}, \qquad 1 \leqslant j \leqslant m \qquad (5.2.13)$$

and plot the diagonal terms $\hat{Q}_{jj}(s)$ on D, $1 \leqslant j \leqslant m$, with superimposed circles of radius $r_j(s)$, $1 \leqslant j \leqslant m$. Write

$$h_{jj}^{-1}(s) = 1 + h_j^{-1}(s), \qquad 1 \leqslant j \leqslant m \qquad (5.2.14)$$

or, equivalently,

$$h_{jj}(s) = \frac{h_j(s)}{1 + h_j(s)}, \qquad 1 \leqslant j \leqslant m \qquad (5.2.15)$$

then $h_{jj}(s)$ can be regarded as the system $h_j(s)$ with unity-negative feedback. The above analysis tells us that, for each s on D, $h_j^{-1}(s)$ lies in a circle of centre $\hat{Q}_{jj}(s)$ and radius $r_j(s) < d_j(s)$. As s goes round D these circles sweep out bands lying inside the Gershgorin bands. These bands will be termed *Ostrowski bands* and the individual circles will be termed *Ostrowski circles*. If the Ostrowski bands are narrow enough, then the closed-loop response can be assessed using the approximation

$$h_{jj}^{-1}(s) \simeq 1 + \hat{Q}_{jj}(s), \qquad 1 \leqslant j \leqslant m, \quad s \text{ on } D, \qquad (5.2.16)$$

assuming that interaction effects are negligible, and applying classical interpretation techniques.

Integrity with respect to sensor failures: One of the important characteristics of the approach is the ability to make graphical assessment of the closed-loop stability in the presence of sensor failures. To do this it is convenient to use the following generalisation of theorem 5.2.1[58]

Theorem 5.2.5: Consider the nonunity-negative feedback system for the $m \times m$ strictly proper, invertible plant $G(s)$ with $m \times m$ proper, invertible forward-path controller $K(s)$ and constant feedback element $F(s) = \text{diag} \{f_j\}_{1 \leqslant j \leqslant m}$. Let $Q(s) = G(s)K(s)$ and let the matrices $F(s) + \hat{Q}(s)$ and $\hat{Q}(s)$ be diagonally- (row or column) dominant at each point s on D. Let the diagonal elements $\hat{Q}_{jj}(s)$, $1 \leqslant j \leqslant m$, of $\hat{Q}(s)$ map D onto closed contours in the complex plane encircling the origin and $(-f_j, 0)$ points $\tilde{n}_j$ and $\hat{n}_j$ times, respectively, $1 \leqslant j \leqslant m$, in a clockwise manner. Then the closed-loop system is asymptotically stable if, and only if,

$$n_0 + \sum_{j=1}^{m} (\hat{n}_j - \tilde{n}_j) = 0 \qquad (5.2.17)$$

Proof: Examine the relation,

$$\frac{\rho_c(s)}{\rho_0(s)} = |I_m + Q(s)F(s)| = \frac{|\text{diag}\,\{f_j\}_{1 \leqslant j \leqslant m} + \hat{Q}(s)|}{|\hat{Q}(s)|} \qquad (5.2.18)$$

and apply theorem 4.6.2.

Exercise 5.2.4
Reformulate theorem 5.2.2 in a similar manner.

Theorem 5.2.5 can be applied to the analysis of sensor failure in a straightforward manner. Suppose, for example, that it is required to assess the stability of the closed-loop system in the presence of a sensor failure in loop k. This can be represented by the feedback matrix

$$F(s) = I_m - e_k e_k^T \qquad (5.2.19)$$

or,

$$f_j = 1 - \delta_{jk}, \qquad 1 \leqslant j \leqslant m \qquad (5.2.20)$$

Simultaneous sensor failure in loops $k_1, \ldots, k_l$ are similarly dealt with by setting

$$f_j = 1 - \delta_{jk_1} - \delta_{jk_2} - \ldots - \delta_{jk_l}, \qquad 1 \leqslant j \leqslant m \quad (5.2.21)$$

Exercise 5.2.5
Using the notation of theorem 5.2.1, suppose that $Q(s)$ is stable (i.e. $n_0 = 0$) and satisfies the dominance conditions and eqn. 5.2.5 with $\hat{n}_j = \tilde{n}_j = 0$, $1 \leqslant j \leqslant m$. Prove that the closed-loop system is stable in the presence of simultaneous failures of sensors in any loops $k_1, \ldots, k_l$. (Hint: diagonal-dominance of $I + \hat{Q}$ and $\hat{Q}$ on D implies diagonal-dominance of $F + \hat{Q}$ on D with f_j as in (5.3.20)).

Exercise 5.2.6
Returning to the analysis of Section 5.1, define the error matrix

$$E(s) = \{I_m + Q(s)\}^{-1}$$

and note that the kth diagonal term takes the form

$$E_{kk}(s) = e_k^T \{I_m + Q(s)\}^{-1} e_k$$

Using the notation of theorem 5.1.1, suppose that $n_0 = 0$ and $n_j = 0$, $1 \leqslant j \leqslant m$, and that $I_m + Q(s)$ is diagonally- (row or column) dominant at each point s on D. Use Ostrowski's theorem to prove that

$$|E_{kk}^{-1}(s) - (1 + Q_{kk}(s))| < \phi_j(s)d_j(s) < d_j(s), \qquad 1 \leqslant j \leqslant m$$

for each s on D. Hence prove that the system is stable in the presence of sensor failure in loop k.

Feedback design procedure: The design procedure suggested by Rosenbrock[58,59] is almost self-evident from the above discussion. For completeness, it is outlined below.

(a) Compute $G(s)$ and $\hat{G}(s)$ and plot the m^2 loci generated by the elements of $\hat{G}(s)$ as s varies on D (This plot is conventionally termed the *inverse Nyquist array*). In particular, examine the loci generated by the diagonal terms $\hat{G}_{jj}(s)$ and superimpose Gershgorin circles based on row (or column) estimates to investigate the degree of dominance.

(b) Choose (if possible) a precompensator $K_c(s)$ such that $\hat{K}_c(s)\hat{G}(s)$ is diagonally- (row or column) dominant at each point s on D. Plot the diagonal terms with associated Gershgorin circles.

(c) Set

$$K(s) = K_c(s) \operatorname{diag}\{k_j(s)\}_{1 \leqslant j \leqslant m} \qquad (5.2.22)$$

and note, in particular, that $\hat{Q}(s) = \operatorname{diag}\{k_j^{-1}(s)\}_{1 \leqslant j \leqslant m}\hat{K}_c(s)\hat{G}(s)$ so that the inverse transfer function $k_j^{-1}(s)$ multiplies the jth diagonal term of $\hat{K}_c(s)\hat{G}(s)$. Choose $k_j(s)$, $1 \leqslant j \leqslant m$, such that $I_m + \hat{Q}(s)$ is diagonally- (row or column) dominant on D and such that the diagonal terms have the required gain and phase characteristics. Apply theorem 5.2.1 (if $\hat{Q}(s)$ is diagonally-dominant on D) or theorem 5.2.2 to assess the stability of the closed-loop system.

(d) Evaluate the performance of the closed-loop system by estimation of $h_j^{-1}(s)$, $1 \leqslant j \leqslant m$, from $\hat{Q}_{jj}(s)$ and plotting the Ostrowski circles.

As a final point, note that, if $\hat{K}_c(s)\hat{G}(s)$ is diagonally row-dominant on D, then $\hat{Q}(s)$ is row dominant on D. Alternatively, if $\hat{K}_c(s)\hat{G}(s)$ is diagonally column-dominant on D, then $\hat{K}_c(s)\hat{G}(s) \operatorname{diag}\{k_j^{-1}(s)\}$ is column-dominant on D when the identity

$$|\hat{Q}(s)| = |\hat{K}_c(s)\hat{G}(s) \operatorname{diag}\{k_j^{-1}(s)\}_{1 \leqslant j \leqslant m}| \qquad (5.2.23)$$

indicates that the result of theorem 5.2.1 is still valid. The diagonal (row or column) dominance of $I_m + \hat{Q}(s)$ is dependent (in general) on the choice of $k_j(s)$, $1 \leqslant j \leqslant m$.

Achieving dominance: The major difficulty in the application of the inverse Nyquist technique and theorem 5.2.1 is the choice of $K_c(s)$ such that $\hat{K}_c(s)\hat{G}(s)$ is diagonally-dominant on D. This can be a difficult exercise, particularly if $m \geqslant 3$. The problem can be eased by the application of systematic trial and error or algorithmic approaches similar in form to those suggested by Rosenbrock.[58]

The simplest technique of achieving row dominance is to use elementary row operations in a sequential manner, by writing

$$\hat{K}_c(s) = \hat{K}_c^{(l)}(s)\hat{K}_c^{(l-1)}(s)\ldots\hat{K}_c^{(2)}(s)\hat{K}_c^{(1)}(s) \qquad (5.2.24)$$

where $\hat{K}_c^{(j)}(s)$, $1 \leqslant j \leqslant l$, are m × m inverse trial precompensators, each taking one of two forms:

(i) permutation matrices, where each column and each row has zero entries except at one point, the exceptional entry being unity e.g.

$$\hat{K}_c^{(j)}(s) = \begin{pmatrix} 0 & 1 & 0 \\ 0 & 0 & 1 \\ 1 & 0 & 0 \end{pmatrix} \qquad (5.2.25)$$

Such compensators essentially renumber the system inputs by permutation of rows.

(ii) elementary matrices of the form

$$\hat{K}_c^{(j)}(s) = \begin{pmatrix} 1 & 0 & \ldots & 0 & \ldots & 0 & \ldots & 0 \\ 0 & 1 & & 0 & & 0 & & 0 \\ \vdots & & & \vdots & & \vdots & & \vdots \\ 0 & 0 & \ldots & 1 & \ldots & \hat{k}_{pq}^{(j)}(s) & \ldots & 0 \\ \vdots & & & \vdots & & \vdots & & \vdots \\ 0 & & \ldots & 0 & \ldots & 0 & \ldots & 1 \end{pmatrix}$$

$$= I_m + \hat{k}_{pq}^{(j)}(s)e_p e_q^T \qquad (5.2.26)$$

where $p \neq q$ and $\hat{k}_{pq}^{(j)}(s)$ is a scalar proper transfer function with poles and zeros in the open left-half plane. The use of $\hat{K}_c^{(j)}(s)$ has the effect of adding $\hat{k}_{pq}^{(j)}$ times the qth row to the pth row of $\hat{K}_c^{(j-1)}(s)\ldots$ $K_c^{(1)}(s)\hat{G}(s)$ and leaving other rows unchanged.

In case (i), $K_c^{(j)}(s)$ is easily obtained by inversion. In case (ii), it is easily verified that

$$K_c^{(j)}(s) = I_m - \hat{k}_{pq}^{(j)}e_p e_q^T \qquad (5.2.27)$$

which is hence asymptotically stable and minimum phase. The implementation of the procedure must proceed in a trial and error manner. At each stage, the inverse Nyquist array of $\hat{K}_c^{(j-1)}(s)\ldots\hat{K}_c^{(1)}(s)\hat{G}(s)$ must be examined and a suitable choice of $\hat{K}_c^{(j)}(s)$ made to improve the dominance of $\hat{K}_c^{(j)}(s)\ldots\hat{K}_c^{(1)}(s)\hat{G}(s)$. For example, consider the system,

$$\hat{G}(s) = \begin{pmatrix} 1 & s+20 \\ s+11 & s+21 \end{pmatrix} \qquad (5.2.28)$$

which is not row-dominant on D. Multiply by the permutation matrix corresponding to interchange of rows gives

$$\hat{K}_c^{(1)}(s)\hat{G}(s) = \begin{pmatrix} s+11 & s+21 \\ 1 & s+20 \end{pmatrix} \qquad (5.2.29)$$

Choosing the elementary matrix corresponding to subtraction of row two from row one, gives

$$\hat{K}_c^{(2)}(s)\hat{K}_c^{(1)}(s)\hat{G}(s) = \begin{pmatrix} 1 & -1 \\ 0 & 1 \end{pmatrix} \begin{pmatrix} s+11 & s+21 \\ 1 & s+20 \end{pmatrix}$$

$$= \begin{pmatrix} s+10 & 1 \\ 1 & s+20 \end{pmatrix} \qquad (5.2.30)$$

which is row- (and column!) dominant on D. The desired precompensator is

$$K_c(s) = K_c^{(1)}(s)K_c^{(2)}(s) = \begin{pmatrix} 0 & 1 \\ 1 & 0 \end{pmatrix} \begin{pmatrix} 1 & 1 \\ 0 & 1 \end{pmatrix} = \begin{pmatrix} 0 & 1 \\ 1 & 1 \end{pmatrix} \qquad (5.2.31)$$

If attention is restricted to constant precompensators $K_c(s)$, it is possible to apply the numerical technique of *pseudodiagonalisation* formulated by Hawkins[12] and described in detail by Rosenbrock.[58] Choose a point $s = i\omega$ on D at which it is desired to improve the degree of row dominance. Write

$$\hat{G}(i\omega) = [v_1, v_2, \ldots, v_m], \qquad \hat{K}_c(s) = \begin{pmatrix} \hat{k}_1^T \\ \vdots \\ \hat{k}_m^T \end{pmatrix} \qquad (5.2.32)$$

where v_j, $1 \leqslant j \leqslant m$, are the columns of $\hat{G}(i\omega)$ and $\hat{k}_j^T$ are constant *real* row vectors. It is easily verified that

$$\hat{K}_c(i\omega)\hat{G}(i\omega) = \begin{pmatrix} \hat{k}_1^T v_1 & \ldots & \hat{k}_1^T v_m \\ \vdots & & \vdots \\ \hat{k}_m^T v_1 & \ldots & \hat{k}_m^T v_m \end{pmatrix} \qquad (5.2.33)$$

and that $\hat{K}_c \hat{G}$ is diagonally- (row) dominant at $s = i\omega$ if, and only if,

$$|k_j^T v_j| > \sum_{\substack{l=1 \\ l \neq j}}^{m} |k_j^T v_l|, \qquad 1 \leqslant j \leqslant m \qquad (5.2.34)$$

The choice of k_j, $1 \leqslant j \leqslant m$, to satisfy eqn. 5.2.34 is attempted by the choice of k_j to minimise the functionals

$$\psi_j = \sum_{\substack{l=1 \\ l \neq j}}^{m} |k_j^T v_l|^2 \qquad (5.2.35)$$

subject to

$$k_j^T k_j = 1, \qquad 1 \leqslant j \leqslant m \qquad (5.2.36)$$

Note that the optimisation problems are independent (making solution an easy task) but that these solutions of the weaker problem eqns. 5.2.35–5.2.36 may not satisfy eqn. 5.2.34. Writing v_l in real and imaginary parts,

$$v_l = \alpha_l + i\beta_l, \qquad 1 \leqslant l \leqslant m \qquad (5.2.37)$$

yields,

$$\psi_j = k_j^T A_j k_j, \qquad 1 \leqslant j \leqslant m \qquad (5.2.38)$$

where

$$A_j = \sum_{\substack{l=1 \\ l \neq j}}^{m} \{\alpha_l \alpha_l^T + \beta_l \beta_l^T\} \qquad (5.2.39)$$

is symmetric and positive-semidefinite. Using a Lagrange multiplier λ, the Lagrangian

$$k_j^T A_j k_j + \lambda\{1 - k_j^T k_j\} \qquad (5.2.40)$$

has a stationary point at the point k_j if, and only if,

$$A_j k_j = \lambda k_j, \qquad k_j^T k_j = 1 \qquad (5.2.41)$$

when

$$\psi_j = k_j^T A_j k_j = \lambda k_j^T k_j = \lambda \qquad (5.2.42)$$

It follows that k_j can be calculated as an eigenvector of A_j corresponding to the smallest eigenvalue of A_j and normalised to satisfy eqn. 5.2.36. This procedure can be generalised in several ways.[58] In particular, the alignment algorithm could be applied by maximising

$$\psi_j = \frac{|k_j^T v_j|^2}{\sum_{\substack{l=1 \\ l \neq j}}^{m} |k_j^T v_l|^2 + \epsilon k_j^T k_j}$$

$$= \frac{|v_j^T k_j|^2}{\sum_{\substack{l=1 \\ l \neq j}}^{m} |v_l^T k_j|^2 + \epsilon k_j^T k_j}, \qquad 1 \leqslant j \leqslant m \qquad (5.2.43)$$

with ϵ small and positive, in the manner described in Section 4.5. Again, the solution is not guaranteed to satisfy eqn. 5.2.34.

In Chapter 3, minor-loop compensation networks played an important role in the construction of analytic solutions. They can also help in the achievement of diagonal-dominance. Suppose that $G(s)$ is generated from the original plant $G_1(s)$ by the use of minor-loop compensation $H(s)$

$$G(s) = \{I_m + G_1(s)H(s)\}^{-1} G_1(s) \qquad (5.2.44)$$

or

$$\hat{G}(s) = H(s) + \hat{G}_1(s) \qquad (5.2.45)$$

The term $H(s)$ can be used to improve the degree of dominance of $\hat{G}(s)$, before choice of precompensator $K_c(s)$ is attempted. This may simplify the structure of $K_c(s)$ but care must be taken to ensure that the construction is not sensitive to modelling errors in $\hat{G}_1(s)$.

Exercise 5.2.7

(a) If $G(0)$ is finite and nonsingular, show that the choice of $K_c(s) = G^{-1}(0)$ produces dominance at low frequencies.

(b) If $G_\infty^{(k)} = \lim_{s \to \infty} s^k G(s)$ is finite and nonsingular for some $k \geqslant 1$, show that $K_c(s) = (G_\infty^{(k)})^{-1}$ produces dominance at high frequencies.

(c) Consider the effect of choosing $K_c(s) = (G_\infty^{(k)})^{-1} + \dfrac{c}{s} G^{-1}(0)$, $c > 0$.

Illustrative examples: Consider, initially the liquid level system of Section 2.5,

$$\hat{G}(s) = \begin{pmatrix} a_1 s + \beta & -\beta \\ -\beta & a_2 s + \beta \end{pmatrix} \qquad (5.2.46)$$

and note that $\hat{G}(s)$ is diagonally- (row) dominant on D except in the vicinity of $s = 0$. Choosing the data $a_1 = a_2 = 1$, $\beta = 2$, the inverse Nyquist array can be represented by the single plot shown in Fig. 5.2.1a. Applying theorem 5.2.2 and noting that $G(s)$ has no zeros, the reader can verify that the closed-loop system is stable with $K_c(s) = I_2$, and proportional controls $k_j(s) = k_j$, $j = 1,2$ whenever $k_1 > 0$, $k_2 > 0$. Choose $k_1 = k_2 = 4$ when the inverse Nyquist array can be represented by the single plot in Fig. 5.2.1b. The Ostrowski bands are shown in Fig. 5.2.1c and enable a visual inspection of closed-loop performance. Note, however, that the system has interaction effects of the order of 25% (examine the steady-state behaviour of the off-diagonal terms in

$H_c(s)$) indicating that diagonal-dominance does not necessarily imply small interaction. It is left as an exercise for the reader to show that interaction can be suppressed by increasing the gains k_1 and k_2 e.g. $k_1 = k_2 \gg \beta$.

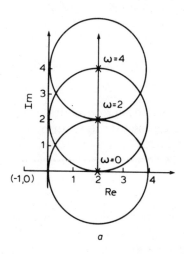

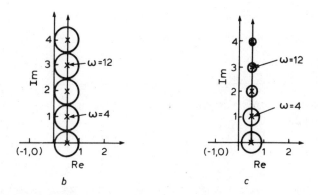

Fig. 5.2.1 Inverse Nyquist loci for liquid level system
    a Plant with $a_1 = a_2 = 1$ $\beta = 2$
    b Gershgorin circles for $k_1 = k_2 = 4$
    c Ostrowski circles for $k_1 = k_2 = 4$

Consider the three-vessel system of Section 3.14,

$$\hat{G}(s) = \beta^{-1} \begin{pmatrix} \beta s + 2\beta + 1 & -(s + 2\beta + 1) \\ -(s + 2\beta + 1) & s^2 + 2(1 + \beta)s + 2\beta + 1 \end{pmatrix} \quad (5.2.47)$$

which is row-dominant on D if, and only if,

$$|\beta s + 2\beta + 1| > |s + 2\beta + 1| \qquad (5.2.48)$$

and

$$|s^2 + 2(1 + \beta)s + 2\beta + 1| > |s + 2\beta + 1| \qquad (5.2.49)$$

for all s on D. Choosing $s = i\omega$, expr. 5.2.48 becomes

$$\beta^2 \omega^2 + (2\beta + 1)^2 > \omega^2 + (2\beta + 1)^2 \qquad (5.2.50)$$

i.e. the first row of $\hat{G}$ is dominant for $\omega \neq 0$ if, and only if, $\beta > 1$. The reader can easily verify that, in this case, the first row of $\hat{G}$ is dominant on the whole of D except in the vicinity of $s = 0$. Expr. 5.2.49 is satisfied on the semicircular part of D so set $s = i\omega$ to give

$$(2\beta + 1 - \omega^2)^2 + 4(1 + \beta)^2 \omega^2 > (2\beta + 1)^2 + \omega^2 \quad (5.2.51)$$

which is satisfied for all $\omega \neq 0$ and $\beta > 0$.

If $\beta < 1$ then the technique would appear to hit severe problems. The absence of any degree of dominance suggests that precompensation is required. The constant precompensator

$$\hat{K}_c(s) = \begin{pmatrix} 1 & \alpha \\ 0 & 1 \end{pmatrix} \qquad (5.2.52)$$

leaves row two invariant and adds a multiple of row two to row one. This operation has the effect of introducing a term in s^2 into the $(1,2)$ position when row dominance cannot be achieved at high frequency.

Exercise 5.2.8
Show that column dominance cannot be achieved for $0 < \beta < 1$ using eqn. 5.2.52 (Hint: note that the first column of $\hat{G}(s)$ requires that $(\beta - \alpha)^2 > 1$ while the second column requires $(1 - \alpha)^2 < 1$).

Choosing $\beta = 2$ (as in Section 3.14), the diagonal elements of the inverse Nyquist array are shown in Fig. 5.2.2 with Gershgorin circles based on row estimates, and illustrates the diagonal dominance except in the vicinity of $\omega = 0$,

$$\hat{G}_{11}(s) = s + \tfrac{5}{2}$$

$$\hat{G}_{22}(s) = \tfrac{1}{2}(s^2 + 6s + 5) = \tfrac{1}{2}(s + 1)(s + 5) \qquad (5.2.47)$$

Noting that the system has no zeros, application of theorem 5.2.2 with $K_c(s) = I_2$ and proportional controllers $k_1(s) = k_1$, $k_2(s) = k_2$ indicates that the closed-loop system is stable for all $k_1 > 0$, $k_2 > 0$.

Exercise 5.2.9

Choose appropriate values of k_1, k_2 and sketch the inverse Nyquist array of $\hat{Q}(s)$ with superimposed Ostrowski circles. Consider the effect of the use of phase-compensation networks in $k_2(s)$.

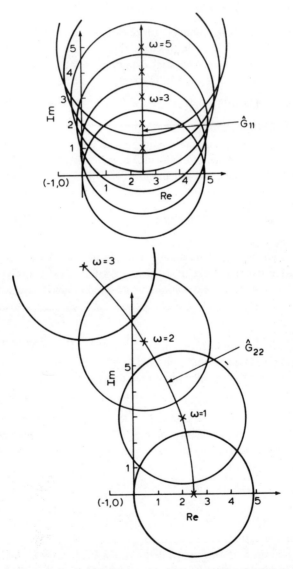

Fig. 5.2.2 Diagonal elements of inverse Nyquist array with Gershgorin circles

5.3 Transformations and origin shifts

A comparison of the inverse-Nyquist-array technique with the characteristic locus and method of dyadic expansion suggests a great similarity but fundamental differences in emphasis. The characteristic locus and method of dyadic expansion place great emphasis on the accurate estimation and compensation of characteristic loci by transforming $G(s)$ to approximately diagonal form over a range of frequencies of interest, whereas the inverse Nyquist method uses precompensation techniques to force $Q(s)$ into approximately diagonal form. Transformation techniques may introduce conceptual difficulties in the interpretation of closed-loop dynamics in terms of eigenvalue characteristics whereas the precompensation methods may introduce difficulties due to an inability to construct a precompensator of suitably simple form. In this Section, the techniques are merged to provide a general approach to stability analysis.[47]

Use of constant transformations: Consider the design of a unity-negative feedback system for the $m \times m$ strictly proper, invertible system $G(s)$ and write,

$$P_2 \hat{G}(s) P_1 = \hat{H}(s) \qquad (5.3.1)$$

where P_1, P_2 are constant, nonsingular $m \times m$ matrices chosen so that $\hat{H}(s)$ has a simple form. For example, if $G(s)$ is a dyadic transfer-function matrix it is always possible to choose P_1, P_2 so that $H(s)$ is a diagonal matrix. If $G(s)$ is not dyadic then it is, in general, possible to choose P_1, P_2 so that $H(s)$ is diagonal at a specified frequency $s = i\omega_1$ of interest and diagonally- (row or column) dominant in the vicinity of that point. Alternatively P_1, P_2 may be chosen from physical considerations.

Let $K(s)$ be an $m \times m$ proper forward-path controller for $G(s)$ and write

$$K_1(s) = P_2 K(s) P_1 \qquad (5.3.2)$$

Then the identity,

$$|T(s)| = |I_m + G(s)K(s)| = |I_{\bar{m}} + P_1 H(s) P_2 P_2^{-1} K_1(s) P_1^{-1}|$$
$$= |I_m + H(s)K_1(s)| \qquad (5.3.3)$$

indicates that the closed-loop systems

$$H_c(s) = \{I_m + G(s)K(s)\}^{-1} G(s)K(s) \qquad (5.3.4)$$

$$H_c^{(1)}(s) = \{I_m + H(s)K_1(s)\}^{-1} H(s)K_1(s) \qquad (5.3.5)$$

have identical stability characteristics. The reader should verify that

$$H_c(s) = P_1 H_c^{(1)}(s) P_1^{-1} \qquad (5.3.6)$$

and hence that the output responses are related by the transformation matrix P_1. The control analysis could now be formulated as the choice of $K_1(s)$ for $H(s)$ to produce a stable closed-loop system and investigation of the closed-loop response using eqn. 5.3.6 and the techniques of Chapter 4. In particular, it is possible to write

$$K_1(s) = K_c(s) \operatorname{diag} \{k_j(s)\}_{1 \leqslant j \leqslant m}$$

$$K(s) = P_2^{-1} K_1(s) P_1^{-1} = P_2^{-1} K_c(s) \operatorname{diag} \{k_j(s)\}_{1 \leqslant j \leqslant m} P_1^{-1} \qquad (5.3.7)$$

where $K_c(s)$ is a precompensator for $H(s)$ and $k_j(s)$ are single-loop controllers for $H(s)K_c(s)$, and apply the inverse-Nyquist-array approach to the design of eqn. 5.3.5.

These results may have application in those cases when dominance is difficult to achieve in the application of the inverse-Nyquist-array technique to $G(s)$, when the choice of P_1, P_2 by the method of dyadic expansion guarantees dominance at a specified frequency and diagonal dominance in the vicinity of that frequency point. (Compare with the method of pseudodiagonalisation which sets $P_1 = I_m$). The choice of precompensator $K_c(s)$ for $H(s)$ may enable diagonal-dominance to be achieved at every point D.

Exercise 5.3.1
Compare the above theory with the examples of Section 4.7 and 5.2 with P_1, P_2 defined by exprs. 4.7.5 and 4.7.8 and $\hat{H}(s) = \hat{H}(s, \infty)$ given in eqn. 4.7.9. Note that the transformation method improves the degree of dominance.

Use of origin shifts: An alternative approach to stability analysis using dominance conditions is to use the loose concept of *origin shifts*.[47] Write

$$K(s) = K_c(s) \{\operatorname{diag} \{k_j(s)\}_{1 \leqslant j \leqslant m} + K_0(s)\} \qquad (5.3.8)$$

where $K_c(s)$ is a proper $m \times m$, minimum-phase, asymptotically stable precompensator, the loop transfer functions $k_j(s)$, $1 \leqslant j \leqslant m$, are minimum-phase and stable (with the exception of integral terms) and $K_0(s)$ is a stable 'origin shift' term. Closed-loop stability is assessed by the return-difference determinant,

$$|T(s)| = |I_m + G(s)K(s)| = |G(s)||\hat{G}(s) + K(s)|$$

$$= |G(s)K_c(s)||\hat{K}_c(s)\hat{G}(s) + K_0(s) + \operatorname{diag} \{k_j(s)\}_{1 \leqslant j \leqslant m}|$$

$$= |G(s)K_c(s) \text{ diag } \{k_j(s)\}|$$

$$|\text{diag } \{k_j^{-1}(s)\}_{1 \leqslant j \leqslant m} (\hat{K}_c(s)\hat{G}(s) + K_0(s)) + I_m| \qquad (5.3.9)$$

More compactly, define

$$Q_0(s) = G(s)K_c(s) \text{ diag } \{k_j(s)\}_{1 \leqslant j \leqslant m}$$

$$\hat{Q}_1(s) = \text{diag } \{k_j^{-1}(s)\}_{1 \leqslant j \leqslant m} (\hat{K}_c(s)\hat{G}(s) + K_0(s)) \qquad (5.3.10)$$

when eqn. 5.3.9 becomes

$$|T(s)| = \frac{\rho_c(s)}{\rho_0(s)} = |Q_0(s)\| \hat{Q}_1(s) + I_m| \qquad (5.3.11)$$

Theorem 5.3.1: Let $I_m + \hat{Q}_1(s)$ be diagonally (row or column) dominant at each point s on D. Let the diagonal terms $(\hat{Q}_1(s))_{jj}$, $1 \leqslant j \leqslant m$, of $\hat{Q}_1(s)$ map D onto closed-contours in the complex plane encircling the $(-1,0)$ point $\hat{n}_j$ times, $1 \leqslant j \leqslant m$, in a clockwise manner. Let $G(s)$ have n_z^+ zeros in the interior of D. Then the closed-loop system is asymptotically stable if, and only if,

$$n_z^+ + \sum_{j=1}^{m} \hat{n}_j = 0 \qquad (5.3.12)$$

Proof: If $Q_0(s)$ has a zero polynomial $z(s)$, then $\rho_0(s)|Q_0(s)| = z(s)f(s)$ where $f(s)$ is a polynomial which divides the characteristic polynomial of $K_0(s)$ and hence has roots with negative real parts. The result follows by examination of the identity

$$\rho_c(s) = z(s)f(s)|I_m + \hat{Q}_1(s)| \qquad (5.3.13)$$

and application of theorem 4.6.2, noting that $z(s)$ has n_z^+ roots in the interior of D.

Exercise 5.3.2
Write,

$$K(s) = K_c(s) \text{ diag } \{k_j(s)\}_{1 \leqslant j \leqslant m} (I_m + K_0(s)) \qquad (5.3.14)$$

and show that

$$|T(s)| = |Q_0(s)\| I_m + \hat{Q}_0(s) + K_0(s)| \qquad (5.3.15)$$

Formulate and prove an analogue of theorem 5.3.1 in this case.

If $K_0(s) \equiv 0$ both theorem 5.3.1 and the result implied by Exercise 5.3.2 reduce to theorem 5.2.2 and can be applied in the form of the inverse-Nyquist-array design technique. Suppose, however, that it is difficult to obtain dominance of $I_m + \hat{Q}_0(s)$ on D using the precompensator $K_c(s)$, then the extra term $K_0(s)$ in eqns. 5.3.10 or 5.3.14 provides extra degrees of freedom to achieve dominance by

(a) approximate cancellation of off-diagonal terms to reduce the magnitude of the Gershgorin circles over a frequency range of interest.

(b) increasing the magnitude of diagonal terms to improve the degree of dominance.

Exercise 5.3.3

Using the controller (eqn. 5.3.8), show that

$$\hat{H}_c(s) = \{I_m + \text{diag}\{k_j^{-1}(s)\}_{1 \leqslant j \leqslant m} K_0(s)\}^{-1}(I_m + \hat{Q}_1(s)) \qquad (5.3.16)$$

and hence that the closed-loop response can be examined by analysis of $\hat{Q}_1(s)$ if the gains $k_j(s)$, $1 \leqslant j \leqslant m$, are sufficiently large (compared with the elements of $K_0(s)$).

For the controller represented by 5.3.14, show that

$$\hat{H}_c(s) = \{I_m + K_0(s)\}^{-1}(I_m + \hat{Q}_0(s) + K_0(s)) \qquad (5.3.17)$$

Note that, in this case, the relation between the inverse Nyquist analysis and time response may be weak and the technique is primarily geared to ensuring closed-loop stability.

To illustrate the application of theorem 5.3.1, consider the $m \times m$ first-order lag

$$\hat{G}(s) = sA_0 + A_1, \quad |A_0| \neq 0 \qquad (5.3.18)$$

with $K_c(s) = A_0$, $K_0(s) = -A_0^{-1}A_1$ and $k_j(s) = k_j$, $1 \leqslant j \leqslant m$, then

$$\hat{Q}_1(s) = \text{diag}\{k_j^{-1}\}_{1 \leqslant j \leqslant m}(A_0^{-1}(sA_0 + A_1) - A_0^{-1}A_1)$$

$$= \text{diag}\left\{\frac{s}{k_j}\right\}_{1 \leqslant j \leqslant m} \qquad (5.3.19)$$

which is diagonal. Noting that $G(s)$ has no zeros, it follows from theorem 5.3.1 that the closed-loop system is stable for all $k_j > 0$, $1 \leqslant j \leqslant m$. The controller

$$K(s) = A_0(\text{diag}\{k_j\}_{1 \leqslant j \leqslant m} - A_0^{-1}A_1)$$

$$= A_0 \text{diag}\{k_j\}_{1 \leqslant j \leqslant m} - A_1 \qquad (5.3.20)$$

is simply the controller used in Section 3.5. It is left as an exercise for the reader to show that the specified $K_0(s)$ simply cancels the off-diagonal terms of $\hat{K}_c(s)\hat{G}(s)$ to 'reduce' the size of the Gershgorin circles.

Consider now the $m \times m$ second-order lag

$$\hat{G}(s) = s^2 A_0 + s A_1 + A_2, \quad |A_0| \neq 0 \qquad (5.3.21)$$

Assume that $A_0^{-1} A_1$ is diagonally- (row) dominant but that $A_0^{-1} A_2$ is not dominant. This implies that the choice of $\hat{K}_c(s) = A_0^{-1}$ will not produce a dominant $\hat{K}_c(s)\hat{G}(s)$ at all frequencies. This does not prevent the application of theorem 5.2.2 as high gains in $k_j(s)$, $1 \leqslant j \leqslant m$, may ensure that $I_m + \hat{Q}(s)$ is diagonally dominant on D. The situation can be improved by the use of the origin shift $K_0(s) = -A_0^{-1} A_2$ to increase dominance at low frequencies, when

$$\hat{Q}_1(s) = \text{diag}\{k_j^{-1}(s)\}_{1 \leqslant j \leqslant m}(A_0^{-1}(s^2 A_0 + s A_1 + A_2) - A_0^{-1} A_2)$$
$$= \text{diag}\{k_j^{-1}(s)\}_{1 \leqslant j \leqslant m} s(s I_m + A_0^{-1} A_1) \qquad (5.3.22)$$

which is diagonally- (row) dominant on D except in the vicinity of $s = 0$. In particular, the Gershgorin circles have small radii at low frequencies aiding the attempt to make $I_m + \hat{Q}_1(s)$ diagonally-dominant on D. The controller takes the form

$$K(s) = A_0 \text{ diag}\{k_j(s)\}_{1 \leqslant j \leqslant m} - A_2 \qquad (5.3.23)$$

which should be compared with eqn. 3.9.13.

Exercise 5.3.4
Investigate the stability of the unity-negative feedback system

$$\hat{G}(s) = s^2 \begin{pmatrix} 1 & 1 \\ 0 & 1 \end{pmatrix} + s \begin{pmatrix} 3 & 4 \\ 1 & 3 \end{pmatrix} + \begin{pmatrix} 2 & 6 \\ 2 & 0 \end{pmatrix}$$

$$K(s) = \begin{pmatrix} k_1 - 2 & k_2 - 6 \\ 2 & k_2 \end{pmatrix}$$

(Hint: express $K(s)$ in the form of eqn. 5.3.23.)

Combined transformations and origin shifts: Express $\hat{G}(s)$ in the form of eqn. 5.3.1 and set

$$K(s) = P_2^{-1} K_c(s) \{\text{diag}\{k_j(s)\}_{1 \leqslant j \leqslant m} + K_0(s)\} P_1^{-1} \qquad (5.3.24)$$

when, by comparison with eqn. 5.3.2, the controller

$$K_1(s) = K_c(s) \{\text{diag}\{k_j(s)\}_{1 \leqslant j \leqslant m} + K_0(s)\} \qquad (5.3.25)$$

operates on the transformed plant $H(s)$. In this way, the transformation simplifies the system structure and the stability analysis may be approached by the use of precompensation and origin shifts to achieve diagonal dominance and application of theorem 5.3.1 with $\hat{H}(s)$ replacing $\hat{G}(s)$ in eqn. 5.3.10.

The simplest general illustration of the technique is obtained by consideration of a mixed-type structure of the form considered in Section 3.13 with $m = 2$, $r = 1$, when there exists nonsingular constant transformations P_1, P_2 so that (eqn. 3.13.7)

$$P_2 \hat{G}(s) P_1 = \begin{pmatrix} g_1^{-1}(s) & A_{12} \\ A_{21} & g_2^{-1}(s) \end{pmatrix} = \hat{H}(s) \qquad (5.3.26)$$

where $g_1(s), g_2(s)$ are scalar first and second order lags, respectively, and A_{12}, A_{21} are real scalars. Note that the Gershgorin circles of $\hat{H}(s)$ have constant radii on D and that $\hat{H}(s)$ is diagonally- (row and column) dominant at high frequencies. Choose $K(s)$ by eqn. 5.3.24 with $K_c(s) = I_2$ (to retain high-frequency dominance) and

$$K_0(s) = \begin{pmatrix} 0 & \alpha_{12} \\ \alpha_{21} & 0 \end{pmatrix} \qquad (5.3.27)$$

then

$$\hat{K}_c(s)\hat{H}(s) + K_0(s) = \begin{pmatrix} g_1^{-1}(s) & A_{12} + \alpha_{12} \\ A_{21} + \alpha_{21} & g_2^{-1}(s) \end{pmatrix} \qquad (5.3.28)$$

The constant parameters can now be used to improve dominance at low frequency. In particular, choosing $\alpha_{12} = -A_{12}, \alpha_{21} = -A_{21}$ a diagonal system is generated. The reader should investigate the relationship of this construction to the techniques of Section 3.13.

Exercise 5.3.5

The system defined by

$$\hat{G}(s) = \begin{pmatrix} s^3 + 2s^2 + 2s + 1 & s^2 + 3s + 2 \\ s^3 + 3s + 2 & s^3 + 2s^2 + 2s + 1 \end{pmatrix}$$

has no zeros and is diagonally-dominant at high frequencies but non-dominant at low frequencies. Apply the origin-shift technique with $K_c(s) = I_2$ (to retain high-frequency dominance),

$$K_0(s) = \frac{(2 + 3s)}{(1 + 0 \cdot 15s)} \begin{pmatrix} 0 & -1 \\ -1 & 0 \end{pmatrix}$$

to attain diagonal dominance of $\hat{K}_c\hat{G} + K_0$ at low frequencies and $k_1(s) = k_2(s) = k$. Find the range of k such that $I_2 + \hat{Q}_1(s)$ is diagonally-dominant on D and apply theorem 5.3.1 to ensure closed-loop stability.

Exercise 5.3.6
Repeat Exercise 5.3.5 with $K_c(s) = I_2$,

$$\hat{G}(s) = \begin{pmatrix} s^2 + 3s + 1 & s + 2 \\ s + 3 & 2s + 1 \end{pmatrix}$$

and

(a) $K_0(s) = \begin{pmatrix} 0 & -2 \\ -3 & 0 \end{pmatrix}$

(b) $K_0(s) = \begin{pmatrix} 0 & \dfrac{-20(s + 2)}{(s + 20)} \\ \dfrac{-30(s + 3)}{s + 30} & \end{pmatrix}$

and proportional loop elements $k_1(s) = k_1$, $k_2(s) = k_2$. Use the techniques of Section 3.13 to show that

$$\hat{H}(s) = P_2\hat{G}(s)P_1 = \begin{pmatrix} 1 & -0.5 \\ 0 & 0.5 \end{pmatrix} \hat{G}(s) \begin{pmatrix} 0.4 & 0 \\ -0.2 & 1.0 \end{pmatrix}$$

$$= \begin{pmatrix} 0.4s^2 + s - 0.5 & 1.5 \\ 0.5 & s + 0.5 \end{pmatrix}$$

which is dominant at high frequencies. Apply the combined transformation and origin-shift technique with $K_c(s) = I_2$ and

$$K_0(s) = \begin{pmatrix} 1.0 & -1.5 \\ -0.5 & 0 \end{pmatrix}$$

to generate a stable closed-loop system.

Exercise 5.3.7
Consider the application of the origin-shift technique to the minimum-phase plant

$$\hat{G}(s) = sA_0 + A_1 + H(s), \quad |A_0| \neq 0$$

with $H(s)$ proper, $A_0^{-1}A_1$ row dominant, $K_c(s) = A_0$, $K_0(s) = -A_0^{-1}H(0)$.

5.4 Sequential return differences

The technique discussed in this Section differs in basic concept from those in previous sections and chapters. Here, all elements of approximation disappear, providing an exact technique for stability analysis. This does introduce difficulties in implementation, but the analysis does parallel a commonly used practical technique for online system tuning.

Basic stability analysis: Consider the analysis of a unity-negative feedback system for the control of the $m \times m$ invertible, strictly proper plant $G(s)$ with $m \times m$ proper forward path control system, constrained to take the form

$$K(s) = \text{diag}\{k_j(s)\}_{1 \leqslant j \leqslant m} \tag{5.4.1}$$

where $k_j(s)$, $1 \leqslant j \leqslant m$, are scalar loop transfer functions. The stability of the closed-loop system is described by the return difference $T(s) = I_m + G(s)K(s)$,

$$\frac{\rho_c(s)}{\rho_0(s)} = |T(s)| = |I_m + G(s)K(s)| \tag{5.4.2}$$

In the absence of diagonal-dominance conditions or freedom to choose all elements of $K(s)$ to manipulate the system characteristic loci, the analysis of eqn. 5.4.2 is a complex task. Given a specific choice of $k_j(s)$, $1 \leqslant j \leqslant m$, eqn. 5.4.2 can be used directly to assess stability. In the absence of stability, however, eqn. 5.4.2 provides little insight into the choice of compensation elements. The stability analysis can be approached by regarding the problem as a sequence of single-loop designs in the manner suggested by Mayne.[15,25,26] To formulate the approach, write

$$K_j(s) = \text{diag}\{k_1(s), \ldots, k_j(s), 0, \ldots, 0\}, \qquad 1 \leqslant j \leqslant m \tag{5.4.3}$$

as the effective controller if loops $j+1, j+2, \ldots, m$ are opened (i.e. if the controller ignores the error signals $e_{j+1}(s), \ldots, e_m(s)$). A more compact form of eqn. 5.4.3 is

$$K_0(s) = 0$$

$$K_j(s) = K_{j-1}(s) + k_j(s)e_je_j^T, \qquad 1 \leqslant j \leqslant m$$

$$K_m(s) = K(s) \tag{5.4.4}$$

Associated with each controller (eqn. 5.4.4) is a matrix return difference

$$T_j(s) = I_m + G(s)K_j(s), \qquad 0 \leqslant j \leqslant m \tag{5.4.5}$$

describing the stability of the system with loops $j + 1, \ldots, m$ open.

The foundations of the stability analysis are formulated in terms of relations between successive return-difference determinants, provided by the identities, $1 \leqslant j \leqslant m$

$$
\begin{aligned}
|T_j(s)| &= |I_m + G(s)K_j(s)| \\
&= |I_m + G(s)K_{j-1}(s) + k_j(s)G(s)e_j e_j^T| \\
&= |T_{j-1}(s) + k_j(s)G(s)e_j e_j^T| \\
&= |T_{j-1}(s)\|I_m + k_j(s)T_{j-1}^{-1}(s)G(s)e_j e_j^T| \\
&= |T_{j-1}(s)| \{1 + e_j^T T_{j-1}^{-1}(s)G(s)e_j k_j(s)\}
\end{aligned}
\tag{5.4.6}
$$

More compactly, defining the scalar return-differences

$$t_j(s) = 1 + \{e_j^T T_{j-1}^{-1}(s)G(s)e_j\}k_j(s), \qquad 1 \leqslant j \leqslant m \tag{5.4.7}$$

and noting that $T_0(s) = I_m$ and $|T_0(s)| = 1$, then

$$|T_k(s)| = \prod_{j=1}^{k} t_j(s), \qquad 1 \leqslant k \leqslant m \tag{5.4.8}$$

In particular, taking $k = m$,

$$|T(s)| = |T_m(s)| = \prod_{j=1}^{m} t_j(s) \tag{5.4.9}$$

It follows directly that the closed-loop system is stable if the zeros of $t_j(s)$, $1 \leqslant j \leqslant m$, all have strictly negative real parts. Alternatively, if the scalar return-differences $t_j(s)$, $1 \leqslant j \leqslant m$, satisfy the scalar Nyquist stability criterion.

The stability analysis can now be approached by sequential addition of the loop transfer functions $k_1(s), k_2(s), \ldots, k_m(s)$ and analysis of the scalar return-differences $t_j(s)$, $1 \leqslant j \leqslant m$. Note that the dynamic characteristics of $t_j(s)$ depend upon the loop transfer function $k_j(s)$ explicitly and on the transfer functions $k_l(s)$, $1 \leqslant l \leqslant j - 1$ in the form of $T_{j-1}(s)$.

(a) Set $j = 1$ and $T_{j-1}(s) = I_m$

(b) Compute $e_j^T T_{j-1}^{-1}(s)G(s)e_j$ and apply classical techniques to choose $k_j(s)$ ensuring that the zeros of $t_j(s)$ have strictly negative real parts. The calculation is simplified by noting that $G(s)e_j$ is simply the jth column of $G(s)$.

(c) If $j = m$, stop. Otherwise continue to (d).

(d) Compute $T_j^{-1}(s)$ from the relation (the reader should verify this)

$$T_j^{-1}(s) = \left\{ I_m - \frac{k_j(s)}{t_j(s)} T_{j-1}^{-1}(s)G(s)e_je_j^T \right\} T_{j-1}^{-1}(s) \qquad (5.4.10)$$

(e) Set $j = j + 1$ and return to (b).

Exercise 5.4.1

Suppose that $t_j(s)$, $1 \leqslant j \leqslant k$, possess only zeros with strictly negative real parts. Show that the closed-loop system is stable in the presence of simultaneous failure of sensors (or actuators) in loops $k + 1, \ldots, m - 1, m$.

Use of precompensation: The controller structure (eqn. 5.4.1) limits the attainable closed-loop performance. For example, although the use of high gains and integral action will suppress low-frequency interaction, high-frequency interaction can only be significantly suppressed if $Q(s) = G(s)K(s)$ is approximately diagonal at high frequencies. In general, this cannot be achieved using eqn. 5.4.1. There is an easy route out of this problem by the use of precompensation

$$K(s) = K_c(s) \, \text{diag} \, \{k_j(s)\}_{1 \leqslant j \leqslant m} \qquad (5.4.11)$$

Replacing $G(s)$ by $G(s)K_c(s)$ in the above, it is left as an exercise for the reader to show that, if

$$K_0(s) = 0, \quad K_j(s) = K_{j-1}(s) + k_j(s)e_je_j^T, \qquad 1 \leqslant j \leqslant m$$

$$T_j(s) = I_m + G(s)K_c(s)K_j(s), \qquad 0 \leqslant j \leqslant m$$

$$t_j(s) = 1 + k_j(s)e_j^T T_{j-1}^{-1}(s)G(s)K_c(s)e_j, \qquad 1 \leqslant j \leqslant m$$

$$T_j^{-1}(s) = \{ I_m - \frac{k_j(s)}{t_j(s)} T_{j-1}^{-1}(s)G(s)K_c(s)e_je_j^T \}T_{j-1}^{-1}(s),$$

$$1 \leqslant j \leqslant m \qquad (5.4.12)$$

then,

$$|T_k(s)| = \prod_{j=1}^{k} t_j(s), \qquad 1 \leqslant k \leqslant m$$

$$|T(s)| = |T_m(s)| \qquad (5.4.13)$$

The choice of precompensator $K_c(s)$ is available for design and improving system performance. For example, it may be possible to choose $K_c(s)$ such that

(i) the transfer functions $e_j^T T_{j-1}^{-1}(s) G(s) K_c(s) e_j$, $1 \leqslant j \leqslant m$, are minimum-phase (a necessary condition if the gain of $k_j(s)$ is to be high).

(ii) $G(s)K_c(s)$ is diagonally column dominant at high frequencies, ensuring that $Q(s) = G(s)K(s)$ is column dominant at high frequencies (hence reducing high-frequency interaction). For example, $K_c(s)$ could be specified by application of the alignment algorithm, or the use of pseudodiagonalisation methods.

Exercise 5.4.2
Suppose that $t_j(s)$, $1 \leqslant j \leqslant k$, are stable. Show that the closed-loop system is stable in the presence of simultaneous failure of sensors in loops $k + 1, \dots, m$. (Note that this is not, in general, true for actuator failure if $K_c(s)$ is nondiagonal).

An important observation from eqn. 5.4.12 is that, for $1 \leqslant k \leqslant m$, both $T_j(s)$ and $t_j(s)$, $1 \leqslant j \leqslant k$, are independent of the $k + 1, k + 2, \dots$, mth columns of $K_c(s)$. In these cases where $K_c(s)$ is not prespecified by the control designer, this degree of freedom can be used, at each stage, to simplify and improve the structure of $t_j(s)$. For example, write

$$K_c(s) = [k_c^{(1)}(s), k_c^{(2)}(s), \dots, k_c^{(m)}(s)] \qquad (5.4.14)$$

then

$$t_j(s) = 1 + k_j(s) e_j^T T_{j-1}^{-1}(s) G(s) k_c^{(j)}(s), \qquad 1 \leqslant j \leqslant m \qquad (5.4.15)$$

The effect of $k_c^{(j)}(s)$ is to generate a transfer function in the form of a linear combination of the elements of the jth row of $T_{j-1}^{-1}(s) G(s)$ e.g. by suitable choice of elements of $k_c^{(j)}(s)$ it may be possible to ensure the minimum-phase property for $e_j^T T_{j-1}^{-1}(s) G(s) k_c^{(j)}(s)$.

Retention of full output feedback: The above procedure uses only limited output information at each stage of the design and activates (if precompensation is used) all system inputs $u_1(s), \dots, u_m(s)$. An alternative approach has been suggested by Owens[44] using full output information at each stage but activating only limited control action. The application of the technique is similar to the above, so we simply state the basic recurrence relations. Write

$$K(s) = \begin{pmatrix} \alpha_1^T(s) \\ \vdots \\ \alpha_m^T(s) \end{pmatrix} \qquad (5.4.16)$$

and
$$K_0(s) = 0$$
$$K_j(s) = K_{j-1}(s) + e_j\alpha_j^T(s), \qquad 1 \leqslant j \leqslant m$$
$$K(s) = K_m(s) \tag{5.4.17}$$

Note that $K_j(s)$ represents the situation when $u_{j+1}(s), \ldots, u_m(s)$ remain unactivated. Denote

$$T_j(s) = I_m + G(s)K_j(s), \qquad 0 \leqslant j \leqslant m$$
$$t_j(s) = 1 + \alpha_j^T(s)T_{j-1}^{-1}(s)G(s)e_j, \qquad 1 \leqslant j \leqslant m \tag{5.4.18}$$

when it is easily verified that

$$|T(s)| = |T_m(s)|, \quad |T_k(s)| = \prod_{j=1}^{k} t_j(s), \qquad 1 \leqslant k \leqslant m \tag{5.4.19}$$

Exercise 5.4.3
Verify that exercise 5.4.2 is valid if we replace the sensor failures by actuator failures.

Exercise 5.4.4
Extend the above algorithm to cope with nonsquare $m \times l$ systems $G(s)$ (Hint: note that $K_c(s)$ is $l \times m$ in eqn. 5.4.11 and $K(s)$ is $l \times m$ in eqn. 5.4.16).

Use of transformations: The sequential return difference techniques described above can be used in the general context of transformation techniques discussed in Section 5.3. Suppose that[45]

$$G(s) = P_1 H(s) P_2 \tag{5.4.20}$$

where P_1, P_2 are constant nonsingular matrices and write

$$K(s) = P_2^{-1} K_1(s) P_1^{-1} \tag{5.4.21}$$

then
$$|T(s)| = |I_m + G(s)K(s)| = |I_m + H(s)K_1(s)| \tag{5.4.22}$$

and $K_1(s)$ can be designed by application of a sequential return-difference technique to $H(s)$. This approach may have usefulness if diagonal dominance can only be achieved over a small frequency range, when the above techniques provide an exact approach to stability design.

5.5 Contraction-mapping algorithm and system approximation

It is well known that many high order scalar transfer functions can be approximated, for the purposes of feedback control systems design, by low-order transfer functions owing to the presence of approximate pole-zero cancellation. This observation can be expected to hold, in some sense, in the multivariable situation and has already been illustrated in Sections 3.7 and 3.15. It might also be anticipated that the approximation procedure could be based, roughly speaking, on the idea of diagonal dominance which has been of great help in preceding sections. The rigorous formulation of these ideas was originally provided by Freeman[8] and modified by Owens,[50] and uses the idea of *contraction mappings.*[6, 10] As in the case of the diagonal dominance theorems, the technique only provides sufficient conditions for closed-loop stability.

The mathematical background is beyond the scope of this text and the reader is referred to the references for technical details. The basic result is provided by Freeman.[8]

Theorem 5.5.1: Consider a unity-negative feedback system with $m \times m$ strictly proper forward-path transfer-function matrix $Q(s) = G(s)K(s)$ derived from a *controllable and observable, asymptotically stable* state-vector model. Let $Q_A(s)$ be a stable approximate form of $Q(s)$ such that the unity-negative feedback system with forward path transfer function matrix $Q_A(s)$ is asymptotically stable. Then a sufficient condition for closed-loop stability is that

$$\max_{1 \leqslant j \leqslant m} \max_{s \in D} \sum_{l=1}^{m} |L_{jl}(s)| < 1 \qquad (5.5.1)$$

where

$$L(s) = \{I_m + Q_A(s)\}^{-1}\{Q_A(s) - Q(s)\} \qquad (5.5.2)$$

In practical terms, the result states that, if $G(s)$ is approximated by $G_A(s)$ for the purposes of design and the controller $K(s)$ is designed for $G_A(s)$ to ensure that the closed-loop system is stable, then the original closed-loop system is stable if the *contraction condition* expr. 5.5.1 is satisfied with $Q_A(s) = G_A(s)K(s)$.

Exercise 5.5.1

Suppose that $Q_A(s)$ is derived from the diagonal terms of $Q(s)$ i.e.

$$Q_A(s) = \text{diag} \{Q_{jj}(s)\}_{1 \leqslant j \leqslant m} \qquad (5.5.3)$$

and that the scalar feedback systems $(1 + Q_{jj}(s))^{-1} Q_{jj}(s)$ are stable.

270   *Noneigenvalue methods in feedback design*

Show that the contraction condition is equivalent to

$$|1 + Q_{jj}(s)| > \sum_{\substack{l=1 \\ l \neq j}}^{m} |Q_{jl}(s)|, \quad 1 \leqslant j \leqslant m \qquad (5.5.4)$$

for all s on D i.e. $I_m + Q(s)$ must be diagonally-dominant on D (compare with Section 5.1).

The major constraint in theorem 5.5.1 is that $Q(s)$ be asymptotically stable. This precludes the application of the result to open-loop unstable plants $G(s)$ and, in principle, prevents the use of integral-control action. This is not a constraint in practice as pure integral action can rarely be achieved. The following result makes possible the analysis of open-loop unstable plants,[50] although it requires that the system be minimum phase.

Theorem 5.5.2: Suppose that $Q(s)$ is invertible and minimum phase and that $Q_A(s)$ is invertible and minimum phase. Then a sufficient condition for closed-loop stability is that expr. 5.5.1 holds with,

$$L(s) = \{I_m + \hat{Q}_A(s)\}^{-1}\{\hat{Q}_A(s) - \hat{Q}(s)\} \qquad (5.5.5)$$

Exercise 5.5.2
If

$$\hat{Q}_A(s) = \text{diag}\{\hat{Q}_{jj}(s)\}_{1 \leqslant j \leqslant m} \qquad (5.5.6)$$

and the scalar feedback systems $(1 + \hat{Q}_{jj}(s))^{-1}$, $1 \leqslant j \leqslant m$, are stable, show that the contraction condition is equivalent to

$$|1 + \hat{Q}_{jj}(s)| > \sum_{\substack{l=1 \\ l \neq j}}^{m} |\hat{Q}_{jl}(s)|, \quad 1 \leqslant j \leqslant m \qquad (5.5.7)$$

for all s on D i.e. $I_m + \hat{Q}(s)$ must be diagonally-dominant on D (compare with Section 5.2).

The contraction conditions expr. 5.5.1 can be checked by examination of the functions

$$f_j(s) = \sum_{l=1}^{m} |L_{jl}(s)| \qquad (5.5.8)$$

at selected points on D. Alternatively, the results can be regarded purely as a justification for the use of approximation methods, the stability of the closed-loop system being checked by simulation.

The theory has great generality but does not provide any guidelines as to the choice of $Q_A(s)$. Some examples are provided by exercises 5.5.1 and 5.5.2 and the technique of Section 3.7. Let $G(s)$ be $m \times m$, strictly proper, minimum phase and invertible, with (see Section 3.7)

$$\hat{G}(s) = sA_0 + A_1 + A_0 H(s), \quad |A_0| \neq 0, \quad H(s) \text{ proper,}$$

$$H(0) = 0 \tag{5.5.9}$$

and use the first-order approximation

$$\hat{G}_A(s) = sA_0 + A_1 \tag{5.5.10}$$

with the controller

$$K(s) = kA_0 - A_1, \quad k > 0 \tag{5.5.11}$$

and $Q_A(s) = G_A(s)K(s)$. It is known (Section 3.5) that the unity-negative feedback system with forward-path element $Q_A(s)$ is stable. Using theorem 5.5.2,

$$L(s) = \{I_m + \hat{K}\hat{G}_A\}^{-1}\{\hat{K}\hat{G}_A - \hat{K}\hat{G}\}$$

$$= \{K + \hat{G}_A\}^{-1}\{\hat{G}_A - \hat{G}\} = \frac{(-1)}{s+k}H(s) \tag{5.5.12}$$

so that the closed-loop system is asymptotically stable if

$$\max_{1 \leqslant j \leqslant m} \max_{s \in D} \frac{1}{|s+k|} \sum_{l=1}^{m} |H_{jl}(s)| < 1 \tag{5.5.13}$$

which should be compared with exprs. 3.7.6 and 3.7.7. More generally, suppose that $G(s)$ is strictly proper, invertible and minimum phase with

$$\hat{G}(s) = s^k A_0 + s^{k-1}A_1 + \ldots + A_k + H(s), \quad H(s) \text{ proper,}$$

$$H(0) = 0 \tag{5.5.14}$$

and use the kth-order approximation

$$\hat{G}_A(s) = s^k A_0 + s^{k-1}A_1 + \ldots + A_k \tag{5.5.15}$$

then

$$L(s) = \{K + \hat{G}_A(s)\}^{-1}(\hat{G}_A - \hat{G})$$

$$= \{K + \hat{G}_A(s)\}^{-1}(-1)H(s) \tag{5.5.16}$$

suggests intuitively that stability will be obtained if high gains are used or $H(s)$ is 'small' in some sense. In such cases the analytic techniques of chapter three could be used to design $K(s)$, although some approximation to $H(s)$ must be included in the reduced model $\hat{G}_A(s)$ if the zeros of the system are important in closed-loop dynamic behaviour.

Exercise 5.5.3

Suppose that (see eqns. 5.4.20, 5.4.21)

$$G(s) = P_1 H(s) P_2 \qquad (5.5.17)$$

where P_1, P_2 are constant, nonsingular matrices and

$$K(s) = P_2^{-1} K_1(s) P_1^{-1} \qquad (5.5.18)$$

(Note: $H(s)$ is not to be confused with $H(s)$ in eqn. 5.5.9). Use eqn. 5.4.22 to formulate analogues to theorems 5.5.1 and 5.5.2 in terms of $H(s)$ and $K_1(s)$. Consider the application of your results to stability analysis where P_1, P_2 are derived (say) from the method of dyadic expansion.

5.6 Summary

This chapter has reviewed the available theoretical methods lying under the broad title of noneigenvalue-type methods, with particular emphasis on the well established inverse-Nyquist-array design technique. The reader should have noted the great importance of diagonal-dominance type approximation schemes in stability analysis and the need for ingenuity in the achievement of diagonal dominance. An important general comment on the material of Chapters 3 to 5 is that the primary theoretical objective has been the reduction of the complex multi-input/multi-output control problem to m individual classical design problems by a combination of transformation techniques, approximation of eigenvalue dynamics and the use of precompensation and origin shifts. An attempt at a unified approach is provided in Section 5.3 but this is not totally satisfactory. It does suggest, however, that the difference between the characteristic-locus technique, the method of dyadic expansion and the inverse Nyquist array is simply one of emphasis and approximation procedures. In this sense it is anticipated that they can usefully be combined as valid design tools for a particular application.

5.7 Problems and Exercises

1 Consider the system (see Section 2.5)

$$G(s) = \frac{1}{s(s+2\beta)} \begin{pmatrix} s+\beta & \beta \\ \beta & s+\beta \end{pmatrix}$$

with forward-path controller

$$K(s) = \text{diag}\{k_1, k_2\}$$

Use theorem 5.1.1 to investigate the stability of the closed-loop system as a function of k_1, k_2. Repeat the analysis with the first-order-type controller

$$K(s) = k \begin{pmatrix} 1 & 0 \\ 0 & 1 \end{pmatrix} - \begin{pmatrix} \beta & -\beta \\ -\beta & \beta \end{pmatrix}$$

2 Write $|T(s)| = |I_m + G(s)K(s)| = |G(s)||\hat{G}(s) + K(s)|$ (valid if G is invertible). Suppose that $K(s)$ is asymptotically stable and that $\hat{G}(s) + K(s)$ is diagonally- (row or column) dominant at every point s on D. Let $G(s)$ have n_z^+ zeros in the interior of D and suppose that the jth element of $\hat{G} + K$ maps D onto closed contours encircling the origin of the complex plane n_j times in a clockwise manner. Prove that the closed-loop system is stable if, and only if,

$$n_z^+ + \sum_{j=1}^{m} n_j = 0$$

Writing $K(s) = K_1(s)K_2(s)$ where $K_1(s)$ is minimum phase, show that $|T(s)| = |G(s)K_1(s)||\hat{K}_1(s)\hat{G}(s) + K_2(s)|$. Formulate and prove an equivalent result in this case.

3 Show that it is impossible to construct a constant nonsingular precompensator for the plant

$$\hat{G}(s) = \begin{pmatrix} s & 1 \\ 1 & s \end{pmatrix}$$

such that $\hat{K}_c\hat{G}$ is diagonally-dominant on D. Apply theorem 5.2.2 with $K_c(s) = I_2, k_1(s) = k_1, k_2(s) = k_2$ to find the gains k_1, k_2 such that the closed-loop system is stable.

4 A 2×2 plant with inverse transfer-function matrix

$$\hat{G}_1(s) = s^2 \begin{pmatrix} 1 & 1 \\ 0 & 1 \end{pmatrix} + s \begin{pmatrix} 3 & 3 \\ 2 & 1 \end{pmatrix} + \begin{pmatrix} 4 & 3 \\ 1 & 2 \end{pmatrix}$$

is subject to minor-loop rate feedback $u(s) = v(s) - sH_1 y(s)$ where H_1 is a constant 2×2 matrix yielding $y(s) = G(s)v(s)$ where

$$G(s) = \{I_m + sG_1(s)H_1\}^{-1}G_1(s)$$

Design a unity-negative feedback system for $G(s)$ ensuring that $\hat{Q}(s)$ is diagonally-dominant on D by suitable choice of constant precompensator $K_c(s)$ and rate feedback element H_1 (Hint: note that $G(s)$ is a second-order lag and apply theorem 5.2.2 with $K_c(s) = A_0$ and suitable H_1).

5 Consider a unity-negative feedback system for the control of the $m \times m$ strictly proper, invertible plant $G(s)$ with forward-path controller,

$$K(s) = \text{diag} \{k_j(s)\}_{1 \leqslant j \leqslant m}$$

Use the identity,

$$\rho_c(s) = z(s)|I_m + \hat{K}(s)\hat{G}(s)|$$

where $z(s)$ is the zero polynomial of GK. Defining,

$$\hat{K}_0(s) = 0, \quad \hat{K}_j(s) = \hat{K}_{j-1}(s) + e_j e_j^T k_j^{-1}(s), \qquad 1 \leqslant j \leqslant m$$

$$N_j(s) = I_m + \hat{K}_j(s)\hat{G}(s), \qquad 1 \leqslant j \leqslant m$$

show that

$$\rho_c(s) = z(s) \prod_{j=1}^m t_j(s)$$

where, $1 \leqslant j \leqslant m$,

$$t_j(s) = 1 + k_j^{-1}(s) e_j^T \hat{G}(s) N_{j-1}^{-1}(s) e_j$$

6 Apply the sequential return-difference method to the system of problem 1.

7 Regarding $Q(s)$ as an exact physical model of the plant plus forward-path controller and $Q_A(s)$ as a mathematical model (including modelling errors and other unavoidable features), interpret the results of Section 5.5 in terms of the sensitivity of the closed-loop design to modelling and approximation errors.

8 Apply the precompensation and origin-shift technique to the stability analysis of the system

$$\hat{G}(s) = s^2 \begin{pmatrix} 1 & 1 \\ 0 & 1 \end{pmatrix} + s \begin{pmatrix} 6 & 4 \\ 2 & 3 \end{pmatrix} + \begin{pmatrix} 3 & 3 \\ 2 & 1 \end{pmatrix}$$

ensuring that $\hat{K}_c(s)\hat{G}(s) + K_0(s)$ is diagonally-dominant on D (Hint: choose $K_c(s)$ to ensure that $\hat{K}_c\hat{G}$ is diagonal at high frequencies). Consider the possibility of applying transformation methods such that the off-diagonal terms of $P_2\hat{G}P_1$ are frequency-independent.

Chapter 6

Introduction to multivariable root-loci

The material described in this Chapter represents a summary of some important aspects of recent work on the analysis of the root-loci of linear multivariable systems (References 14, 61, 42, 48, 49, 52, 22, 55). The field is new and the ultimate impact of the results cannot yet be assessed. For this reason, our attention will be limited to conceptual discussion and the description of computational methods.

6.1 Basic concepts

The classical root-locus technique[58] for the analysis and compensation of scalar feedback systems is well established as a useful design tool. It is natural, therefore, to consider the possibility of extending the techniques to the analysis of the multi-input/multi-output case. It is not clear at the present time if a full extension is possible but useful and important light has been shed into the structure of such systems and the asymptotic properties of their root-loci plots.

Consider an $m \times m$ strictly proper plant with invertible transfer function matrix $G(s)$ subject to unity-negative feedback control with proper, invertible forward-path controller transfer-function matrix $K(s)$. The stability of the closed-loop system is described by the relation

$$\frac{\rho_c(s)}{\rho_0(s)} = |T(s)| = |I_m + Q(s)| \qquad (6.1.1)$$

where $Q(s) = G(s)K(s)$. The basic concept of a system root-locus plot is to consider the graphical variation of the roots of the closed-loop characteristic polynomial $\rho_c(s)$ as the controller gains vary in some unbounded interval. The simultaneous variation of the m^2 gains of the

elements of $K(s)$ in an independent manner is not a practical proposition so attention is restricted to the case

$$K(s) = pK_1(s), \quad Q_0(s) = G(s)K_1(s) \qquad (6.1.2)$$

where $K_1(s)$ is a specified control system (designed, perhaps, using one
of the techniques described in previous chapters) and $p > 0$ is a real
'overall gain' parameter. The root-locus plot of the closed-loop system
is then defined to be the graphical representation of the variation of the
roots of $\rho_c(s)$ as p varies in the interval $0 \leqslant p < +\infty$.

Exercise 6.1.1
Show that the closed-loop poles coincide with the open-loop poles
when $p = 0$.

In general, it is not possible to obtain analytical expressions for the
closed-loop poles. It is, therefore, necessary to consider approximation
methods, if theoretical results are to be obtained. In particular, the
following problems can be posed:
(a) obtain asymptotic expressions for the closed-loop poles as $p \to +\infty$
(b) assess the effect of the choice of $K_1(s)$ on the root-locus plot
(c) relate the overall characteristics of the root-locus plot to the transient performance of the closed-loop system.
As yet, little information is available concerning the practical solution
of (c). Useful results have been obtained, however, providing an
approach to the solution of (a) and (b). The rather artificial device of
letting $p \to +\infty$ does not necessarily preclude the application of the
results in practical situations if it is assumed that high-controller gains
are to be used to ensure fast response speed, small interaction effects at
low frequency and small steady-state errors in response to unit-step
demands.
In the scalar case ($m = 1$)

$$Q_0(s) = G(s)K_1(s) = g \frac{\prod\limits_{j=1}^{n_z} (s - z_j)}{\prod\limits_{j=1}^{n} (s - p_j)}, \quad k = n - n_z > 0 \qquad (6.1.3)$$

and the system root-locus has *finite-limit poles* (more precisely, finite
cluster points) at the *zeros* z_j, $1 \leqslant j \leqslant n_z$, and k *unbounded poles* of
the form, $1 \leqslant j \leqslant k$,

$$s = p^{1/k} \eta_j \alpha + \epsilon_j(p)$$

$$\lim_{p \to \infty} \epsilon_j(p) = 0 \qquad\qquad (6.1.4)$$

where $p^{1/k}$ is the positive-real kth root of p, η_j, $1 \leqslant j \leqslant k$, are the distinct kth roots of $-g$, and the *intercept* α is given by

$$k\alpha = \sum_{j=1}^{n} p_j - \sum_{j=1}^{n_z} z_j \qquad\qquad (6.1.5)$$

The reader should recollect the graphical interpretation of expr. 6.1.4 and the effect of k, g, α on closed-loop stability at high gains, and note that the unbounded poles are said to approach the *asymptotes* $p^{1/k} \eta_j + \alpha$, $1 \leqslant j \leqslant k$, as $p \to +\infty$.

The essential nature of the root-locus of a multivariable system is suggested by considering the special case when $G(s) = P_1$ diag $\{g_j(s)\}_{1 \leqslant j \leqslant m} P_2$ and $K_1(s) = P_2^{-1}$ diag $\{k_j(s)\}_{1 \leqslant j \leqslant m} P_1^{-1}$ are dyadic i.e.

$$\frac{\rho_c(s)}{\rho_0(s)} = \prod_{j=1}^{m} (1 + p g_j(s) k_j(s)) \qquad\qquad (6.1.6)$$

and the system root-locus has the structure of m superimposed scalar root-loci. This is not exactly the case in general (when $g_j k_j$ must, in principle, be replaced by the characteristic transfer functions of $Q_0(s)$) but certain features can be retained (Fig. 6.1.1), namely,
(a) The root-locus has finite cluster points at the zeros of $Q_0(s)$ (Section 3.20), and
(b) a variety of unbounded poles of the form

$$s_{jl} = p^{1/\nu_j} \eta_{jl} + \alpha_j + \epsilon_{jl}(p)$$

$$\lim_{p \to \infty} \epsilon_{jl}(p) = 0, \qquad 1 \leqslant l \leqslant \nu_j, \quad 1 \leqslant j \leqslant m \quad (6.1.7)$$

where η_{jl}, $1 \leqslant l \leqslant \nu_j$, are the distinct ν_jth roots of a nonzero (complex) number $-\lambda_j$. Relation 6.1.7 is said to represent an *infinite zero of order* ν_j with *asymptotic directions* η_{jl} and *pivot* α_j. The pivot plays the role of the intercept in the classical root-locus plot but may be complex (Fig. 6.1.2). A multivariable system may possess distinct orders of infinite zeros and the orders need not be integer e.g. consider the example

$$Q_0(s) = \begin{pmatrix} 0 & \dfrac{1}{s} \\ \dfrac{1}{s^2} & 0 \end{pmatrix} \qquad\qquad (6.1.8)$$

yielding

$$\frac{\rho_c(s)}{\rho_0(s)} = \frac{s^3 - p^2}{s^3} \tag{6.1.9}$$

and the system has three infinite zeros of order 3/2. For practical purposes, however, such cases can be dismissed as[48] it can be shown

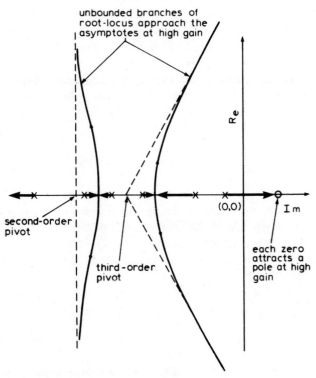

Fig. 6.1.1 Schematic multivariable root-locus with two second-order and three third-order infinite zeros and one finite zero
——— root-locus
– – – asymptotes
 x   open-loop poles
 ○   system zeros

(using a canonical form due to Morse[31]) that it is always possible to choose $K_1(s)$ such that only integer-order infinite zeros exist. In fact, a 'random' choice of $K_1(s)$ will achieve this objective with probability one.

Exercise 6.1.2

Replacing $Q_0(s)$ by $Q_0(s) \begin{pmatrix} 0 & 1 \\ 1 & 0 \end{pmatrix}$ in eqn. 6.1.8, show that the system has infinite zeros of order 1,2.

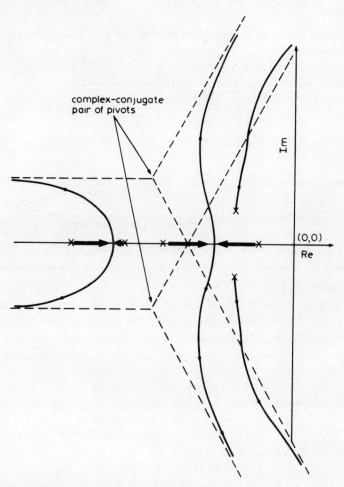

Fig. 6.1.2 Multivariable root-locus with six third-order infinite zeros and complex (conjugate) pivots

Finally, suppose that $Q_0(s)$ can be derived from a state-vector model (A, B, C), then

$$\sum \text{(closed-loop poles)} = \text{tr}\,\{A - pBC\}$$

$$= \text{tr}\,A - p\,\text{tr}\,CB \qquad (6.1.10)$$

Using expr. 6.1.7 and denoting the zeros of $Q_0(s)$ by z_j, $1 \leqslant j \leqslant n_z$, gives

$$\sum_{j=1}^{m} \sum_{l=1}^{\nu_j} s_{jl} + \sum_{j=1}^{n_z} z_j - \text{tr}\,A + p\,\text{tr}\,CB \to 0 \qquad (p \to +\infty) \qquad (6.1.11)$$

Noting that the asymptotic directions for $\nu_j > 1$ cancel in the summation gives

$$p \sum_{\nu_j=1} \eta_{jl} + \sum_{j=1}^{m} \nu_i \alpha_j + \sum_{j=1}^{m} \sum_{l=1}^{\nu_j} \epsilon_{jl}(p) - \text{tr}\,A + p\,\text{tr}\,CB + \sum_{j=1}^{n_z} z_j$$

$$\to 0 \qquad (p \to +\infty) \qquad (6.1.12)$$

Using expr. 6.1.7, the terms linear in p can be cancelled, from which, letting $p \to +\infty$,

$$\sum_{j=1}^{m} \nu_j \alpha_j = \text{sum of the open-loop poles}$$

$$- \text{sum of the system zeros} \qquad (6.1.13)$$

which is a multivariable generalisation of eqn. 6.1.5.

Exercise 6.1.3
If $m = 1$ it is well known that a closed-loop pole cannot 'pass through' a system zero. Show by example that this is no longer the case if $m > 1$ (Hint: choose $Q_1(s)$ diagonal).

6.2 Finite-limit poles

If $Q_0(s)$ is invertible, suppose that some closed-loop pole remains finite as $p \to +\infty$, then

$$0 = \frac{\rho_c(s)}{\rho_0(s)} = |I_m + pQ_0(s)| = p^m |p^{-1} I_m + Q_0(s)| \quad (6.2.1)$$

The closed-loop pole is hence a zero of

$$\rho_0(s)|p^{-1} I_m + Q_0(s)| \to \rho_0(s)|Q_0(s)| = z(s) \qquad (p \to +\infty) \qquad (6.2.2)$$

i.e. the finite limit poles of the root-locus are simply zeros of $Q_0(s)$. The converse is also true and, in fact, every zero of $Q_0(s)$ with multiplicity d will attract d closed-loop poles. It is now possible to state a useful identity

$$n = n_z + \sum_{j=1}^{m} \nu_j \qquad (6.2.3)$$

by noting that the root-locus has n_z finite cluster points and $\sum\limits_{j=1}^{m} \nu_j$ unbounded roots.

Exercise 6.2.1

A system of state dimension $n = 5$ and $m = 2$ is known to have two zeros and integer order-infinite zeros. If the system has only one first-order infinite zero, show that it has two second-order infinite zeros.

Exercise 6.2.2

Show that a nonminimum phase system is always unstable at high gain.

6.3 Uniform rank systems: a special case

The calculation of the orders, asymptotic directions and pivots of the root-locus is undertaken by analysis of the series (valid for all large $|s|$) about the point at infinity,

$$Q_0(s) = C(sI_n - A)^{-1}B = s^{-1}Q_1 + s^{-2}Q_2 + s^{-3}Q_3 + \ldots \qquad (6.3.1)$$

where the system 'Markov parameters' are given by

$$Q_j = CA^{j-1}B, \qquad j \geqslant 1 \qquad (6.3.2)$$

A special case of significance in the following Sections is when

$$Q_j = 0, \qquad 1 \leqslant j < k$$

$$|Q_k| \neq 0 \qquad (6.3.3)$$

when the system is said to have *uniform rank* k. Suppose that s is a closed-loop pole and that $|s| \to +\infty$ as $p \to +\infty$, then

$$0 = |T(s)| = \left| I_m + \frac{p}{s^k} Q_k + \frac{p}{s^{k+1}} Q_{k+1} + O\left(\frac{p}{s^{k+2}}\right) \right| \qquad (6.3.4)$$

where the notation $O\left(\dfrac{p}{s^l}\right)$ will be used to represent the fact that $p^{-1}s^l O\left(\dfrac{p}{s^l}\right)$ remains finite as $p \to +\infty$. Multiplying eqn. 6.3.4 by $(p^{-1}s^k)^m$ yields

$$0 = \left| \frac{s^k}{p} I_m + Q_k + O(s^{-1}) \right| \qquad (6.3.5)$$

Letting $p \to +\infty$, the term $O(s^{-1})$ becomes negligible and $p^{-1}s^k$ must have only finite cluster-points λ satisfying

$$|\lambda I_m + Q_k| = 0 \qquad (6.3.6)$$

i.e. $Q_0(s)$ has mk kth-order infinite zeros of the form

$$\lim_{p \to \infty} \frac{s^k}{p} = -\lambda_j \qquad (6.3.7)$$

where λ_j, $1 \leqslant j \leqslant m$, are the eigenvalues of Q_k (all nonzero owing to eqn. 6.3.3).

Exercise 6.3.1
Prove that $Q_0(s)$ cannot have infinite zeros of any other order (Hint: suppose $Q_0(s)$ has an infinite zero of order $\nu \neq k$. If $\nu < k$ use eqn. 6.3.4 to obtain a contradiction. If $\nu > k$, use eqn. 6.3.5 in a similar manner.)

Eqn. 6.3.7 indicates that the infinite zeros take the form

$$s = p^{1/k}\eta_{ij} + \mu_{ij}(p), \qquad 1 \leqslant i \leqslant k, \quad 1 \leqslant j \leqslant m \qquad (6.3.8)$$

where η_{ij}, $1 \leqslant i \leqslant k$, are the distinct kth roots of $-\lambda_j$ and

$$\lim_{p \to \infty} p^{-1/k}\mu_{ij}(p) = 0 \qquad (6.3.9)$$

Comparing eqn. 6.3.8 with eqn. 6.1.7 it is seen that the pivot can only be obtained by analysis of the terms $\mu_{ij}(p)$. Suppose that the eigenvalues λ_j, $1 \leqslant j \leqslant m$, consist of l distinct terms η_j, $1 \leqslant j \leqslant l$, of multiplicity d_j, $1 \leqslant j \leqslant l$ and that Q_k has a nonsingular eigenvector matrix T_0

$$T_0^{-1} Q_k T_0 = \text{block diag } \{\eta_j I_{d_j}\}_{1 \leqslant j \leqslant l} \qquad (6.3.10)$$

and write

$$T_0^{-1} Q_{k+1} T_0 = \begin{pmatrix} N_{11} & \cdots & N_{1l} \\ \vdots & & \vdots \\ N_{l1} & \cdots & N_{ll} \end{pmatrix} \tag{6.3.11}$$

where N_{ij} has dimension $d_i \times d_j$, $1 \le i \le l$, $1 \le j \le l$. Examining the identity

$$0 = \left| \frac{s^{k+1}}{p} T_0^{-1} T(s) T_0 \right|$$

$$= \left| s \left\{ \frac{s^k}{p} I_m + \text{block diag } \{\eta_i I_{d_i}\}_{1 \le i \le l} \right\} \right.$$

$$\left. + T_0^{-1} Q_{k+1} T_0 + O\left(\frac{1}{s}\right) \right| \tag{6.3.12}$$

and supposing that $p^{-1} s^k \to -\eta_j (p \to +\infty)$, application of Schur's formula yields

$$\lim_{p \to \infty} |s\{p^{-1}s^k + \eta_j\} I_{d_j} + N_{jj}| = 0 \tag{6.3.13}$$

and hence

$$\lim_{p \to \infty} s\{p^{-1}s^k + \eta_j\} = -\alpha_{jr} \tag{6.3.14}$$

where α_{jr} is an eigenvalue of N_{jj}. Substitution from eqn. 6.3.8 followed by binomial expansion of s^k and the use of expr. 6.3.9 yields the formula,

$$\lim_{p \to \infty} \mu_{ij}(p) = \frac{\alpha_{jr}}{k\eta_j} \tag{6.3.15}$$

The infinite zeros of $Q_0(s)$ can now be listed in the form,

$$s_{ijr}(p) = p^{1/k} \eta_{ij} + \frac{\alpha_{jr}}{k\eta_j} + \epsilon_{ijr}(p),$$

$$\lim_{p \to \infty} \epsilon_{ijr}(p) = 0, \qquad 1 \le i \le k, \quad 1 \le r \le d_j, \quad 1 \le j \le l \tag{6.3.16}$$

where $p^{1/k}$ is the positive real kth root of p, η_{ij} $(1 \le i \le k)$ are the distinct kth roots of $-\eta_j$, and α_{jr}, $1 \le r \le d_j$, are the eigenvalues of N_{jj}. Note that, for $m > 1$, both η_j and α_{jr} may be complex but the fact that system closed-loop eigenvalues exist in complex conjugate pairs indicates that the system asymptotes are symmetric under reflection in the real axis of the complex plane.

Exercise 6.3.2
Deduce from the above that a system of uniform rank k has $n - km$ zeros (c.f. Theorem 2.20.3).

To illustrate the application of the technique, consider the coupled spring-mass-damper system described in Section 2.6 by the state-vector model (eqn. 2.6.2). Considering unity-negative feedback control with $K_1(s) = I_2$, the relevant Markov parameters are given by

$$Q_1 = CB = 0, \quad Q_2 = CAB = \begin{pmatrix} \dfrac{k_1}{m_1} & 0 \\ 0 & \dfrac{k_2}{m_2} \end{pmatrix} \quad (6.3.17)$$

and the system has uniform rank $k = 2$. We will require the third Markov parameter matrix,

$$Q_3 = CA^2B = \begin{pmatrix} \dfrac{-ck_1}{m_1^2} & \dfrac{ck_2}{m_1 m_2} \\ \dfrac{ck_1}{m_2 m_1} & \dfrac{-ck_2}{m_2^2} \end{pmatrix} \quad (6.3.18)$$

Case One: $k_1 m_2 \neq k_2 m_1$, when $l = 2$, $d_1 = d_2 = 1$ and $\eta_1 = k_1/m_1$, $\eta_2 = k_2/m_2$. The eigenvector matrix of Q_2 is simply $T_0 = I_2$ and hence $T_0^{-1} Q_3 T_0 = Q_3$ giving

$$N_{11} = \dfrac{-ck_1}{m_1^2}, \quad N_{22} = \dfrac{-ck_2}{m_2^2} \quad (6.3.19)$$

from which $\alpha_{11} = N_{11}$, $\alpha_{21} = N_{22}$ and the system has four second-order infinite zeros of the asymptotic form (with $i^2 = -1$ and neglecting the terms tending to zero as $p \to +\infty$),

$$s(p) \simeq \pm i \sqrt{\dfrac{k_j}{m_j}} \, p^{1/2} - \dfrac{c}{2m_j}, \quad (p \to +\infty), \quad j = 1,2 \quad (6.3.20)$$

indicating stability at high gain (the pivots are real and negative!) and the presence of oscillation (consistent with the physical nature of the system!).

Cast two: $k_1 m_2 = k_2 m_1$ when $l = 1, d_1 = 2$ and $\eta_1 = k_1/m_1 = k_2/m_2$. Again $T_0 = I_2$ but, in this case, $T_0^{-1} Q_3 T_0 = Q_3 = N_{11}$ yielding

$$\alpha_{11} = 0, \quad \alpha_{12} = -c \frac{k_1}{m_1} \left\{ \frac{1}{m_1} + \frac{1}{m_2} \right\} \qquad (6.3.21)$$

The sytem hence has four second-order infinite zeros of the form $(p \to \infty)$

$$s(p) \simeq \pm i \sqrt{\frac{k_1}{m_1}} \, p^{1/2}$$

$$s(p) \simeq \pm i \sqrt{\frac{k_1}{m_1}} \, p^{1/2} - \frac{c}{2} \left\{ \frac{1}{m_1} + \frac{1}{m_2} \right\} \qquad (6.3.22)$$

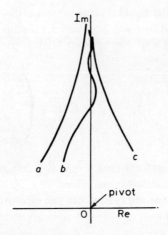

Fig. 6.3.1 Approach to the asymptote

The stability of the closed-loop system at high gain cannot be deduced in this case from the approximation (expr. 6.3.22) owing to the presence of two asymptotes with pivot at the origin of the complex plane. This is most easily explained by noting that two closed-loop poles will asymptotically approach the imaginary axis of the complex plane in one of the ways illustrated in Fig. 6.3.1. Stability for all high-enough gains is ensured only in case (*a*) and, in all cases, the damping ratio approaches zero indicating severe oscillation in the closed-loop response.

Exercise 6.3.3
In the above example, using $K_1(s) = \begin{pmatrix} -1 & 0 \\ 0 & 1 \end{pmatrix}$, show that the closed-
loop system has four second-order infinite zeros of the asymptotic form
$(p \to \infty)$

$$s(p) \simeq \pm \sqrt{\frac{k_1}{m_1}} p^{1/2} - \frac{c}{2m_1}$$

$$s(p) \simeq \pm i \sqrt{\frac{k_2}{m_2}} p^{1/2} - \frac{c}{2m_2}$$

and hence that the closed-loop system is unstable for all high-enough
gains $p \geqslant 0$. Provide a physical interpretation of this result.

Turning now to the liquid storage system of Section 2.5 with state-
vector model defined by eqns. 2.5.4 and 2.5.5 subject to unity-negative
feedback with $K_1(s) = I_2$. The relevant Markov parameters are seen to
be

$$Q_1 = CB = \begin{pmatrix} a_1^{-1} & 0 \\ 0 & a_2^{-1} \end{pmatrix}, \quad Q_2 = CAB = \begin{pmatrix} -\dfrac{\beta}{a_1^2} & \dfrac{\beta}{a_1 a_2} \\ \dfrac{\beta}{a_1 a_2} & -\dfrac{\beta}{a_2^2} \end{pmatrix} \quad (6.3.23)$$

and the system has uniform rank $k = 1$. It is left as an exercise for the
reader to verify the following predictions,
(i) $a_1 \neq a_2$ implies that the system has two first-order infinite zeros of
the asymptotic form

$$s(p) \simeq -a_j^{-1} p - \frac{\beta}{a_j}, \quad j = 1,2 \quad (6.3.24)$$

(ii) $a_1 = a_2$ implies that the system has two first-order infinite zeros of
the asymptotic form

$$s(p) \simeq -a_1^{-1} p - \frac{2\beta}{a_1}, \quad s(p) \simeq -a_1^{-1} p \quad (6.3.25)$$

In both cases the closed-loop system is stable for all high-enough gains
$p > 0$.

Exercise 6.3.4
Check eqn. 6.1.13 for all the above examples.

Knowledge of the asymptotic directions and pivots of the root-locus plot provides useful information concerning the behaviour of the closed-loop poles. In particular, it can indicate any incompatibility between the need to use high gains (to reduce steady-state error and low-frequency interaction and to increase response speeds) and the requirement of closed-loop stability. This can be expressed in the form of the following theorem:

Theorem 6.3.1: Suppose that the $m \times m$ strictly proper system $Q_0(s)$ has uniform rank $k \geqslant 1$. Then conditions for the closed-loop system to be stable at high gains are that
(*a*) $Q_0(s)$ is minimum-phase and $k \leqslant 2$
(*b*) If $k = 1$, then Q_1 has only eigenvalues with strictly positive real parts
(*c*) If $k = 2$, then Q_2 has only real, strictly positive eigenvalues and all pivots have strictly negative real parts.

Exercise 6.3.5
Prove Theorem 6.3.1 (Hint: consider the behaviour of expr. 6.3.16 as $p \to +\infty$ and, in particular, the cases when the eigenvalues of Q_k are real-positive, real-negative, complex and with positive or negative real parts).

Exercise 6.3.6
If $Q_0(s)$ has uniform rank $k = 1$ and Q_1 has eigenvalues with strictly positive real parts, show that the closed-loop system is asymptotically stable for all high enough gains p.

In all cases the numerical values of the asymptotic directions can be manipulated by choice of $K_1(s)$. In the cases of $k \geqslant 2$, the numerical magnitude of the pivots can be interpreted in terms of gain and phase margins. It is to be anticipated that an improvement can be obtained by the use of phase-compensation networks to shift the pivots further into the left-half complex plane. This is easily achieved by replacing $K_1(s)$ by $K_1(s)K_2(s)$ where $K_2(s)$ is the dyadic transfer-function matrix

$$K_2(s) = T_0 \text{ block diag } \{K_2^{(j)}(s)\}_{1 \leqslant j \leqslant l} T_0^{-1}$$

$$K_2^{(j)}(s) = \text{diag} \left\{ \frac{s + a_{jr}}{s + b_{jr}} \right\}_{1 \leqslant r \leqslant d_j}, \qquad 1 \leqslant j \leqslant l \quad (6.3.26)$$

and choosing T_0 to ensure that $N_{jj} = \text{diag}\{\alpha_{jr}\}_{1 \leqslant r \leqslant d_j}$, $1 \leqslant j \leqslant l$. The reader should verify that the composite system has uniform rank k, that

$$Q_0(s)K_2(s) = s^{-k}Q_k + s^{-(k+1)}\{Q_{k+1} + Q_kR\} + \ldots \quad (6.3.27)$$

where

$$R = T_0 \text{ block diag } \{R_j\}_{1 \leqslant j \leqslant l} T_0^{-1}$$

$$R_j = \text{diag}\{a_{jr} - b_{jr}\}_{1 \leqslant r \leqslant d_j}, \qquad 1 \leqslant j \leqslant l \quad (6.3.28)$$

and hence that the system has mk kth-order infinite zeros of the form

$$s = p^{1/k}\eta_{ij} + k^{-1}\left\{\frac{\alpha_{jr}}{\eta_j} + a_{jr} - b_{jr}\right\} + \epsilon_{ijr}(p)$$

$$\lim_{p \to \infty} \epsilon_{ijr}(p) = 0, \quad 1 \leqslant i \leqslant k, \quad 1 \leqslant r \leqslant d_j, \quad 1 \leqslant j \leqslant l$$

$$(6.3.29)$$

A comparison of exprs. 6.3.29 and 6.3.16 indicates that the inclusion of $K_2(s)$ enables the systematic and independent shifting of the pivots of the root-locus plot to be achieved by the use of suitable phase-compensation networks in eqn. 6.3.26.

Exercise 6.3.7
If $Q_0(s)$ has uniform rank k and $K_2(s) = \frac{(s + a)}{(s + b)} I_m$, show that K_2 has the effect of moving all pivots of the root-locus by the amount $k^{-1}(a - b)$.

Exercise 6.3.8
By suitable choice of $K_1(s)$ suppose that $Q_k = \text{diag}\{\lambda_j\}_{1 \leqslant j \leqslant m}$ where $\lambda_1, \ldots, \lambda_m$ are distinct nonzero real numbers. Show that the closed-loop system possesses small interaction and alignment of the characteristic directions with the natural basis at high frequencies. Consider the effect of the inclusion of the control factor

$$K_2(s) = \text{diag}\left\{\frac{(s + a_j)}{(s + b_j)}\right\}_{1 \leqslant j \leqslant m}$$

on the structure of the root-locus at high gains, and relate to the discussion of alignment in Chapter 4.

6.4 Computation of the asymptotes

In more general cases when the condition represented by eqn. 6.3.3 is violated the series eqn. 6.3.1 can still be used to compute the asymptotic directions and pivots of the root-locus.[49] The theoretical background is relatively complex although, as will be seen below, the computational procedure reduces to sequential application of the techniques of the previous section.

6.4.1 Decomposition of $Q_0(s)$

Suppose that $Q_0(s)$ is $m \times m$, strictly proper and invertible and define the unique integer $k_1 \geqslant 1$ such that $\lim_{s \to \infty} s^{k_1} Q_0(s)$ is finite and nonzero.

Equivalently (c.f. eqn. 6.3.3)

$$Q_j = 0, \quad 1 \leqslant j < k_1, \quad Q_{k_1} \neq 0 \tag{6.4.1}$$

$$Q_0(s) = s^{-k_1} Q_{k_1} + s^{-(k_1+1)} Q_{k_1+1} + O(s^{-(k_1+2)}) \tag{6.4.2}$$

Exercise 6.4.1
Use the Cayley-Hamilton theorem to show that $1 \leqslant k_1 \leqslant n$.

Let $d_1 = \operatorname{rank} Q_{k_1}$ and suppose that there exists a constant $m \times m$ transformation T_1 such that

$$T_1^{-1} Q_{k_1} T_1 = \begin{pmatrix} \Lambda_1 & 0 \\ 0 & 0 \end{pmatrix} \tag{6.4.3}$$

where the $d_1 \times d_1$ matrix Λ_1 is nonsingular. In effect, it is assumed that the zero eigenvalues have simple structure ie they contribute only diagonal blocks to the Jordan form of Q_{k_1}. Applying T_1 to eqn. 6.4.2

$$T_1^{-1} Q_0(s) T_1 = \begin{pmatrix} G_1(s) & O(s^{-(k_1+1)}) \\ O(s^{-(k_1+1)}) & O(s^{-(k_1+1)}) \end{pmatrix} \tag{6.4.4}$$

where the $d_1 \times d_1$ transfer-function matrix $G_1(s)$ has uniform rank k_1. Suppose that $d_1 < m$ and that the (2,1) block of eqn. 6.4.4 takes the form $s^{-(k_1+1)} \tilde{R}_1 + O(s^{-(k_1+2)})$ and define

$$L_1^{(1)}(s) = \begin{pmatrix} I_{d_1} & 0 \\ -s^{-1} \tilde{R}_1 \Lambda_1^{-1} & I_{m-d_1} \end{pmatrix}, \quad |L_1^{(1)}(s)| \equiv 1 \tag{6.4.5}$$

giving

$$L_1^{(1)}(s)T_1^{-1}Q_0(s)T_1 = \begin{pmatrix} G_1(s) & O(s^{-(k_1+1)}) \\ O(s^{-(k_1+2)}) & O(s^{-(k_1+1)}) \end{pmatrix} \quad (6.4.6)$$

where the order of the (2,1) element has been reduced by unity. Repeated application of the procedure with

$$L_1^{(j)}(s) = \begin{pmatrix} I_{d_1} & 0 \\ -s^{-j}\tilde{R}_j\Lambda_1^{-1} & I_{m-d_1} \end{pmatrix} \quad (6.4.7)$$

and defining

$$L_1(s) = L_1^{(n+1-k_1)}(s)\ldots L_1^{(2)}(s)L_1^{(1)}(s)$$

$$= \begin{pmatrix} I_{d_1} & 0 \\ O(s^{-1}) & I_{m-d_1} \end{pmatrix}, \quad |L_1(s)| \equiv 1 \quad (6.4.8)$$

gives

$$L_1(s)T_1^{-1}Q_0(s)T_1 = \begin{pmatrix} G_1(s) & O(s^{-(k_1+1)}) \\ O(s^{-(n+2)}) & O(s^{-(k_1+1)}) \end{pmatrix} \quad (6.4.9)$$

In a similar manner, it is possible to construct a transformation of the form

$$M_1(s) = \begin{pmatrix} I_{d_1} & O(s^{-1}) \\ 0 & I_{m-d_1} \end{pmatrix}, \quad |M_1(s)| \equiv 1 \quad (6.4.10)$$

to continue the reduction,

$$L_1(s)T_1^{-1}Q_0(s)T_1M_1(s) = \begin{pmatrix} G_1(s) & O(s^{-(n+2)}) \\ O(s^{-(n+2)}) & H_2(s) \end{pmatrix} \quad (6.4.11)$$

Exercise 6.4.2

Prove that $|Q_0(s)| \not\equiv 0$ implies that $|H_2(s)| \not\equiv 0$ (Hint: note that $|Q(s)| = O(s^{-(n-n_z)})$) and hence that

$$k_1 d_1 + r_2 = n - n_z$$

where $|H_2(s)| = O(s^{-r_2})$.

Let $k_2 > k_1$ be the unique integer such that $\lim_{s \to \infty} s^{k_2}H_2(s)$ is finite and nonzero. Application of the above procedure to $H_2(s)$ with the simple structure assumption guarantees the existence of

$$T_2 = \begin{pmatrix} I_{d_1} & 0 \\ 0 & \tilde{T}_2 \end{pmatrix}, \quad |T_2| \neq 0$$

$$L_2(s) = \begin{pmatrix} I_{d_1} & 0 & 0 \\ 0 & I_{d_2} & 0 \\ 0 & O(s^{-1}) & I_{m-d_1-d_2} \end{pmatrix}, \quad |L_2(s)| \equiv 1$$

$$M_2(s) = \begin{pmatrix} I_{d_1} & 0 & 0 \\ 0 & I_{d_2} & O(s^{-1}) \\ 0 & 0 & I_{m-d_1-d_2} \end{pmatrix}, \quad |M_2(s)| \equiv 1 \tag{6.4.12}$$

such that

$$L_2(s)T_2^{-1}L_1(s)T_1^{-1}Q_0(s)T_1 M_1(s)T_2 M_2(s)$$

$$= \begin{pmatrix} G_1(s) & 0 & 0 \\ 0 & G_2(s) & 0 \\ 0 & 0 & H_3(s) \end{pmatrix} + O(s^{-(n+2)}) \tag{6.4.13}$$

where the $d_2 \times d_2$ transfer-function matrix $G_2(s)$ has uniform rank $k_2 > k_1$, $H_3(s)$ is strictly proper and $|H_3(s)| \not\equiv 0$. Continuing by induction, using the simple structure assumption at each stage, it can be verified that there exists an integer q and integers d_j, $1 \leq j \leq q$, and k_j, $1 \leq j \leq q$, such that $k_1 < k_2 < \ldots < k_q$,

$$\sum_{j=1}^{q} d_j = m$$

$$\sum_{j=1}^{q} d_j k_j = n - n_z \tag{6.4.14}$$

and transformations T_j, $1 \leq j \leq q$,

$$T_j = \begin{pmatrix} I_{d_1} & \cdots & \cdots & 0 \\ \vdots & I_{d_{j-1}} & 0 & \vdots \\ 0 & \cdots & 0 & \tilde{T}_j \end{pmatrix}, \quad |T_j| \neq 0 \tag{6.4.15}$$

together with dynamic transformations $L_j(s)$, $M_j(s)$, $1 \leqslant j \leqslant q$, of the form,

$$L_j(s) = \begin{pmatrix} I_{d_1} & \cdots & \cdots & \cdots & 0 \\ \vdots & I_{d_j} & & \dot{0} \\ 0 & \cdots & O(s^{-1}) & I_{m-d_1-\ldots-d_j} \end{pmatrix}, \quad |L_j(s)| \equiv 1$$

$$M_j(s) = \begin{pmatrix} I_{d_1} & \cdots & \cdots & 0 \\ \vdots & I_{d_j} & O(\dot{s}^{-1}) \\ 0 & \cdots & 0 & I_{m-d_1-\ldots-d_j} \end{pmatrix}, \quad |M_j(s)| \equiv 1 \tag{6.4.16}$$

such that

$$L_q(s)T_q^{-1}L_{q-1}(s)T_{q-1}^{-1}\ldots L_1(s)T_1^{-1}Q_0(s)T_1M_1(s)\ldots T_qM_q(s)$$
$$= \text{block diag } \{G_j(s)\}_{1 \leqslant j \leqslant q} + O(s^{-(n+2)}) \tag{6.4.17}$$

where $G_j(s)$ are $d_j \times d_j$ and of uniform rank k_j, $1 \leqslant j \leqslant q$.

An important simplification is obtained by noting that, by replacing T_1 by $T_1T_2T_3\ldots T_q$, it is possible to assume that $T_j = I_m$, $2 \leqslant j \leqslant q$, without changing the structure of $M_j(s)$, $L_j(s)$, $1 \leqslant j \leqslant q$, and hence that

$$L(s) = L_q(s)L_{q-1}(s)\ldots L_1(s)$$

$$= \begin{pmatrix} I_{d_1} & 0 & \cdots & \cdots & 0 \\ O(s^{-1}) & I_{d_2} & & \dot{0} \\ O(s^{-1}) & \cdots & O(s^{-1}) & I_{d_q} \end{pmatrix}, \quad |L(s)| \equiv 1$$

$$M(s) = M_1(s)M_2(s)\ldots M_q(s)$$

$$= \begin{pmatrix} I_{d_1} & O(s^{-1}) & \cdots & O(s^{-1}) \\ 0 & I_{d_2} & & \vdots \\ \vdots & & \ddots & O(s^{-1}) \\ 0 & \cdots & 0 & I_{d_q} \end{pmatrix}, \quad |M(s)| \equiv 1 \tag{6.4.18}$$

giving

$$L(s)T_1^{-1}Q_0(s)T_1M(s) = \text{block diag } \{G_j(s)\}_{1 \leqslant j \leqslant q} + O(s^{-(n+2)}) \tag{6.4.19}$$

This is the decomposition of $Q_0(s)$ used in the following characterisation of the root-locus.

Exercise 6.4.2
Prove the existence of a nonsingular $m \times m$ constant controller K_2 such that $Q_0(s)K_2$ satisfies the simple structure assumptions in the above decomposition, by writing

$$K_2 = K_2^{(1)} T_1 K_2^{(2)} T_2 K_2^{(3)} T_3 \ldots T_{q-1} K_2^{(q)} T_{q-1}^{-1} T_{q-2}^{-1} \ldots T_1^{-1}$$

$$K_2^{(j)} = \begin{pmatrix} I_{d_1} & \cdots & \cdots & 0 \\ \vdots & I_{d_{j-1}} & & \vdots \\ \vdots & & & 0 \\ 0 & \cdots & 0 & \tilde{K}_j^{(2)} \end{pmatrix}, \qquad 1 \leqslant j \leqslant q$$

and choosing $\tilde{K}_j^{(2)}$ such that the simple structure assumption is satisfied at each stage.

6.4.2 Asymptotic behaviour of the root-locus
The asymptotic behaviour of the unbounded closed-loop poles can be investigated by the use of eqn. 6.4.19 and the analysis of the unbounded solutions of[49]

$$0 = |T(s)| = |I_m + pQ_0(s)|$$

$$= |L(s)T_1^{-1}\{I_m + pQ_0(s)\}T_1 M(s)|$$

$$= |L(s)M(s) + p \text{ block diag } \{G_j(s)\}_{1 \leqslant j \leqslant q} + pO(s^{-(n+2)})|$$

$$= |I_m + \{L(s)M(s)\}^{-1} p \text{ block diag } \{G_j(s)\}_{1 \leqslant j \leqslant q} + pO(s^{-(n+2)})|$$

$$(6.4.20)$$

and noting that both $L(s)M(s)$ and $\{L(s)M(s)\}^{-1}$ take the form,

$$\begin{pmatrix} I_{d_1} + O(s^{-2}) & O(s^{-1}) & \cdots & O(s^{-1}) \\ \vdots & & & O(s^{-1}) \\ & & & \vdots \\ O(s^{-1}) & O(s^{-1}) & & I_{d_q} + O(s^{-2}) \end{pmatrix} \qquad (6.4.21)$$

In particular eqn. 6.4.20 takes the form

$$\begin{vmatrix} I_{d_1} + pG_1(s) + O(ps^{-(k_1+2)}) & O(ps^{-(k_2+1)}) \ldots \ldots \\ \quad O(ps^{-(k_1+1)}) & \\ \quad \vdots & \\ \quad O(ps^{-(k_1+1)}) & O(ps^{-(k_2+1)}) \ldots \ldots \ldots \\ & & O(ps^{-(k_q+1)}) \\ & & O(ps^{-(k_q+1)}) \\ & & I_{d_q} + pG_q(s) + O(ps^{-(k_q+2)}) \end{vmatrix}$$

$$= 0 \qquad (6.4.22)$$

Noting that ps^{-k_j}, $1 \leqslant j \leqslant q$, cannot all tend to zero as $p \to \infty$, suppose that $ps^{-k_j} \to 0$, $2 \leqslant j \leqslant q$, when application of Schur's formula yields

$$|I_{d_1} + pG_1(s) + O(ps^{-(k_1+2)}) + O(p^2 s^{-(k_1+k_2+2)})| = 0 \quad (6.4.23)$$

indicating that the system has $k_1 d_1$ k_1th-order infinite zeros governed by the behaviour of $G_1(s)$. In particular the terms $O(ps^{-(k_1+2)}) + O(p^2 s^{-(k_1+k_2+2)}) = O(ps^{-(k_1+2)})$ have no effect on both the asymptotic directions and pivots of these branches of the root-locus (which depend only on terms of the form $pO(s^{-k_1})$ and $pO(s^{-(k_1+1)})$, respectively) suggesting that it is only necessary to use the approximation

$$|I_{d_1} + pG_1(s)| = 0 \qquad (6.4.24)$$

in the calculation of these important feedback quantities.

Assume now that ps^{-k_1} is unbounded as $p \to \infty$. Application of Schur's formula to eqn. 6.4.22 gives

$$\begin{vmatrix} I_{d_2} + pG_2(s) + O(ps^{-(k_2+2)}) & O(ps^{-(k_3+1)}) \ldots \ldots O(ps^{-(k_q+1)}) \\ \quad O(ps^{-(k_2+1)}) & \vdots \\ \quad \vdots & \vdots \\ \quad O(ps^{-(k_2+1)}) \ldots \ldots \ldots \ldots I_{d_q} + pG_q(s) + O(ps^{-(k_q+2)}) \end{vmatrix}$$

$$= 0 \qquad (6.4.25)$$

which has a similar structure to eqn. 6.4.22. It is now possible to apply induction using similar reasoning to the above to prove that the system has $k_j d_j$ k_jth-order infinite zeros, $1 \leqslant j \leqslant q$, with asymptotic directions and pivots obtained directly from the uniform rank problems

$$|I_{d_j} + pG_j(s)| = 0, \qquad 1 \leqslant j \leqslant q \qquad (6.4.26)$$

by application of the methods of Section 6.3.

6.4.3 Computational algorithm

The calculation of the asymptotic directions and pivots of $Q_0(s)$ can now be regarded as the calculation of the dominant pairs of Markov parameters of the uniform rank systems $G_j(s)$, $1 \leqslant j \leqslant q$. In particular it is only necessary to consider the first k_{q+1} Markov parameters of $Q_0(s)$ as the term $O(s^{-(n+2)})$ can be replaced in eqn. 6.4.19 by $O(s^{-(k_q+2)})$ without changing the results of Section 6.4.2 and the problem reduces to the reduction of the truncated series

$$Q_T(s) = s^{-1}Q_1 + s^{-2}Q_2 + \ldots + s^{-(k_q+1)}Q_{k_q+1} \qquad (6.4.27)$$

to block diagonal form with uniform rank blocks using transformations of the form discussed in Section 6.4.1 and neglecting terms of the form $O(s^{-(k_q+2)})$. These operations can be regarded as algebraic operations on the matrix

$$M_l = [Q_1, Q_2, \ldots, Q_{l-1}, Q_l] \qquad (6.4.28)$$

for some $l \geqslant k_q + 1$. In general, k_q is unknown initially and hence must be estimated from physical information or, to be sure, it may be convenient to take $l = n + 1$.

The operations considered take the form of

(*a*) similarity transformations $Q_T(s) \to V^{-1}Q_T(s)V$ equivalent to the operation

$$M_l \to [V^{-1}Q_1 V, V^{-1}Q_2 V, \ldots, V^{-1}Q_l V]$$

(*b*) elementary row operations of the form

$$Q_T(s) \to \left\{ I_m + \frac{\beta_{ij}}{s^k} e_i e_j^T \right\} Q_T(s), \qquad k \geqslant 1$$

equivalent to the addition of β_{ij} times the jth row of Q_r to the ith row of Q_{r+k}, $1 \leqslant r \leqslant l - k$. Note that $L(s)$ can always be represented as a product of such transformations

(*c*) elementary column operations of the form

$$Q_T(s) \to Q_T(s) \left\{ I_m + \frac{\beta_{ij}}{s^k} e_i e_j^T \right\}, \qquad k \geqslant 1$$

equivalent to the addition of β_{ij} times the ith column of Q_r to the jth column of Q_{r+k}, $1 \leqslant r \leqslant l - k$.

The computational algorithm can now be stated in the form

(i) Set $j = 1$ and construct $M_l^{(j)} = [Q_1, Q_2, \dots, Q_l]$ for some $l > 1$.

(ii) Evaluate k_j as the index of the first nonzero block in $M_l^{(j)}$. If $l < k_j + 1$, return to (i) with l increased.

(iii) Use a transformation V_j of type (a) to reduce Q_{k_j} to the form

$$Q_{k_j} = \begin{pmatrix} G_j^{(k_j)} & 0 \\ 0 & 0 \end{pmatrix}$$

where $d_j = \text{rank } Q_{k_j}$ and $G_j^{(k_j)}$ is $d_j \times d_j$. If this is not possible the algorithm terminates as the simple structure assumption is violated (Note from Exercise 6.4.2, however, that suitable modifications to the control system will remove this difficulty).

(iv) Use operations of type (b) and (c) to reduce $M_l^{(j)}$ to the form

$$M_l^{(j)} = \left(0, 0, \dots, 0, \begin{pmatrix} G_j^{(k_j)} & 0 \\ 0 & H_j^{(k_j)} \end{pmatrix}, \dots, \begin{pmatrix} G_j^{(l)} & 0 \\ 0 & H_j^{(l)} \end{pmatrix} \right)$$

ensuring that the (1,1) blocks of each block entry remain invariant.

(v) Read off

$$G_j(s) = s^{-k_j} G_j^{(k_j)} + s^{-(k_j+1)} G_j^{(k_j+1)} + O(s^{-(k_j+2)})$$

and compute the $k_j d_j$ k_jth-order infinite zeros using the techniques of Section 6.3.

(vi) If $d_1 + d_2 + \dots + d_j = m$, stop.

(vii) Set $Q_i = 0$, $1 \leqslant i \leqslant k_j - 1$, $Q_i = H_j^{(i)}$, $k_j \leqslant i \leqslant l$ (Note the reduction in dimension) and set $M_l^{(j+1)} = [Q_1, Q_2, \dots, Q_l]$.

(viii) Replace $j + 1$ by j and go to (ii)

To illustrate the application of the technique, consider the liquid-level system of Section 3.14 with state-vector model (eqn. 3.14.3), $\beta = 2$ and $K_1(s) = I_2$. Taking $l = 3$, the relevant Markov parameter matrices are

$$Q_1 = CB = \begin{pmatrix} 1 & 0 \\ 0 & 0 \end{pmatrix}, \quad Q_2 = CAB = \begin{pmatrix} -2 & 1 \\ 1 & 2 \end{pmatrix},$$

$$Q_3 = CA^2 B = \begin{pmatrix} 6 & -3 \\ -3 & -11 \end{pmatrix}$$

so that

$$M_1^{(3)} = \left\{ \begin{pmatrix} 1 & 0 \\ 0 & 0 \end{pmatrix}, \begin{pmatrix} -2 & 1 \\ 1 & 2 \end{pmatrix}, \begin{pmatrix} 6 & -3 \\ -3 & -11 \end{pmatrix} \right\}$$

and $d_1 = k_1 = 1$. The matrix Q_1 is in the desired form so, continuing to the row operations to eliminate the (2,1) entry of the second block gives

$$M_1^{(3)} \to \left\{ \begin{pmatrix} 1 & 0 \\ 0 & 0 \end{pmatrix}, \begin{pmatrix} -2 & 1 \\ 0 & 2 \end{pmatrix}, \begin{pmatrix} 6 & -3 \\ -1 & -12 \end{pmatrix} \right\}$$

Elimination of the (2,1) entry of the third block yields

$$M_1^{(3)} \to \left\{ \begin{pmatrix} 1 & 0 \\ 0 & 0 \end{pmatrix}, \begin{pmatrix} -2 & 1 \\ 0 & 2 \end{pmatrix}, \begin{pmatrix} 6 & -3 \\ 0 & -12 \end{pmatrix} \right\}$$

which, after suitable column operations, becomes

$$M_1^{(3)} \to \left\{ \begin{pmatrix} 1 & 0 \\ 0 & 0 \end{pmatrix}, \begin{pmatrix} -2 & 0 \\ 0 & 2 \end{pmatrix}, \begin{pmatrix} 6 & 0 \\ 0 & -12 \end{pmatrix} \right\}$$

giving

$$G_1(s) = s^{-1} - 2s^{-2} + O(s^{-3})$$
$$M_2^{(3)} = \{0, \quad 2, \quad -12\}$$

so that $d_2 = 1, k_2 = 2$ and

$$G_2(s) = 2s^{-2} - 12s^{-3} + O(s^{-4})$$

The system hence has one first-order infinite zero of the asymptotic form $-p-2$ and two second-order infinite zeros of the asymptotic form $\pm i\sqrt{2}p^{1/2} - 3$. This is verified by the exact root-locus shown in Fig. 6.4.1 and is consistent with the mixed first-, and second-order type classification discussed in Section 3.13.

Exercise 6.4.3
Show that T_1 in (6.4.19) can be set equal to

$$T_1 = V_1 \begin{pmatrix} I_{d_1} & 0 \\ 0 & V_2 \end{pmatrix} \dots \begin{pmatrix} I_{d_1+\dots+d_{q-1}} & 0 \\ 0 & V_q \end{pmatrix}$$

6.4.4 Compensation

Suppose that $Q_0(s) = G(s)K_1(s)$ has a decomposition of the form of eqn. 6.4.19 and consider the inclusion of a second controller factor $K_2(s)$ of the form,

$$K_2(s) = T_1 \text{ block diag } \{K_2^{(j)}(s)\}_{1 \leqslant j \leqslant q} T_1^{-1} \qquad (6.4.29)$$

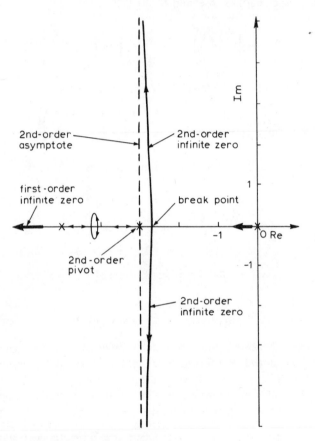

Fig. 6.4.1 Root-locus for liquid level system
 x = open-loop pole

where the $d_j \times d_j$ transfer-function matrices $K_2^{(j)}(s)$ are proper, minimum phase and $\lim_{s \to \infty} K_2^{(j)}(s)$ is nonsingular, $1 \leqslant j \leqslant q$. Then

$$L(s)T_1^{-1}\{Q_0(s)K_2(s)\}T_1\tilde{M}(s)$$

$$= L(s)T_1^{-1}Q_0(s)T_1 \text{ block diag } \{K_2^{(j)}(s)\}_{1 \leqslant j \leqslant q}\tilde{M}(s)$$

$$= L(s)T_1^{-1}Q_0(s)T_1M(s) \text{ block diag } \{K_2^{(j)}(s)\}_{1 \leqslant j \leqslant q}$$

$$= \text{block diag } \{G_j(s)K_2^{(j)}(s)\}_{1 \leqslant j \leqslant q} + O(s^{-(n+2)}) \qquad (6.4.30)$$

where $\tilde{M}(s)$, defined by

$$\text{block diag } \{K_2^{(j)}(s)\}_{1 \leqslant j \leqslant q}\tilde{M}(s)$$
$$= M(s) \text{ block diag } \{K_2^{(j)}(s)\}_{1 \leqslant j \leqslant q}, \qquad (6.4.31)$$

has the same structure as $M(s)$. It follows directly that the composite system has $k_j d_j$ k_jth-order infinite zeros, $1 \leqslant j \leqslant q$, with asymptotic directions and pivots obtained from the *uniform rank* problems

$$|I_{d_j} + p\,G_j(s)K_2^{(j)}(s)| = 0, \qquad 1 \leqslant j \leqslant q \qquad (6.4.32)$$

i.e. the compensation of $Q_0(s)$ can be regarded as the compensation of the uniform rank subproblems followed by the construction of $K_2(s)$ as in eqn. 6.4.29.

Exercise 6.4.4
In the example of Section 6.4.3 show that $T_1 = I_2$. Hence, consider the effect on the root-locus of the inclusion of the controller factor,

$$K_2(s) = \begin{pmatrix} k_1 & 0 \\ 0 & k_2 \dfrac{(s+a)}{(s+b)} \end{pmatrix}, \quad k_1 > 0, \quad k_2 > 0$$

6.5 Sensitivity and the approach to the asymptotes

Attention is restricted in this Section to uniform-rank systems but note that the results of Section 6.4 indicate that the discussion also applies to nonuniform rank systems. A glance at the examples of Section 6.3 indicates that the asymptotic directions of $Q_0(s)$ are continuous functions of the parameters in $Q_0(s)$ but that pivots can be discontinuous functions of plant parameters. For example, consider $Q_0(s)$ defined by

$$A = \begin{pmatrix} -2 & 1 \\ 1 & -2 \end{pmatrix}, \quad B = \begin{pmatrix} 1+\epsilon & 0 \\ 0 & 1 \end{pmatrix}, \quad C = \begin{pmatrix} 1 & 0 \\ 0 & 1 \end{pmatrix}$$

$$(6.5.1)$$

where $k = 1$, and

$$Q_0(s) = s^{-1} \begin{pmatrix} 1 + \epsilon & 0 \\ 0 & 1 \end{pmatrix} + s^{-2} \begin{pmatrix} -2(1 + \epsilon) & 1 \\ (1 + \epsilon) & -2 \end{pmatrix} + O(s^{-3}) \quad (6.5.2)$$

If $\epsilon \neq 0$, the system has two first-order infinite zeros of the asymptotic forms,

$$s(p) \simeq -(1 + \epsilon)p - 2, \quad s(p) \simeq -p - 2 \quad (6.5.3)$$

If $\epsilon = 0$, the system has two first-order infinite zeros of the asymptotic forms,

$$s(p) \simeq -p - 1, \quad s(p) \simeq -p - 3 \quad (6.5.4)$$

Note the discontinuous behaviour of the pivots at $\epsilon = 0$ when Q_k has multiple eigenvalues. This can be verified by direct evaluation of the roots of the closed-loop polynomial $\rho_c(s) = |sI_2 - A + pBC|$. In practical terms, if ϵ is small but nonzero, the root locus will behave over the practical range of gains as if the asymptotes are expr. 6.5.4, the approach to the real asymptotes (expr. 6.5.3) being slow. In effect, the erroneous asymptotes (expr. 6.5.4) are better estimates of the behaviour of closed-loop poles at finite gains than the (real) asymptotes (expr. 6.5.3). This anomaly is of particular significance if $k \geqslant 2$ when the pivots have particular relevance to high gain stability.

Exercise 6.5.1

Consider the asymptotic directions and pivots of the system

$$Q_0(s) = s^{-2} \begin{pmatrix} 1 + \epsilon & 0 \\ 0 & 1 \end{pmatrix} + s^{-3} \begin{pmatrix} -2(1 + \epsilon), & 10 \\ 10(1 + \epsilon), & -2 \end{pmatrix} + O(s^{-3})$$

for $\epsilon > 0$, and $\epsilon = 0$. Show that the closed-loop system is stable for all high-enough gains $p > 0$, if, and only if, $\epsilon \neq 0$. Interpret this result in terms of the approach to the asymptote if ϵ is small and nonzero.

The above analysis is of significance in applications if it is remembered that the design condition of low-high-frequency interaction can be interpreted as requiring that Q_k is approximately diagonal i.e. $Q_k \simeq$ diag $\{\mu_1, \mu_2, \ldots, \mu_m\}$. If similar rise times are required in each loop, then $\mu_j \simeq \mu_l$ $1 \leqslant j \leqslant l \leqslant m$, which is precisely the situation of maximum sensitivity of the pivots. In such situations, a better estimate of closed-loop poles at finite gains may be obtained by setting $\mu_j = \mu_l$, $1 \leqslant j \leqslant l \leqslant m$.

6.6 Root-loci and the inverse system

A single-input/single-output system of order n with transfer function $g(s)$ and n_z zeros has an inverse system of the form

$$g^{-1}(s) = a_0 s^k + a_1 s^{k-1} + \ldots + a_k + h(s), \qquad k \geq 1 \qquad (6.6.1)$$

where $a_0 \neq 0$, $h(s)$ is strictly proper and the system has only kth-order infinite zeros with intercept (or pivot) $-a_1/ka_0$ and asymptotic directions described by a_0. In effect the asymptotic behaviour of the unbounded branches of the root-locus can be described by the higher order terms in the polynomial part of the inverse system. It can be proved[52] that similar results hold in the multivariable case by the argument developed in the following sections. The results provide a natural simplification of the root-locus analysis and could, in principle, be used in conjunction with any of the previously described design techniques based on the inverse system.

Effect of minor loop feedback: Consider the $m \times m$ invertible, strictly proper system $G(s)$ subjected to unity-negative feedback with forward-path controller of the form (compare with eqn. 6.1.2)

$$K(s) = pK_1(s)K_2(s) \qquad (6.6.1)$$

where the factors $K_1(s)$ and $K_2(s)$ are proper, $m \times m$ and invertible and p is a scalar gain. Consider now the inclusion of the minor-loop feedback element $H(s)$ as indicated in Fig. 6.6.1.

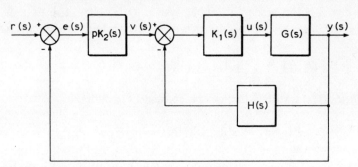

Fig. 6.6.1 Feedback system with minor-loop feedback

Theorem 6.6.1: The orders, asymptotic directions and pivots of the infinite zeros of the system depicted in Fig. 6.6.1 are independent of the minor-loop feedback if

$$\lim_{s \to \infty} sG(s)K_1(s)H(s) = 0 \qquad (6.6.2)$$

(Note: we use the notation $O(s^{-l})$ to indicate that $\lim_{s \to \infty} s^l O(s^{-l})$ is finite when expr. 6.6.2 becomes $G(s)K_1(s)H(s) = O(s^{-2})$).

Proof: The closed-loop poles are described by the relation

$$0 = |I_m + (I_m + G(s)K_1(s)H(s))^{-1}G(s)K(s)|$$

$$= \frac{|I_m + G(s)K_1(s)H(s) + G(s)K(s)|}{|I_m + G(s)K_1(s)H(s)|} \quad (6.6.3)$$

Considering only unbounded solutions and setting $Q_0(s) = G(s)K_1(s)K_2(s)$, we need only consider the identity,

$$|I_m + G(s)K_1(s)H(s) + pQ_0(s)| = 0 \quad (6.6.4)$$

Using the decomposition eqn. 6.4.19 it can easily be verified that

$$|I_m + (L(s)(I_m + O(s^{-2}))M(s))^{-1}L(s)T_1^{-1}Q_0(s)T_1M(s)| = 0 \quad (6.6.5)$$

or, noting that $L(s)(I_m + O(s^{-2}))M(s)$ takes the same form as $L(s)M(s)$ (eqn. 6.4.21) and using the analysis of Section 6.4.2, the system has k_jd_j infinite zeros of order k_j, $1 \leq j \leq q$, whose asymptotic directions and pivots are described by the uniform rank problems,

$$|I_{d_j} + pG_j(s)| = 0, \quad 1 \leq j \leq q \quad (6.6.6)$$

The result is now proved as the $G_j(s)$, $1 \leq j \leq m$, are dependent only on $Q_0(s)$.

Asymptotic behaviour and the inverse system: Consider now the $m \times m$ strictly proper invertible system $Q_0(s)$ subjected to unity-negative feedback with scalar gain $p \geq 0$ and write $Q_1(s) = G(s)K_1(s)$ with

$$Q_1^{-1}(s) = \sum_{j=0}^{k} s^j A_{k-j} + H_0(s), \quad A_0 \neq 0, \quad k \geq 1 \quad (6.6.7)$$

where $H_0(s)$ is strictly proper. It is convenient to define

$$P_l(s) = \sum_{j=l}^{k} s^j A_{k-j}, \quad H_l(s) = Q_1^{-1}(s) - P_l(s),$$

$$0 \leq l \leq k \quad (6.6.8)$$

when, applying theorem 3.13.1 and Exercise 3.13.1,

Theorem 6.6.2: If $k^* \geq 1$ is the unique integer such that $\lim_{s \to \infty} s^{k^*}Q_1(s)$ exists and is nonzero, then

$$|P_l(s)| \not\equiv 0$$

and

$$\lim_{s \to \infty} s^{k^*} P_l^{-1}(s) = \lim_{s \to \infty} s^{k^*} Q_1(s), \qquad 0 \leqslant l \leqslant k^* \qquad (6.6.9)$$

Proof: Follow directly from theorem 3.13.1 noting that

$$\lim_{s \to \infty} Q_1(s) H_l(s) = 0, \qquad 0 \leqslant l \leqslant k^* \qquad (6.6.10)$$

and using the identity, $0 \leqslant l \leqslant k^*$,

$$Q_1(s) = (P_l(s) + H_l(s))^{-1} = (I_m + P_l^{-1}(s) H_l(s))^{-1} P_l^{-1}(s) \qquad (6.6.11)$$

Of particular interest are the formulas,

$$\lim_{s \to \infty} s P_l^{-1}(s) H_l(s) = 0, \qquad 0 \leqslant l \leqslant k^* - 1 \qquad (6.6.12)$$

which lead to the following main result:

Theorem 6.6.3: The orders, asymptotic directions and pivots of the invertible system $Q_0(s) = G(s) K_1(s) K_2(s)$ subjected to unity-negative feedback with scalar gain $p \geqslant 0$ are identical to those of the invertible systems $P_l^{-1}(s) K_2(s), 0 \leqslant l \leqslant k^* - 1$.

Proof: Eqn. 6.6.11 indicates that $Q_1(s) = G(s) K_1(s)$ can be regarded as a system $P_l^{-1}(s)$ with the dynamic feedback loop $H_l(s)$. The result now follows directly from theorem 6.6.1 using expr. 6.6.12.

In effect, the asymptotic properties of the root-locus can be deduced from the higher-order terms in the polynomial component of $Q_1^{-1}(s)$. To illustrate the approach, consider the important case when $K_2(s) = I_m$ and $Q_0(s)$ has uniform rank k i.e. $K(s) = p K_1(s), Q_1(s) \equiv Q_0(s)$ and

$$|A_0| \neq 0, \qquad k = k^* \qquad (6.6.13)$$

Theorem 6.6.3 states that the orders, asymptotic directions and pivots can be deduced from the uniform-rank system

$$P_{k-1}^{-1}(s) = \frac{1}{s^{k-1}} (s A_0 + A_1)^{-1} \qquad (6.6.14)$$

using the techniques of Section 6.3 and the series expansion

$$P_{k-1}^{-1}(s) = \frac{1}{s^k} A_0^{-1} - \frac{1}{s^{k+1}} A_0^{-1} A_1 A_0^{-1} + O(s^{-(k+2)}) \qquad (6.6.15)$$

or other techniques.[42]

Computation of the asymptotes: Theorem 6.6.3 indicates that we need only consider any one of the systems $P_l^{-1}(s) K_2(s), 0 \leqslant l \leqslant k^* - 1$. If k^* is known then $P_{k^*-1}^{-1}(s) K_2(s)$ is the best bet. If k^* is not known then it is always possible to use $P_0^{-1}(s)K_2(s)$. In either case the techniques of Section 6.4 can be applied to series expansions about the point at infinity. Alternatively, the following analysis could be applied directly to the inverse system.

Suppose that $K_2(s) = I_m$ and, by an obvious parallel to the techniques of Section 6.4, suppose the existence of integers $q \geqslant 1$, $k_1 < k_2 \ldots < k_q$ and d_j, $1 \leqslant j \leqslant q$, and a nonsingular transformation T_1, together with unimodular matrices $L(s), M(s)$ of the form indicated in eqn. 6.4.18 such that

$$L(s)T_1^{-1}Q_0^{-1}(s)T_1 M(s)$$
$$= \text{block diag} \{G_{q+1-j}^{-1}(s)\}_{1 \leqslant j \leqslant q} + O(s^{k_1-2}) \qquad (6.6.16)$$

where the $d_j \times d_j$ transfer-function matrices $G_j(s)$ have uniform rank k_j, $1 \leqslant j \leqslant q$, with inverses of the form

$$G_j^{-1}(s) = s^{k_j}A_0^{(j)} + s^{k_j-1}A_1^{(j)} + O(s^{k_j-2})$$
$$|A_0^{(j)}| \neq 0, \qquad 1 \leqslant j \leqslant q \qquad (6.6.17)$$

The matrices $A_0^{(j)}, A_1^{(j)}$, $1 \leqslant j \leqslant q$, can be obtained by direct application of the algorithm of Section 6.4.3 to the matrix

$$[A_0, A_1, \ldots, A_l] \qquad (6.6.18)$$

for some l in the range $k - k^* + 1 \leqslant l$

Exercise 6.6.1
Show that the integers q, k_j, d_j, $1 \leqslant j \leqslant q$ are identical to those used in Section 6.4.

Writing $|I_m + pQ_0(s)| = p^m |Q_0(s)| |I_m + p^{-1}Q_0^{-1}(s)|$, the infinite zeros are the unbounded solutions of

$$0 = |I_m + p^{-1}Q_0^{-1}(s)| = |L(s)M(s) + p^{-1}L(s)T_1^{-1}Q_0^{-1}(s)T_1 M(s)|$$

$$= \left| \begin{pmatrix} I_{d_q} + O(s^{-2}) + p^{-1}G_q^{-1}(s) & \cdots & O(s^{-1}) \\ O(s^{-1}) & \ddots & \vdots \\ \vdots & \ddots & O(s^{-1}) \\ O(s^{-1}) & \cdots & I_{d_1} + O(s^{-2}) + p^{-1}G_1^{-1}(s) \end{pmatrix} + p^{-1}O(s^{k_1-2}) \right|$$

$$\qquad (6.6.19)$$

where we have used eqns. 6.6.16 and 6.4.21. Note that $p^{-1}s^{k_j}$, $1 \leqslant j \leqslant q$, cannot all tend to zero as $p \to +\infty$ and suppose that $p^{-1}s^{k_q}$

has a finite cluster point. Application of Schur's formula yields the relation

$$|I_{d_q} + p^{-1}G_q^{-1}(s) + O(s^{-2}) + p^{-1}O(s^{k_1-2})| = 0 \qquad (6.6.20)$$

or, after some manipulation,

$$|I_{d_q} + (I_{d_q} + G_q(s)O(s^{k_1-2}))^{-1}pG_q(s)(I_{d_q} + O(s^{-2}))| = 0 \qquad (6.6.21)$$

Noting that $G_q(s)O(s^{k_1-2}) = O(s^{-2})$ we can use theorem 6.6.1 to reduce eqn. 6.6.21 to the form

$$|I_{d_q} + pG_q(s)(I_{d_q} + O(s^{-2}))| = 0 \qquad (6.6.22)$$

if attention is restricted to asymptotic directions and pivots only. However, the results of Section 6.3 state that the asymptotic directions and pivots of a uniform rank system can be deduced from the first two terms in its series expansion about the point at infinity i.e. the system has $d_q k_q$ infinite zeros of order k_q with asymptotic directions and pivots obtained from solution of the uniform rank problem,

$$|I_{d_q} + pG_q(s)| = 0 \qquad (6.6.23)$$

Suppose now that $p^{-1}s^{k_q}$ is unbounded, then, noting that $p^{-1}s^{k_1}$ must be finite (Section 6.4), Schur's formula reduces eqn. 6.6.19 to

$$\left| \begin{pmatrix} I_{d_{q-1}} + p^{-1}G_{q-1}^{-1}(s) + O(s^{-2}) & \cdots & \cdots & O(s^{-1}) \\ O(s^{-1}) & \ddots & & \vdots \\ \vdots & & \ddots & O(s^{-1}) \\ O(s^{-1}) & \cdots & \cdots & I_{d_1} + p^{-1}G_1^{-1}(s) + O(s^{-2}) \end{pmatrix} + p^{-1}O(s^{k_1-2}) \right| = 0 \qquad (6.6.24)$$

which has a similar form. Applying induction it follows that

Theorem 6.6.4: The $m \times m$ invertible, strictly proper system $Q_0(s)$, subjected to unity-negative feedback with scalar gain $p \geqslant 0$ and having a decomposition of the form specified in eqn. 6.6.16, has $k_j d_j$ infinite zeros of order k_j, $1 \leqslant j \leqslant q$, whose asymptotic directions and pivots are defined by the uniform rank problems

$$|I_{d_j} + pG_j(s)| = 0, \qquad 1 \leqslant j \leqslant q \qquad (6.6.25)$$

Writing (eqn. 6.6.17), $1 \leqslant j \leqslant q$,

$$G_j(s) = s^{-k_j}(A_0^{(j)})^{-1} - s^{-(k_j+1)}(A_0^{(j)})^{-1}A_1^{(j)}(A_0^{(j)})^{-1} + O(s^{-(k_j+2)}) \qquad (6.6.26)$$

then the asymptotes can be computed using the methods of Section 6.3.

Finally, the following useful identity follows from eqn. 6.6.16

$$k^* = k_1 < k_2 < \ldots < k_q = k \qquad (6.6.27)$$

and proves the following result.

Theorem 6.6.5: The $m \times m$ strictly proper invertible system $Q_0(s)$, subjected to unity-negative feedback with scalar gain $p \geqslant 0$ can only have infinite zeros of integer order ν in the range

$$k^* \leqslant \nu \leqslant k \qquad (6.6.28)$$

where k^* (resp. k) is the unique integer $\geqslant 1$ such that

$$\lim_{s \to \infty} s^{k^*} Q_0(s) \qquad (\text{resp. } \lim_{s \to \infty} s^{-k} Q_0^{-1}(s))$$

is finite and nonzero.

An approach to compensation: The results of Section 6.4.4 can be generalised to the use of the inverse system. Suppose that $Q_0(s)$ satisfies eqn. 6.6.16 and consider the inclusion of the nonunity controller factor of the form

$$K_2(s) = T_1 \text{ block diag } \{K_2^{(q+1-j)}(s)\}_{1 \leqslant j \leqslant q} T_1^{-1} \qquad (6.6.29)$$

where the $d_j \times d_j$ transfer function matrices $K_2^{(j)}(s)$ are proper, minimum phase and $\lim_{s \to \infty} K_2^{(j)}(s)$ is nonsingular, $1 \leqslant j \leqslant q$. Defining the matrix $\tilde{L}(s)$ by the relation

$$L(s) \text{ block diag } \{K_2^{(q+1-j)}(s)\}_{1 \leqslant j \leqslant q}$$
$$= \text{ block diag } \{K_2^{(q+1-j)}(s)\}_{1 \leqslant j \leqslant q} \tilde{L}(s) \qquad (6.6.30)$$

then $\tilde{L}(s)$ has the same structure as $L(s)$ (see eqn. 6.4.18) and the identity

$$\tilde{L}(s) T_1^{-1} K_2^{-1}(s) Q_0^{-1}(s) T_1 M(s)$$
$$= \text{ block diag } \{(K_2^{(q+1-j)}(s))^{-1} G_{q+1-j}^{-1}(s)\}_{1 \leqslant j \leqslant q} + O(s^{k_1-2}) \qquad (6.6.31)$$

indicates immediately that the closed-loop system has $k_j d_j$ infinite zeros of order k_j, $1 \leqslant j \leqslant q$, with asymptotic directions and pivots that can be computed from the uniform rank problems

$$|I_{d_j} + p G_j(s) K_2^{(j)}(s)| = 0, \qquad 1 \leqslant j \leqslant q \qquad (6.6.32)$$

In particular the asymptotic directions and pivots can be systematically manipulated using, for example, the methods of Section 6.3.

A note on systems with polynomial inverses: The result of theorem 6.6.3 has an interesting interpretation in terms of the techniques discussed in Chapter 3. Let us interpret $K_1(s)$ as a precompensator included to modify the structure of the plant $G(s)$ and interpret $K_2(s)$ as the matrix of dynamic compensation elements to be designed to ensure the desired closed-loop performance. Theorem 6.6.3 can now be interpreted as stating that dynamic compensation of the composite system $G(s)K_1(s)$ (if regarded as manipulation of asymptotic directions and pivots) can be achieved by compensation of any $P_l^{-1}(s)$, $0 \leqslant l \leqslant k^* - 1$. Noting that $P_l^{-1}(s)$ has a polynomial matrix inverse it follows that the study of such systems could have an important impact on design theory (see Sections 3.5, 3.8, 3.9, 3.11–3.13), particularly if minor-loop compensation is to be included.

To illustrate this concept consider the configuration of Fig. 6.6.1 and, for simplicity, denote the inverse of $Q_1(s) = G(s)K_1(s)$ by (see eqn. 6.6.8)

$$Q_1^{-1}(s) = P_0(s) + H_0(s) \tag{6.6.33}$$

and let $Q_2(s)$ denote the transfer-function matrix between $v(s)$ and $y(s)$,

$$Q_2(s) = \{I_m + Q_1(s)H(s)\}^{-1}Q_1(s) \tag{6.6.34}$$

It follows directly that

$$Q_2^{-1}(s) = Q_1^{-1}(s) + H(s) = \{P_0(s) + H(s)\} + H_0(s) \tag{6.6.35}$$

and hence that the minor-loop element could be used to structure the polynomial part of $Q_2^{-1}(s)$ and hence manipulate the pivots of the root-locus of the closed-loop system. More precisely, let $H(s)$ be the polynomial transfer-function matrix regarded as a minor-loop state feedback for the plant $P_0^{-1}(s)$, then $(P_0(s) + H(s))^{-1}$ exists and is strictly proper. In particular, theorem 6.6.3 states that $H_0(s)$ can be neglected if attention is restricted to asymptotic directions and pivots only, and $G(s)$ replaced by $P_0^{-1}(s)$ in Fig. 6.6.1. If $P_0(s)$ is interpreted as the inverse transfer-function matrix of a kth-order lag (Sections 3.5, 3.8, 3.9, 3.12) or a mixed-type system (Section 3.13) then the system design could proceed along the lines suggested in Chapter 3.

Exercise 6.6.2
Show that the above discussion is valid if $P_0^{-1}(s)$ is replaced by $P_l^{-1}(s)$ for any, $0 \leqslant l \leqslant k^* - 1$.

Exercise 6.6.3
Suppose that $G(s)$ has uniform rank $k \geqslant 1$ with inverse system of the form

$$G^{-1}(s) = s^k A_0 + s^{k-1} A_1 + \ldots + A_k + H_0(s)$$

with $|A_0| \neq 0$ and $H_0(s)$ strictly proper. Set $K_1(s) = A_0$ and

$$H(s) = s^{k-1}H_1 + s^{k-2}H_2 + \ldots + H_k$$

Show that the asymptotic directions and pivots of the closed-loop system are identical to those of the unity-negative feedback system with forward-path transfer-function matrix

$$\frac{p}{s^{k-1}} (sI_m + A_0^{-1}A_1 + H_1)^{-1}K_2(s)$$

Hence assess the effect on the root-locus plot of the choice of

$$H_1 = \operatorname{diag}\{h_j\}_{1 \leqslant j \leqslant m} - A_0^{-1}A_1, \quad K_2(s) = \operatorname{diag}\left\{g_j \frac{(s+a_j)}{(s+b_j)}\right\}_{1 \leqslant j \leqslant m}$$

where h_j, g_j, a_j, b_j are real numbers and $g_j \neq 0, 1 \leqslant j \leqslant m$.

Exercise 6.6.4
Consider how the techniques indicated in Exercise 6.6.3 could be used to design rate (resp. constant) minor-loop feedback elements for a uniform rank two (respt. one) plant $G(s)$.

Exercise 6.6.5
Consider the design of $H(s), K_1(s), K_2(s)$ if

$$G^{-1}(s) = s^2 A_0 + sA_1 + A_2 + H_0(s)$$

where $H_0(s)$ is strictly proper, $A_0 \neq 0, |A_0| = 0$ by using the techniques suggested in Section 3.13.

6.7 Summary and conclusions

The material presented in this Chapter represents a fairly complete discussion of the basic concepts of multivariable root-loci, computational techniques for the calculation of the asymptotic directions and pivots of the root-locus in terms of the inverse system or in terms of the state matrices (A, B, C), the existence of suitable compensation elements and the sensitivity problems associated with the pivots. The author regrets the absence of space available for the description of the algebraic methods developed by MacFarlane and Postlethwaite[22] and Postlethwaite.[55] There are many remaining problems, concerning

(a) the unification of root-locus concepts with the techniques of previous chapters,

(b) the physical interpretation of T_1 in (6.5.19) and its use in design,

(c) the relationship of the structure of the root-locus plot to transient performance, and

(d) the derivation of alternative compensation schemes, and, in particular, the investigation of the potential impact of minor-loop feedback elements.

It is not clear, at the present time, if the picture can be clarified. Certainly, the sensitivity problems and associated slow movement to the asymptotes could be regarded as a bad sign if it expected that the theory and application of multivariable root-loci will reach the same degree of sophistication and acceptability as the scalar root-locus. It is feasible, however, that useful insight can be gained by their study. The interested reader is encouraged to have a go!

6.8 Problems and Exercises

1 Show that the system $Q_0(s)$ defined by

$$A = \begin{pmatrix} 0 & 0 & 1 & 0 \\ 0 & 0 & 0 & 1 \\ 1 & 1 & -1 & 3 \\ 0 & 0 & 2 & -1 \end{pmatrix}, \quad B = \begin{pmatrix} 0 & 0 \\ 0 & 0 \\ 2 & 1 \\ 0 & 1 \end{pmatrix}$$

$$C = \begin{pmatrix} 1 & 0 & 0 & 0 \\ 0 & 1 & 0 & 0 \end{pmatrix}$$

has uniform rank $k = 2$. Prove that the system has no zeros and calculate the asymptotic directions and pivots of the root-locus plot. Check your results by substitution into eqn. 6.1.13 and direct evaluation of the root-locus plot.

2 Suppose that $G(s) = \{I_m + G_0(s)H\}^{-1} G_0(s)$ is derived from the $m \times m$ strictly proper invertible plant $G_0(s)$ subject to minor-loop compensation with constant minor-loop element. Defining $K(s) = pK_1(s) - H$, show that the *finite* and *infinite* zeros of the closed-loop system can be derived from the analysis of

$$|T_0(s)| = |I_m + pG_0(s)K_1(s)|$$

Justify the result from physical considerations.

3 Given the system

$$G(s) = s^{-2}\begin{pmatrix} 1 & 0 \\ 0 & 1 \end{pmatrix} + s^{-3}\begin{pmatrix} -2 & 1 \\ 1 & -2 \end{pmatrix} + O(s^{-4})$$

with controller

$$K_1(s) = \begin{pmatrix} 1 & 0 \\ 0 & \dfrac{(s+1)}{(s+1+\beta)} \end{pmatrix}, \qquad \beta > 0$$

By evaluation of the asymptotic directions and pivots of the four second-order infinite zeros of $Q_0(s)$, show that the phase advance introduced into the second control loop is shared between the various branches of the root-locus i.e. it cannot be associated with one particular branch. Repeat the analysis for

$$G(s) = s^{-2}\begin{pmatrix} 1+\epsilon & 0 \\ 0 & 1 \end{pmatrix} + s^{-3}\begin{pmatrix} -2 & 1 \\ 1 & -2 \end{pmatrix} + O(s^{-4}), \qquad \epsilon > 0$$

and comment on your results in terms of sensitivity if ϵ is small.

4 Consider the application of the algorithm of Section 6.4.3 to the system $Q_0(s)$ defined by

$$A = \begin{pmatrix} -1 & 1 & 0 & 0 & 1 \\ 1 & -1 & 1 & 0 & 0 \\ 0 & 1 & 0 & 1 & 0 \\ 0 & 0 & 0 & 0 & 1 \\ 0 & 0 & -1 & -3 & -3 \end{pmatrix}, \quad B = \begin{pmatrix} 1 & 0 & 0 \\ 0 & 1 & 0 \\ 0 & 0 & 0 \\ 0 & 0 & 0 \\ 0 & 0 & 1 \end{pmatrix}$$

$$C = \begin{pmatrix} 1 & 0 & 0 & 0 & 0 \\ 0 & 2 & 0 & 0 & 0 \\ 0 & 0 & 8 & 0 & 0 \end{pmatrix}$$

to give the sequence

$$M_4^{(1)} = \left\{ \begin{pmatrix} 1 & 0 & 0 \\ 0 & 2 & 0 \\ 0 & 0 & 0 \end{pmatrix} \begin{pmatrix} -1 & 1 & 1 \\ 2 & -2 & 0 \\ 0 & 8 & 0 \end{pmatrix} \begin{pmatrix} 2 & -2 & -4 \\ -4 & 6 & 2 \\ 8 & -8 & 8 \end{pmatrix} \begin{pmatrix} -4 & 4 & 11 \\ 10 & -12 & -8 \\ -16 & 24 & -16 \end{pmatrix} \right\}$$

$$\rightarrow \left(\begin{pmatrix} 1 & 0 & 0 \\ 0 & 2 & 0 \\ 0 & 0 & 0 \end{pmatrix} \begin{pmatrix} -1 & 1 & 1 \\ 2 & -2 & 0 \\ 0 & 0 & 0 \end{pmatrix} \begin{pmatrix} 2 & -2 & -4 \\ -4 & 6 & 2 \\ 0 & 0 & 8 \end{pmatrix} \begin{pmatrix} -4 & 4 & 11 \\ 10 & -12 & -8 \\ 0 & 0 & -24 \end{pmatrix} \right)$$

$$\rightarrow \left(\begin{pmatrix} 1 & 0 & 0 \\ 0 & 2 & 0 \\ 0 & 0 & 0 \end{pmatrix} \begin{pmatrix} -1 & 1 & 0 \\ 2 & -2 & 0 \\ 0 & 0 & 0 \end{pmatrix} \begin{pmatrix} 2 & -2 & 0 \\ -4 & 6 & 0 \\ 0 & 0 & 8 \end{pmatrix} \begin{pmatrix} -4 & 4 & 0 \\ 10 & -12 & 0 \\ 0 & 0 & -24 \end{pmatrix} \right)$$

yielding $k_1 = 1, d_1 = 2$,

$$G_1(s) = s^{-1} \begin{pmatrix} 1 & 0 \\ 0 & 2 \end{pmatrix} + s^{-2} \begin{pmatrix} -1 & 1 \\ 2 & -2 \end{pmatrix} + O(s^{-3})$$

$$M_4^{(2)} = \{0, \quad 0, \quad 8, \quad -24\}, \quad k_2 = 3, d_2 = 1$$

$$G_2(s) = s^{-3} 8 - s^{-4} 24 + O(s^{-3})$$

Deduce that the system hence has two first-order infinite zeros of the form $s \simeq -p - 1$, $s \simeq -2p - 1$ and three third-order infinite zeros of the form

$$s \simeq 2(-1)^{1/3} p^{1/3} - 1$$

corresponding to the distinct cube roots of -1.

5 In problem (4) deduce that T_1 (eqn. 6.4.19) is the unit 3×3 matrix. Hence deduce the effect of the additional compensation element

$$K_2(s) = \begin{pmatrix} I_2 & 0 \\ 0 & \dfrac{(s+1)}{(s+10)} \end{pmatrix}$$

6 Investigate the sensitivity of the pivots of

$$Q_0(s) = s^{-3} \begin{pmatrix} 1+\epsilon & -\epsilon \\ -\epsilon & 1+\epsilon \end{pmatrix} + s^{-4} \begin{pmatrix} 1 & 2 \\ 3 & 4 \end{pmatrix} + O(s^{-5})$$

to the parameter $\epsilon \geqslant 0$ in the vicinity of $\epsilon = 0$.

7 Show that the system

$$Q_0(s) = \frac{1}{\Delta(s)} \begin{pmatrix} -s^3 - 11s^2 - 29s + 92 & -20s^2 + 35s + 70 \\ 41s^2 - s - 91 & 33s^2 - 170s + 118 \end{pmatrix}$$

$$\Delta(s) = s^4 - s^3 + 2s^2 - 25s + 29$$

has one first-order infinite zero with asymptotic direction 1 and two second-order infinite zeros of the form $s \simeq \pm i\sqrt{3}p^{1/2} - 14 \cdot 5$. (Hint: expand $Q_0(s)$ as a series expansion about the point at infinity, element by element).

8 Generalise Exercise 6.3.7 to the case of nonuniform rank $Q_0(s)$.

9 Investigate the asymptotic behaviour of the root locus of the liquid-level system of Section 3.14 using the technique of Section 6.6. Assume the control configuration of Fig. 6.6.1 with $K_1(s) = I_m$, $H(s) = 0$, $K_2(s) = I_m$. Compare your results with those of Section 6.4.3. Suggest how the analysis of Section 3.13 could be used to assess the effect of the inclusion of nonzero minor-loop feedback (use $K_1(s)$, $K_2(s)$, $H(s)$ as free design variables in this case).

References

1 BELLMAN, R.: 'Introduction to matrix analysis' (McGraw-Hill, 1960)
2 BENGTSSON, G.: 'A theory for control of linear multivariable systems', Lund Institute of Technology, Division of Automatic Control, Sweden, Report 7341, 1973
3 BROCKETT, R.W.: 'Finite dimensional linear systems' (John Wiley & Sons, 1970)
4 BRIGGS, R.W.: 'Stability of a two-degree-of-freedom gyro with external feedback', *IEEE Trans.*, 1965, **AC-9**, pp. 244–249
5 DAVISON, E.J., and CHOW, S.G.: 'An algorithm for the assignment of closed-loop poles using output feedback in linear multivariable systems', *IEEE Trans.*, 1973, **AC-18**, 74–75
6 DIEUDONNE, J.: 'Foundations of modern analysis' (Academic Press, 1969)
7 EDWARDS, J.B., and OWENS, D.H.: '1st-order-type systems for multivariable process control', *Proc. IEE*, 1977, **124**, (11), pp. 1083–1088
8 FREEMAN, E.A.: 'Stability of linear constant multivariable systems: contraction-mapping approach', *ibid.*, 1973, **120**, (3), pp. 379–384
9 GANTMACHER, F.R.: 'Theory of matrices' (Chelsea, New York, 1960)
10 HOLTZMANN, J.H.: 'Nonlinear systems theory: a functional analysis approach' (Prentice-Hall, 1970)
11 HALMOS, P.R.: 'Finite dimensional vector spaces' (Van Nostrand, 1958)
12 HAWKINS, D.J.: 'Pseudodiagonalisation and the inverse-Nyquist-array method', *Proc. IEE*, 1972, **119**, (3), pp. 337–342
13 KOUVARITAKIS, B., and MACFARLANE, A.G.J.: 'Geometric approach to analysis and synthesis of system zeros', *Int. J. Control*, 1976, **23**, pp. 149–182
14 KOUVARITAKIS, B., and SHAKED, U.: 'Asymptotic behaviour of the roots of linear multivariable systems', *ibid.*, 1976, **23**, pp. 297–340
15 LAYTON, J.M.: 'Multivariable control theory' (Peter Peregrinus, 1976)
16 LANG, S.: 'Linear Algebra' (Addison-Wesley, 1966)
17 MACFARLANE, A.G.J., and KARCANIUS, N.: 'Poles and zeros of linear multivariable systems: survey of the algebraic, geometric and complex-variable theory', University of Cambridge Engineering Department Control and Management System Group, Research Report TR 105
18 MACFARLANE, A.G.J.: 'Commutative controller: a new technique for the design of multivariable control systems', *Electron. Lett.*, **1970**, 6, pp.

121–123

19   MACFARLANE, A.G.J.: 'Return-difference and return-ratio matrices and their use in analysis and design of multivariable feedback control systems', *Proc. IEE*, 1970, **117**, (10), pp. 2037–2049

20   MACFARLANE, A.G.J.: 'A survey of some recent results in linear multivariable feedback theory', *Automatica*, 1972, **8**, pp. 455–492

21   MACFARLANE, A.G.J., and BELLETRUTTI, J.J.: 'The characteristic locus design method', *ibid.*, 1973, **9**, pp. 575–588

22   MACFARLANE, A.G.J., and POSTLETHWAITE, I.: 'The generalized Nyquist stability criterion and multivariable root-loci', *Int. J. Control*, 1977, **25**, pp. 81–127

23   MACFARLANE, A.G.J., and KOUVARITAKIS, B.: 'A design technique for linear multivariable feedback systems', *ibid.*, 1977, **25**, 837–874

24   MACFARLANE, A.G.J.: 'Relationships between recent developments in linear control theory and classical design techniques', *Meas. & Control*, 8, pp. 179–187, pp. 219–223, pp. 278–284, pp. 319–323, pp. 371–375 (In Five Parts)

25   MAYNE, D.Q.: 'The design of linear multivariable systems', *Automatica*, 1973, **9**, pp. 201–207

26   MAYNE, D.Q.: 'The effect of feedback on linear multivariable systems', *ibid.*, 1974, **10**, pp. 405–412

27   MAYNE, D.Q., and CHUANG, S.C.: 'Sequential return difference method for designing linear multivariable systems', IEE conference on the computer-aided-design of control systems, Cambridge, England, 1973

28   McMORRAN, P.D.: 'Extension of the inverse Nyquist method', *Electron. Lett.*, 1970, **6**, pp. 800–801

29   MEES, D.H.: 'The level control of coupled evaporator vessels' *in* 3rd IFAC symposium on measurement and control, Institute of Measurement and Control, Manchester, Sept. 1974, F11

30   MIRSKY, L.: 'An introduction to linear algebra' (Addison-Wesley, 1966)

31   MORSE, A.S.: 'Structural invariants of linear multivariable systems', *SIAM J. Control*, 1973, **11**, pp. 446–465

32   MARSHALL, S.A., and OWENS, D.H.: 'Feedforward/Feedback control of linear multivariable systems using dyadic expansions', *Int. J. Control*, 1976, **23**, pp. 693–701

33   OGATA, K.: 'State space analysis of control systems' (Prentice-Hall, 1967)

34   OSTROWSKI, A.M.: 'Note on bounds for determinants with dominant principal diagonal', *Proc. Am. Math. Soc.*, 1952, **3**, pp. 26–30

35   OWENS, D.H.: 'Multivariable control system design concepts in the failure analysis of a class of nuclear reactor spatial control systems', *Proc. IEE*, 1973, **120**, (1), pp. 119–125

36   OWENS, D.H.: 'FADDEEV: A Fortran code for the calculation of the frequency response matrix of multi-input-multi-output systems', AEEW-R816, (HMSO, 1973)

37   OWENS, D.H.: 'Dyadic approximation method for multivariable control systems design with a nuclear-reactor application', *Proc. IEE*, 1973, **120**, (7), pp. 801–809

38   OWENS, D.H.: 'Dyadic expansion for the analysis of linear multivariable systems', *ibid.*, 1974, **121**, (7), pp. 713–716

39   OWENS, D.H.: 'Dyadic expansion, characteristic loci and multivariable-control-systems design', *ibid.*, 1975, **122**, (3), pp. 315–320

40 OWENS, D.H.: 'First-and-second-order-like structures *in* linear multivariable-control-systems design', *ibid.*, 1975, **122**, (9), pp. 935–941

41 OWENS, D.H.: 'Integrity of multivariable first-order-type structures', *Int. J. Control*, 1976, **23**, pp. 827–835

42 OWENS, D.H.: 'Root-loci concepts for kth-order-type multivariable structures', *Proc. IEE*, 1976, **123**, (9), pp. 933–940

43 OWENS, D.H.: 'Cascade canonical form for linear multivariable systems', *Int. J. Control*, 1976, **23**, pp. 837–850

44 OWENS, D.H.: 'Sequential design retaining full output feedback', *Electron. Lett.*, 1974, **10**, pp. 79–80

45 OWENS, D.H.: 'Dyadic modification to the sequential method for multivariable control systems design', *ibid.*, 1974, **10**, pp. 25–26

46 OWENS, D.H.: 'Invariant zeros of linear multivariable systems: a geometric analysis', *Int. J. Control*, 1977, **26**, pp. 537–548

47 OWENS, D.H.: 'Note on diagonal dominance and the stability of multivariable feedback systems', *ibid.*, 1978, **27**, pp. 603–608

48 OWENS, D.H.: 'Structural invariants and the root-loci of linear multivariable systems', *ibid.*, 1978, **28** (to be published)

49 OWENS, D.H.: 'Dynamic transformations and the calculation of multivariable root-loci', *ibid.*, 1978, **28** (to be published)

50 OWENS, D.H.: 'Feedback stability of open-loop unstable systems: contraction-mapping approach', *Electron. Lett.*, 1974, **10**, pp. 238–239

51 ORTEGA, J.M., and RHEINBOLDT, W.C.: 'Iterative solution of nonlinear equations in several variables' (Academic Press, 1970)

52 OWENS, D.H.: 'Multivariable root-loci and the inverse transfer function matrix', *Int. J. Control*, 1978, **28** (to be published)

53 PORTER, B., and CROSSLEY, R.: 'Modal control: theory and application' (Taylor & Francis, 1972)

54 PORTER, W.A.: 'Modern foundations of systems engineering' (MacMillan, 1966)

55 POSTLETHWAITE, I.: 'The asymptotic behaviour, the angles of departure and the angles of approach of the characteristic frequency loci', *Int. J. Control*, 1977, **25**, pp. 677–695

56 ROSENBROCK, H.H., and STOREY, C.: 'Mathematics of dynamical systems' (Nelson, 1970)

57 ROSENBROCK, H.H.: 'State-space and multivariable theory' (Nelson, 1970)

58 ROSENBROCK, H.H.: 'Computer-aided control systems design' (Academic Press, 1974)

59 ROSENBROCK, H.H.: 'Design of multivariable control systems using the inverse Nyquist array', *Proc. IEE*, 1969, **116**, (11), pp. 1929–1936

60 SIMON, J.D., and MITTER, S.K.: 'A theory of modal control', *Inf. & Control*, 1968, **13**, pp. 316–353

61 SHAKED, U.: 'The angles of departure and approach of the root-loci in linear multivariable systems', *Int. J. Control*, 1976, **23**, pp. 445–457

62 SHAKED, U., and KARCANIUS, N.: 'Use of zeros and zero-directions in model reduction', *ibid.*, 1976, **23**, pp. 113–135

63 WOLOVICH, W.A.: 'Linear multivariable systems' (Springer-Verlag, 1974)

64 WONHAM, W.M.: 'Linear multivariable control: a geometric approach' (Springer-Verlag, 1974)

65 ZADEH, L.A., and DESOER, C.A.: 'Linear systems theory' (McGraw-Hill, 1963)

Index